Acing the
New SAT Math

by Thomas Hyun

GREENHALL PUBLISHING
THOUSAND OAKS, CA

This edition published by Greenhall Publishing

Greenhall Publishing
Thousand Oaks, CA 91358
http:// greenhallpublishing.com

Written by Thomas Hyun

Cover design by Hespenheide Design

Printed in the United States of America

ISBN-10: 0-9754753-5-5
ISBN-13: 978-0-9754753-5-5

SAT is a registered trademark of the College Entrance Examination Board, which is not affiliated with this book.

CONTENTS

II. Statistics and Data Analysis

III. Advanced Math

IV. Geometry

To the Students …

If you're reading this, you are on your way to a better score on the New SAT math! Below are guidelines for getting the most out of this book, as well as information about changes to the math section of the New SAT.

Using this Book

⊙ This book helps students review and master mathematical concepts in the most concise and straightforward manner possible.

⊙ Each of the twenty chapters in this book teaches a particular group of mathematical concepts you need to know for the New SAT.
Each chapter contains lessons that convey key concepts along with illustrations and diagrams. Important vocabularies are printed in **boldface**.

⊙ Next to the key terms and illustrations, you will find examples, with complete solutions, that apply the application of the concepts you have just learned. Keep a pencil and sheet of paper handy. Follow along, working out the sample questions yourself – this will help you later in solving the practice problems.

⊙ This book is not only helpful for SAT Math, but is also a very useful supplement for high school math courses.

Exercise Sets and Practice Tests

⊙ Each lesson includes a set of practice problems for the lesson. Each chapter includes a practice test followed by answers and explanations, to ensure that you master the material.

PSAT and SAT Practice Tests

⊙ At the end of the book, you will find one PSAT and two SAT practice tests. For maximum benefit, these should be taken under realistic testing-center conditions – timed and free from outside distractions.

About the New SAT Math

Content

⊙ Starting in spring of 2016, the math portion of the SAT will cover Algebra I and II, Geometry, parts of Trigonometry, and parts of Statistics. For the new exam students must also be familiar with materials typically taught in Algebra II, Trigonometry, and Statistics.

⊙ The math portion of the SAT will consist of two sections – one 25-minute no-calculator section and one 55-minute calculator section., for a total of 80 minutes in math testing.
The new PSAT/NMSQT will also include the new topics, although the SAT will test for these concepts at a higher level. The math portion of the PSAT/NMSQT will consist of two sections – one 25-minute no-calculator section and one 45-minute calculator section, for a total of 70 minutes in math testing.

⊙ Math questions on the SAT and PSAT fall into two main categories: multiple choice (with four answer choices given) and student produced response questions. Student produced response questions, commonly referred to as "grid-ins," require students to formulate their own answers, then enter the numeric values into a special grid. Multiple choice questions have *no penalty for guessing*!

	SAT		PSAT	
No-Calculator Section	Number of Questions	Time Allocated	Number of Questions	Time Allocated
Multiple Choice (MC)	15		13	
Student-Produced Response (SPR - Grid-In)	5	25 minutes	4	25 minutes
Sub Total	20		17	
Calculator Section	Number of Questions	Time Allocated	Number of Questions	Time Allocated
Multiple Choice (MC)	30		27	
Student-Produced Response (SPR - Grid-In)	8	55 minutes	4	45 minutes
Sub Total	38		31	
Total	58	80 minutes	48	70 minutes

Study Timetable

⊙ As with any test, students will see the best results by studying consistently over at least several weeks before the exam date, rather than trying to cram and learn "test tricks" in a day or two. Students studying an hour a day over two months should be more than able to finish all the exercises in this book. The clear subject organization by chapter means you can focus your efforts and spend more time on topics you are struggling with. While chapters can be broken up over a couple sessions, students should finish each practice test in one uninterrupted sitting.

Calculators

⊙ Students may use a four-function, scientific, or graphing calculator during the SAT exam (calculators with QWERTY keyboard are not allowed). Use of a calculator is highly recommended, though most of the problems can be solved without one. Becoming comfortable with your calculator during test preparation will help you use this tool to solve problems more quickly and efficiently during the actual exam.

Scoring

⊙ Scores on the math portion of the SAT range from 200 to 800. An average score on the math section is about 500, but this can vary with each individual test. Consult the College Board Web site (www.collegeboard.com) for further specifics.

Signing Up for the SAT

⊙ Students can register online for the SAT at the College Board Web site. Students can also pick up registration packets at their high schools and sign up via snail mail. Generally the registration deadlines are a little over a month before the actual testing date. Late registrations incur additional fees.

This book was written to be a straightforward study guide for the New SAT Math. There are no shortcuts or gimmicks, but taking the time to work through this book should leave you feeling confident and well prepared for the test.

Good luck!

Math Review

I. Heart of Algebra

II. Statistics and Data Analysis

III. Advanced Math

IV. Geometry

I. Arithmetic and Algebra

CHAPTER 1
The Language and Tools of Algebra

1-1. Variables and Expressions

In algebra, **variables** are symbols used to represent unspecified numbers or values.
An **algebraic expression** is a collection of numbers, variables, operations, and grouping symbols.

	Verbal Phrase	**Algebraic Expressions**
Addition	The *sum* of twenty and a number n	$20 + n$
	Nine *more than* twice a number a	$2a + 9$
	A number m *increased* by 12	$m + 12$
Subtraction	The *difference* between a number x and 7	$x - 7$
	Three *less than* a number b	$b - 3$
	Three times a number k *decreased* by five	$3k - 5$
	Nine *minus* a number n	$9 - n$
Multiplication	Eleven *times* z to the third power	$11z^3$
	The *product of* -2 and a number n	$-2n$
	Two thirds *of* a number x	$\dfrac{2}{3}x$
Division	n *divided* by 8	$n/8$
	The *quotient* of fifteen and a number d	$\dfrac{15}{d}$

Example 1 □ Write an algebraic expression for each verbal expression.

a. Ten less than one-fourth the cube of p.

b. Twice the difference between x and sixteen.

c. Four times the sum of a number and three.

d. Four times a number increased by three.

Solution □ a. $\dfrac{1}{4}p^3 - 10$

b. $2(x - 16)$

c. $4(n + 3)$

d. $4n + 3$

Example 2 □ Mr. and Mrs. Sawyer are taking their three children to an amusement park. The admission is a dollars per adult, c dollars per child and the cost of each ride is r dollars per person.

a. Write an expression for the cost of admission plus 10 rides for the family.

b. Find the cost of admission plus 10 rides if the admission per adult is 20 dollars, the admission per child is 12 dollars, and the cost of each ride is 8 dollars.

Solution □ a. $2a + 3c + 10r$

b. $2 \cdot 20 + 3 \cdot 12 + 10 \cdot 8$ Substitute 20 for a, 12 for c, and 8 for r.
    $= 156$

Exercise - Variables and Expressions

1

Twice the product of m and n decreased by the square of the sum of m and n.

Which of the following is an expression for the statement above?

A) $2mn - (m^2 + n^2)$

B) $2mn - (m + n)^2$

C) $(m + n)^2 - 2mn$

D) $(m^2 + n^2) - 2mn$

2

The product of a number x and four decreased by twelve.

Which of the following is an expression for the statement above?

A) $4x + 12$

B) $4(x + 12)$

C) $4(x - 12)$

D) $4x - 12$

3

The quotient of 19 and a number d increased by seven.

Which of the following is an expression for the statement above?

A) $\dfrac{19}{d} + 7$

B) $\dfrac{d}{19} + 7$

C) $\dfrac{19 + d}{7}$

D) $\dfrac{d + 7}{19}$

4

Mario received y text messages each minute for 10 minutes yesterday and received t text messages each minute for 20 minutes today. What is the total number of text messages he received for two days in terms of y and t?

A) $30yt$

B) $200yt$

C) $20y + 10t$

D) $10y + 20t$

5

Which of the following expressions represents the product of $3k$ and the sum of m and one third of n?

A) $3km + \dfrac{1}{3}n$

B) $3k \cdot \dfrac{1}{3}(m + n)$

C) $3k(m + \dfrac{1}{3}n)$

D) $3k(m + n + \dfrac{1}{3})$

6

The difference between two numbers is eight. If the smaller number is n to the third power what is the greater number?

A) $n^3 - 8$

B) $n^3 + 8$

C) $8 - n^3$

D) $8n^3$

1-2. Exponents and Order of Operations

An expression like 3^5 is called a **power**. The number 3 is the **base**, and the number 5 is the **exponent**.

$$3^5 = \underbrace{3 \cdot 3 \cdot 3 \cdot 3 \cdot 3}_{\text{5 factors of 3}}$$

To evaluate an expression involving more than one operation, we agree to perform operations in the following order .

Order of Operations

1. Simplify the expressions inside grouping symbols, such as parentheses, brackets, and fraction bars.
2. Evaluate all powers.
3. Do all multiplications and divisions in order from left to right.
4. Do all additions and subtractions in order from left to right.

Example 1 □ Evaluate $(11 - 20 \div \dfrac{5^2 - 13}{3} + 8) \times 2$.

Solution □ $(11 - 20 \div \dfrac{5^2 - 13}{3} + 8) \times 2$

$= (11 - 20 \div \dfrac{25 - 13}{3} + 8) \times 2$ Evaluate power inside grouping symbols.

$= (11 - 20 \div \dfrac{12}{3} + 8) \times 2$ Evaluate expression inside grouping symbols.

$= (11 - 20 \div 4 + 8) \times 2$ Evaluate expression inside grouping symbols.

$= (11 - 5 + 8) \times 2$ Divide 20 by 4.

$= (6 + 8) \times 2$ Subtract 5 from 11.

$= (14) \times 2$ Evaluate expression inside grouping symbols.

$= 28$ Multiply.

Example 2 □ Evaluate $a^3 - \dfrac{b^2 + c}{a} + (ab + c)$ if $a = 4$, $b = -3$, and $c = 7$.

Solution □ $a^3 - \dfrac{b^2 + c}{a} + (ab + c)$

$= 4^3 - \dfrac{(-3)^2 + 7}{4} + (4 \cdot (-3) + 7)$ Replace a with 4, b with -3 , and c with 7.

$= 64 - \dfrac{9 + 7}{4} + (-12 + 7)$ Evaluate 4^3 , $(-3)^2$, and $4 \cdot (-3)$.

$= 64 - \dfrac{16}{4} + (-5)$ Evaluate expression inside grouping symbols.

$= 64 - 4 + (-5)$ Divide 16 by 4.

$= 55$ Subtract and add.

Exercise - Exponents and Order of Operations

1

$[(7^2 - 9) \div 8]2 =$

2

$19 - 3[20 - \dfrac{2^4 - 7}{4} \times 8] =$

3

$\dfrac{72 \div 3^2 \cdot 2}{6} =$

4

$5^3 - \dfrac{1}{2}(12 + 12 \div 3) =$

5

What is the value of $(\dfrac{2c}{a})^2 - 10 \times \dfrac{(b+a)}{c}$ if $a = -2$, $b = 3$, and $c = 5$?

6

What is the value of $9 - 2x \div (z - y)^3$ if $x = 4$, $y = -1$, and $z = -3$?

7

What is the value of $\dfrac{7 \div (q)^2 \cdot 2}{2p} \cdot \dfrac{-p + 6q - r}{-q}$ if $p = 4$, $q = \dfrac{1}{2}$, and $r = 2$?

8

What is the value of $\dfrac{c - 2(a+b)}{(c-a)^2}$ if $a = -\dfrac{1}{2}$, $b = \dfrac{3}{2}$, and $c = \dfrac{5}{2}$?

1-3. Simplifying Algebraic Expressions

A **term** is a number, a variable, or a product or quotient of numbers and variables. For example 5, x, $7a$, b^2, and $2m^3n$ are all terms. **Like terms** contain identical variables. For example, in $5x^2 - 3x^2 + 3x$, the terms $5x^2$ and $-3x^2$ are like terms because the variable part of each term is identical.

The **coefficient** of a term is a number that multiplies a variable. For example, in $8x^2y$, the coefficient is 8, and in $\dfrac{4m}{5}$, the coefficient is $\dfrac{4}{5}$.

An expression is in **simplest form** when it is replaced by an equivalent expression having no like terms or parentheses. Simplifying means rewriting in simpler form.

Distributive Property

Symbols   For any real numbers a, b, and c

$a(b+c) = ab + ac$ $\qquad$ $a(b-c) = ab - ac$

Examples $4(7+3) = 4 \cdot 7 + 4 \cdot 3$ $\qquad$ $4(7-3) = 4 \cdot 7 - 4 \cdot 3$

Commutative Property

Symbols   For any real numbers a and b,

$a + b = b + a$ $\qquad$ $a \cdot b = b \cdot a$

Examples $3 + 4 = 4 + 3$ $\qquad$ $3 \cdot 4 = 4 \cdot 3$

Associative Property

Symbols   For any real numbers a, b, and c

$(a+b) + c = a + (b+c)$ $\qquad$ $(ab)c = a(bc)$

Examples $(3+4) + 7 = 3 + (4+7)$ $\qquad$ $(3 \cdot 4) \cdot 7 = 3 \cdot (4 \cdot 7)$

Example 1 $\square$ Simplify each expression.

a. $\dfrac{1}{3}m - 4n + 2\dfrac{2}{3}m$ $\qquad$ b. $4x^3 - 2(x^3 + 3x)$ $\qquad$ c. $a(2-b) - 2(a-b)$

Solution $\square$ a. $\dfrac{1}{3}m - 4n + 2\dfrac{2}{3}m$

$\qquad = (\dfrac{1}{3} + 2\dfrac{2}{3})m - 4n$ $\qquad\qquad$ Combine like terms.

$\qquad = 3m - 4n$ $\qquad\qquad$ Simplify.

b. $4x^3 - 3(x^3 + 2x)$

$\qquad = 4x^3 - 3(x^3) - 3(2x)$ $\qquad\qquad$ Distributive property

$\qquad = 4x^3 - 3x^3 - 6x$ $\qquad\qquad$ Multiply.

$\qquad = x^3 - 6x$ $\qquad\qquad$ Combine like terms.

c. $a(2-b) - 2(a-b)$

$\qquad = 2a - ab - 2a + 2b$ $\qquad\qquad$ Distributive property

$\qquad = 2a - 2a - ab + 2b$ $\qquad\qquad$ Commutative property

$\qquad = -ab + 2b$ $\qquad\qquad$ Simplify.

Exercise - Simplifying Algebraic Expressions

1

Which of the following expressions is equivalent to $\dfrac{2}{3}(a^2 - a - 3) + \dfrac{1}{3}(a^2 + 2a + 6)$?

A) a^2

B) $a^2 + a$

C) $a^2 - a$

D) $a^2 - 1$

2

Which of the following expressions is equivalent to $5.4(x - 2y) - 2.7(x - 3y)$?

A) $2.7(x + y)$

B) $2.7(x - y)$

C) $2.7x + 3.6y$

D) $2.7x - 3.6y$

3

Which of the following expressions is equivalent to $\dfrac{1}{2}(2a + 3b + 4c) - \dfrac{3}{2}(b + 2c)$?

A) $a - 3c$

B) $a + 5c$

C) $a + c$

D) $a - c$

4

Which of the following expressions is equivalent to $a(b - c) - b(a + c) - c(a - b)$?

A) bc

B) $2ac$

C) $-2bc$

D) $-2ac$

5

Which of the following expressions is NOT equivalent to $3[6a - 3(1 - a) - 5(a + 1)]$?

A) $12a - 24$

B) $24(a - \dfrac{1}{2})$

C) $12(a - 2)$

D) $24(\dfrac{1}{2}a - 1)$

6

Which of the following expressions is NOT equivalent to $p - \dfrac{2}{3}(2p - 3q) - \dfrac{1}{3}(p + 4q)$?

A) $-\dfrac{2}{3}(p - q)$

B) $-\dfrac{2}{3}p + \dfrac{2}{3}q$

C) $-\dfrac{2}{3}(p + q)$

D) $-\dfrac{1}{3}(2p - 2q)$

1-4. Rational, Irrational, and Decimal

Numbers can be pictured as points on a horizontal line called a **number line**. The point for 0 is the **origin**. Points to the left of 0 represent **negative numbers**, and points to the right of 0 represent **positive numbers**. Numbers increase in value from left to right. The point that corresponds to a number is called the **graph** of the number. Each number in a pair such as 3 and −3 is called the **opposite** of the other number. The opposite of a is written $−a$.

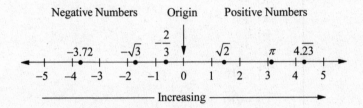

natural numbers: {1, 2, 3, . . .}

whole numbers: {0, 1, 2, 3, . . .}

integers: {. . . , −3, −2, −1, 0, 1, 2, 3, . . .}

rational numbers: A rational number is one that can be expressed as a ratio $\dfrac{a}{b}$, where a and b are

integers and b is not zero, such as $−3.72$, $−\dfrac{2}{3}$, 0, 2, and $4.\overline{23}$. The decimal form

of a rational number is either a terminating or repeating decimal.

irrational numbers   Any real number that is not rational is irrational. $−\sqrt{3}$, $\sqrt{2}$, and π are irrational.

Rounding Decimals

To round a decimal to the desired place, underline the digit in the place to be rounded.
1) If the digit to the right of the underlined digit is 5 or more, increase the underlined digit by one (round up).
2) If the digit to the right of the underlined digit is less than 5, leave the underlined digit as it is (round down).
3) Drop all digits to the right of the underlined digit.

Example 1 □ On the number line below, the marks are equally spaced. What is the coordinate of P?

Solution □ Since the distance between the marks is 0.25, the coordinate of P is $7 \times −0.25$, or $−1.75$.

Example 2 □ Round 52.348 to the nearest a) integer and b) hundredth.

Solution □ a) Underline 2, the digit in the ones place. 5<u>2</u>.348
The digit to the right of the underlined digit is less than 5, keep the underlined digit.
Therefore, 52.348 rounded to the nearest integer is 52.

b) Underline 4, the digit in the hundredths place. 52.3<u>4</u>8
The digit to the right of the underlined digit is more than 5, round up.
Therefore, 52.348 rounded to the nearest hundredths place is 52.35.

Exercise – Rational, Irrational, and Decimal

1

Which of the following shows the numbers arranged in increasing order?

A) $-\sqrt{3},\ -5,\ \dfrac{2}{3},\ 4,\ \sqrt{10}$

B) $-\sqrt{3},\ -5,\ \dfrac{2}{3},\ \sqrt{10},\ 4$

C) $-5,\ -\sqrt{3},\ \dfrac{2}{3},\ \sqrt{10},\ 4$

D) $\dfrac{2}{3},\ -\sqrt{3},\ \sqrt{10},\ 4,\ -5$

2

$11 - 2(2 - 0.8^2) + 24 \div (-4) =$

A) 1.68

B) 2.28

C) 2.78

D) 3.18

3

To the nearest cents, what is the value of $\$500(1 + 0.045)^8 - \$500(1 + 0.04)^8$?

A) \$25.45

B) \$26.00

C) \$26.77

D) \$28.25

4

Which of the following is an irrational number?

A) -1.2

B) $\dfrac{4}{3}$

C) $-\sqrt{16}$

D) $-\sqrt{10}$

5

Which of the following is a rational number?

A) $\sqrt{1.6}$

B) $\sqrt{\dfrac{49}{64}}$

C) $\sqrt{0.9}$

D) $-\sqrt{250}$

6

In three plays, a football team loses 5 yards and then gains 32 yards by completing a pass. Then a penalty was called and the team lost 10 yards. How many yards did the team actually gain?

7

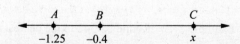

On the number line above, if $BC = 2AB$ what is the value of x ?

Chapter 1 Practice Test

1

Two less than the quotient of three and a number n

Which of the following is an expression for the statement above?

A) $2 - \dfrac{n}{3}$

B) $\dfrac{n}{3} - 2$

C) $\dfrac{3}{n} - 2$

D) $2 - \dfrac{3}{n}$

2

How much greater than $n - 11$ is $n + 3$?

A) 8

B) 10

C) 12

D) 14

3

Johnny received m text messages on Friday, three less than twice as many text messages on Saturday than on Friday, and five more text messages on Sunday than on Saturday. What is the total number of text messages he received over the three days?

A) $4m + 2$

B) $5m - 1$

C) $4m - 2$

D) $5m + 1$

4

What number is halfway between $-\dfrac{5}{6}$ and $\dfrac{1}{3}$ on a number line?

A) $-\dfrac{1}{4}$

B) $-\dfrac{1}{3}$

C) $-\dfrac{1}{2}$

D) $-\dfrac{5}{12}$

5

What is 4.4985 rounded to the nearest hundredth?

A) 4.49

B) 4.498

C) 4.499

D) 4.50

6

Which of the following expressions is equivalent to $3a + \dfrac{1}{2}(b - 2c) - \dfrac{1}{2}(2a + 3b)$?

A) $\dfrac{3}{2}a - \dfrac{1}{2}b - c$

B) $\dfrac{3}{2}a + b - c$

C) $2a - b - c$

D) $2a + b - c$

7

How many minutes are there in $2h$ hours and $6m$ minutes?

A) $60h + 12m$

B) $120h + 6m$

C) $60h + 6m$

D) $120h + 60m$

8

1. Add 5 to a number n.
2. Divide by 8.
3. Subtract by 1.
4. Multiply by 8.

When the sequence of operations above has been completed in order, which of the following is an expression for the statement above?

A) $n - 1$

B) $n - 2$

C) $n - 3$

D) $n - 4$

9

Which of the following expressions is equivalent to $(2y - x) - 2(y - 2z) - 4(x + z)$?

A) $-3x$

B) $-5x$

C) $-3x + 8z$

D) $-5x - 8z$

10

If $x = 10$, what is the value of $\dfrac{x}{2} + \dfrac{x}{20} + \dfrac{x}{200}$?

11

If x and y are positive integers and $2x + 5y = 18$, what is the value of x?

12

If $a = 3$, $b = -1$, and $c = -2$, what is the value of $7 - \dfrac{a - 12 \div (2 - b)}{c + 3}$?

Answer Key

Section 1-1

1. B   2. D   3. A   4. D   5. C

6. B

Section 1-2

1. 10   2. 13   3. 8/3   4. 117   5. 23

6. 10   7. 42   8. $\dfrac{1}{18}$

Section 1-3

1. A   2. B   3. D   4. D   5. B

6. C

Section 1-4

1. C   2. B   3. C   4. D   5. B

6. 17   7. 1.3

Chapter 1 Practice Test

1. C   2. D   3. B   4. A   5. D

6. C   7. B   8. C   9. B   10. 5.55

11. 4   12. 8

Note: Throughout the book, the symbol "$\Rightarrow$" is used to indicate that one step of an equation implies the next step of the equation.

Answers and Explanations

Section 1-1

1. B

$$\underbrace{2mn}_{\substack{\text{twice the product} \\ \text{of } m \text{ and } n}} \underbrace{-}_{\text{decreased by}} \underbrace{(m+n)^2}_{\substack{\text{the square of the} \\ \text{sum of } m \text{ and } n}}$$

2. D

$$\underbrace{4x}_{\substack{\text{the product of} \\ \text{a number } x \text{ and } 4}} \underbrace{-}_{\text{decreased by}} \underbrace{12}_{\text{twelve}}$$

3. A

$$\underbrace{\dfrac{19}{d}}_{\substack{\text{the quotient of 19} \\ \text{and a number } d}} \underbrace{+}_{\text{increased by}} \underbrace{7}_{\text{seven}}$$

4. D

The number of text messages Mario received yesterday $=10y$.

The number of text messages Mario received today $=20t$

The total number of text messages he received for two days $=10y+20t$.

5. C

$$\underbrace{3k}_{3\text{ times }k} \; (\underbrace{m+\dfrac{1}{3}n}_{\substack{\text{sum of } m \text{ and} \\ \text{one third of } n}})$$

$3k(m+\dfrac{1}{3}n)$ stands for $3k\times(m+\dfrac{1}{3}n)$.

6. B

If the smaller number is n to the third power, which is n^3, the greater number is 8 more than n^3, which is n^3+8.

Section 1-2

1. 10

$$[(7^2-9)\div 8]2 = [(49-9)\div 8]2$$
$$=[(40)\div 8]2 = [5]2 = 10$$

2. 13

$$19-3[20-\dfrac{2^4-7}{4}\times 8]$$
$$=19-3[20-\dfrac{16-7}{4}\times 8]$$
$$=19-3[20-\dfrac{9}{4}\times 8] = 19-3[20-\dfrac{72}{4}]$$
$$=19-3[20-18] = 19-3[2]$$
$$=19-6 = 13$$

3. $\dfrac{8}{3}$

$$\dfrac{72\div 3^2\cdot 2}{6} = \dfrac{72\div 9\cdot 2}{6} = \dfrac{8\cdot 2}{6} = \dfrac{16}{6} = \dfrac{8}{3}$$

4. 117

$$5^3-\dfrac{1}{2}(12+12\div 3) = 125-\dfrac{1}{2}(12+4)$$
$$=125-\dfrac{1}{2}(16) = 125-8 = 117$$

5. 23

$$\left(\frac{2c}{a}\right)^2 - 10 \times \frac{(b+a)}{c} = \left(\frac{2 \cdot 5}{-2}\right)^2 - 10 \times \frac{(3+-2)}{5}$$

$$= (-5)^2 - 10 \times \left(\frac{1}{5}\right) = 25 - 2 = 23$$

6. 10

$$9 - 2x \div (z-y)^3 = 9 - 2(4) \div (-3-(-1))^3$$

$$= 9 - 8 \div (-2)^3 = 9 - 8 \div (-8) = 9 - (-1) = 10$$

7. 42

$$\frac{7 \div (q)^2 \cdot 2}{2p} \cdot \frac{-p + 6q - r}{-q}$$

$$= \frac{7 \div \left(\frac{1}{2}\right)^2 \cdot 2}{2(4)} \cdot \frac{-(4) + 6\left(\frac{1}{2}\right) - 2}{-\frac{1}{2}}$$

$$= \frac{7 \div \frac{1}{4} \cdot 2}{8} \cdot \frac{-3}{-\frac{1}{2}} = \frac{28 \cdot 2}{8} \cdot 6 = 7 \cdot 6 = 42$$

8. $\frac{1}{18}$

$$\frac{c - 2(a+b)}{(c-a)^2} = \frac{\frac{5}{2} - 2\left(-\frac{1}{2} + \frac{3}{2}\right)}{\left(\frac{5}{2} - \left(-\frac{1}{2}\right)\right)^2} = \frac{\frac{5}{2} - 2(1)}{(3)^2}$$

$$= \frac{\frac{1}{2}}{9} = \frac{1}{18}$$

Section 1-3

1. A

$$\frac{2}{3}(a^2 - a - 3) + \frac{1}{3}(a^2 + 2a + 6)$$

$$= \frac{2}{3}a^2 - \frac{2}{3}a - 2 + \frac{1}{3}a^2 + \frac{2}{3}a + 2 = a^2$$

2. B

$$5.4(x - 2y) - 2.7(x - 3y)$$

$$= 5.4x - 10.8y - 2.7x + 8.1y$$

$$= 2.7x - 2.7y = 2.7(x - y)$$

3. D

$$\frac{1}{2}(2a + 3b + 4c) - \frac{3}{2}(b + 2c)$$

$$= a + \frac{3}{2}b + 2c - \frac{3}{2}b - 3c$$

$$= a - c$$

4. D

$$a(b-c) - b(a+c) - c(a-b)$$

$$= ab - ac - ab - bc - ac + bc$$

$$= -2ac$$

5. B

$$3[6a - 3(1-a) - 5(a+1)]$$

$$= 3[6a - 3 + 3a - 5a - 5]$$

$$= 3[4a - 8] = 12a - 24$$

All of the answer choices except B are equivalent to $12a - 24$.

6. C

$$p - \frac{2}{3}(2p - 3q) - \frac{1}{3}(p + 4q)$$

$$= p - \frac{4}{3}p + 2q - \frac{1}{3}p - \frac{4}{3}q$$

$$= -\frac{2}{3}p + \frac{2}{3}q$$

All of the answer choices except C are equivalent to $-\frac{2}{3}p + \frac{2}{3}q$.

Section 1-4

1. C

$$-5, \ -\sqrt{3}(\approx -1.73), \ \frac{2}{3}, \ \sqrt{10}(\approx 3.1), \ 4$$

Answer choice C shows the numbers arranged in increasing order.

2. B

$$11 - 2(2 - 0.8^2) + 24 \div (-4)$$

$$= 11 - 2(2 - .64) + (-6)$$

$$= 11 - 2(1.36) - 6 = 2.28$$

3. C

Use calculator.

$500(1+0.045)^8 - 500(1+0.04)^8$

$= 500[(1.045)^8 - (1.04)^8]$

$= 500(0.05353) \approx 26.76578$

26.765 rounded to the nearest hundredth is 26.77.

4. D

$-\sqrt{10}$ is an irrational number.

$-\sqrt{16} = -4$ is not an irrational number.

5. B

$\sqrt{\dfrac{49}{64}} = \dfrac{\sqrt{49}}{\sqrt{64}} = \dfrac{7}{8}$ is a rational number.

6. 17

$-5 + 32 - 10 = 17$

7. 1.3

$BC = 2AB$

$x - (-0.4) = 2[-0.4 - (-1.25)]$

$x + 0.4 = 2(0.85)$

$x + 0.4 = 1.7$

$x = 1.7 - 0.4 = 1.3$

Chapter 1 Practice Test

1. C

The phrase "two less than the quotient of three and a number n" is translated $\dfrac{3}{n} - 2$, not $2 - \dfrac{3}{n}$.

2. D

$(n+3) - (n-11) = n + 3 - n + 11 = 14$

3. B

Number of text messages he received on Friday is m, on Saturday is $2m - 3$, and on Sunday is $2m - 3 + 5$
The total number of text messages he received over the three days is
$m + (2m - 3) + (2m - 3 + 5) = 5m - 1$

4. A

To find a number which is halfway between two numbers, find the average of the two numbers.

$\dfrac{-\dfrac{5}{6} + \dfrac{1}{3}}{2} = \dfrac{(-\dfrac{5}{6} + \dfrac{1}{3})6}{(2)6} = \dfrac{-5 + 2}{12} = \dfrac{-3}{12} = -\dfrac{1}{4}$

5. D

Underline 9, the digit in the hundredths place.
4.4985

The digit to the right of the underlined digit is more than 5, round up. Therefore, 4.4985 rounded to the nearest hundredths place is 4.50.

6. C

$3a + \dfrac{1}{2}(b - 2c) - \dfrac{1}{2}(2a + 3b)$

$= 3a + \dfrac{1}{2}b - c - a - \dfrac{3}{2}b$

$= 2a - b - c$

7. B

There are $2h \times 60$ minutes in $2h$ hours.
There are $(120h + 6m)$ minutes in $2h$ hours and $6m$ minutes.

8. C

1. Add 5 to a number n. $\Rightarrow n + 5$

2. Divide by 8. $\Rightarrow \dfrac{(n+5)}{8}$

3. Subtract by 1. $\Rightarrow \dfrac{(n+5)}{8} - 1$

4. Multiply by 8. $\Rightarrow [\dfrac{(n+5)}{8} - 1] \times 8$

$[\dfrac{(n+5)}{8} - 1] \times 8 = (n + 5) - 8 = n - 3$

9. B

$(2y - x) - 2(y - 2z) - 4(x + z)$

$= 2y - x - 2y + 4z - 4x - 4z$

$= -5x$

10. 5.55

$\dfrac{x}{2} + \dfrac{x}{20} + \dfrac{x}{200} = \dfrac{10}{2} + \dfrac{10}{20} + \dfrac{10}{200}$

$= 5 + 0.5 + 0.05 = 5.55$

11. 4

Choose the first few positive integers for x and make substitutions for the given equation. Construct a table of values.

x	y
1	not an integer
2	not an integer
3	not an integer
4	2

Both x and y are positive integers when x equals 4 and y equals 2. Therefore the value of x is 4.

12. 8

$$7 - \frac{a - 12 \div (2 - b)}{c + 3} = 7 - \frac{3 - 12 \div (2 - (-1))}{-2 + 3}$$
$$= 7 - \frac{3 - 12 \div (3)}{1} = 7 - \frac{3 - 4}{1} = 7 - \frac{-1}{1}$$
$$= 7 + 1 = 8$$

CHAPTER 2
Solving Linear Equations

2-1. Writing Equations

An **equation** is a mathematical sentence with an equal sign. To translate a word sentence into an equation, choose a variable to represent one of the unspecified numbers or measures in the sentence. This is called **defining a variable**. Then use the variable to write equations for the unspecified numbers.

Example 1 □ Translate each sentence into an equation.
    a. Twice a number increased by fourteen is identical to fifty.
    b. Half the sum of seven and a number is the same as the number decreased by two.
    c. The quotient of m and n equals four more than one-third the sum of m and n.
    d. The cube of x plus the square of y is equal to fifty two.

Solution   □ a. Let c be the number.   Define a variable.

$$\underbrace{2c}_{\text{Twice a number } c} \quad \underbrace{+}_{\text{increased by}} \quad \underbrace{14}_{\text{fourteen}} \quad \underbrace{=}_{\text{is identical to}} \quad \underbrace{50}_{\text{fifty.}}$$

b. Let n be the number.   Define a variable.

$$\underbrace{\frac{1}{2}}_{\text{Half}} \quad \underbrace{(7+n)}_{\substack{\text{the sum of 7} \\ \text{and a number}}} \quad \underbrace{=}_{\text{is the same as}} \quad \underbrace{n}_{\text{the number}} \quad \underbrace{-}_{\text{decreased by}} \quad \underbrace{2}_{\text{two.}}$$

c. $$\underbrace{\frac{m}{n}}_{\substack{\text{The quotient} \\ \text{of } m \text{ and } n}} \quad \underbrace{=}_{\text{equals}} \quad \underbrace{4}_{\text{four}} \quad \underbrace{+}_{\text{more than}} \quad \underbrace{\frac{1}{3}}_{\text{one-third}} \quad \underbrace{(m+n)}_{\text{the sum of } m \text{ and } n.}$$

d. $$\underbrace{x^3}_{\text{The cube of } x} \quad \underbrace{+}_{\text{plus}} \quad \underbrace{y^2}_{\text{the square of } y} \quad \underbrace{=}_{\text{is equal to}} \quad \underbrace{52}_{\text{fifty two.}}$$

Consecutive Numbers

Consecutive Integers $\ldots, -3, -2, -1, 0, 1, 2, 3, \ldots$ n, $n+1$, $n+2$ are three consecutive integers if n is an integer.

Consecutive Even Integers $\ldots, -6, -4, -2, 0, 2, 4, 6, \ldots$ n, $n+2$, $n+4$ are three consecutive even integers if n is an even integer.

Consecutive Odd Integers $\ldots, -5, -3, -1, 1, 3, 5, \ldots$ n, $n+2$, $n+4$ are three consecutive odd integers if n is an odd integer.

Example 2 □ Write an equation to represent the given relationship between integers.
    a. The sum of four consecutive integers is -54.
    b. The product of three consecutive odd integers is 693.

Solution   □ a. Let n be the first integer.   Define a variable.

$$\underbrace{n+(n+1)+(n+2)+(n+3)}_{\text{The sum of four consecutive integers}} \quad \underbrace{=}_{\text{is}} \quad \underbrace{-54}_{-54}$$

b. Let n be the first odd integer.   Define a variable.

$$\underbrace{n(n+2)(n+4)}_{\text{The product of three consecutive odd integers}} \quad \underbrace{=}_{\text{is}} \quad \underbrace{693}_{693}$$

Exercise - Writing Equations

1

Eighteen more than the number n is 125.
What is the value of n?

2

Twenty is 7 less than twice the number w.
What is the value of w?

3

Nine less than twice x is three more than x.
What is the value of x?

4

Eight less than four times the number c is twenty.
What is the value of c?

5

The sum of four consecutive odd integers is 296.
What is the greatest of the four consecutive odd integers?

6

The sum of three fourths of the number a and 24 is negative 9. What is the value of a?

A) -44

B) -20

C) 20

D) 44

7

A number g is decreased by 23 and then multiplied by $\dfrac{1}{2}$. The result is 8 more than twice the number g.

A) -13

B) $-\dfrac{34}{3}$

C) $-\dfrac{29}{3}$

D) -8

8

The quotient of p and q is twelve less than three times the sum of p and q.

Which of the following equations represents the statement above?

A) $\dfrac{p}{q} = (3p+q)-12$

B) $\dfrac{p}{q} = 12-(3p+q)$

C) $\dfrac{p}{q} = 3(p+q)-12$

D) $\dfrac{p}{q} = 12-3(p+q)$

2-2. Solving Equations

To solve an equation means to find all values of the variable that make the equation a true statement. One way to do this is to isolate the variable that has a coefficient of 1 onto one side of the equation. You can do this using the rules of algebra called **properties of equality**.

Properties of Equality	Symbols	Examples
1. Addition Property	If $a = b$, then $a + c = b + c$.	If $x - 3 = 5$, then $(x - 3) + 3 = (5) + 3$.
2. Subtraction Property	If $a = b$, then $a - c = b - c$.	If $x + 2 = 6$, then $(x + 2) - 2 = (6) - 2$.
3. Multiplication Property	If $a = b$, then $ca = cb$.	If $\frac{1}{2}x = 3$, then $2 \cdot \frac{1}{2}x = 2 \cdot 3$.
4. Division Property	If $a = b$ and $c \neq 0$, then $\frac{a}{c} = \frac{b}{c}$.	If $3x = 15$, then $\frac{3x}{3} = \frac{15}{3}$.

Example 1 □ Solve each equation.

a. $a + (-11) = -25$ b. $-24 = 8y$

Solution □   a. $a + (-11) = -25$

$a + (-11) + 11 = -25 + 11$ Add 11 to each side.

$a = -14$ $-11 + 11 = 0$ and $-25 + 11 = -14$

b. $-24 = 8y$

$\dfrac{-24}{8} = \dfrac{8y}{8}$ Divide each side by 8.

$-3 = y$ $\dfrac{-24}{8} = 3$ and $\dfrac{8y}{8} = y$

Many equations require more than one operation to solve. Such equations are called **multi-step equations**. To solve multi-step equations, first simplify each side of the equation, if needed, and then use inverse operations to isolate the variable.

Example 2 □ Solve $\dfrac{4}{5}(x - 5) - \dfrac{1}{5}(x - 10) = 21$.

Solution   □ $\dfrac{4}{5}(x - 5) - \dfrac{1}{5}(x - 10) = 19$

$\dfrac{4}{5}x - 4 - \dfrac{1}{5}x + 2 = 19$ Distributive Property

$\dfrac{3}{5}x - 2 = 19$ Simplify.

$\dfrac{3}{5}x - 2 + 2 = 19 + 2$ Add 2 to each side.

$\dfrac{3}{5}x = 21$ Simplify.

$\dfrac{5}{3}(\dfrac{3}{5}x) = \dfrac{5}{3}(21)$ Multiply each side by $\dfrac{5}{3}$.

$x = 35$ Simplify.

Exercise - Solving Equations

1

$$-11 + x = 9$$

Given the above equation, what is the value of $20 - (11 - x)$?

2

If $33 - a = a + 27 - 5a$, what is the value of $33 + 3a$?

3

If $\dfrac{1}{2}x + 3 = \dfrac{3}{4} - x$, what is the value of x ?

4

If $x - (3 - 2x) + (4 - 5x) = -7$, what is the value of x ?

5

If three quarters of a number decreased by twenty is equal to eighty two, what is that number?

6

Two and three fifths of a number equals -26. What is the number?

A) -15

B) -10

C) -5

D) 10

7

There are one hundred forty-two students in a high school band. These students represent two ninth of the total students in the high school. How many students attend the school?

A) 587

B) 613

C) 639

D) 665

8

$$820c + 380r = 4{,}360$$

The above equation models the amount of calories in a snack of c cups of cashews and r cups of raisins. The amount of calories per cup of cashews is 820 and the amount of calories per cup of raisins is 380. According to the equation, how many cups of raisins are used, if 3 cups of cashews are used to make the snack?

A) 3

B) 4

C) 5

D) 6

2-3. Solving Equations with Variables on Both Sides

Some equations have variables on both sides. To solve such equations, first use the Addition or Subtraction Property of Equality to write an equivalent equation that has all of the variables on one side. Then use the Multiplication or Division Property of Equality to simplify the equation if necessary. When solving equations that contain grouping symbols, use the Distributive Property to remove the grouping symbols.

Example 1 □ Solve each equation.

a. $\dfrac{7}{3}x - 8 = 6 + \dfrac{1}{3}x$

b. $5 - 3(k+1) = -k$

Solution □ a. $\dfrac{7}{3}x - 8 = 6 + \dfrac{1}{3}x$

$\dfrac{7}{3}x - 8 - \dfrac{1}{3}x = 6 + \dfrac{1}{3}x - \dfrac{1}{3}x$ Subtract $\dfrac{1}{3}x$ from each side.

$2x - 8 = 6$ Simplify.

$2x - 8 + 8 = 6 + 8$ Add 8 to each side.

$2x = 14$ Simplify.

$\dfrac{2x}{2} = \dfrac{14}{2}$ Divide each side by 2.

$x = 7$ Simplify.

b. $5 - 3(k+1) = -k$

$5 - 3k - 3 = -k$ Distributive Property

$2 - 3k = -k$ Simplify.

$2 - 3k + k = -k + k$ Add k to each side.

$2 - 2k = 0$ Simplify.

$2 - 2k - 2 = 0 - 2$ Subtract 2 from each side.

$-2k = -2$ Simplify.

$\dfrac{-2k}{-2} = \dfrac{-2}{-2}$ Divide each side by -2.

$k = 1$ Simplify.

Example 2 □ Four times the sum of three and a number equals nine less than the number.

a. Write an equation for the problem.

b. Then solve the equation.

Solution □ a. $4(3+n) = n - 9$

b. $12 + 4n = n - 9$ Distributive Property

$12 + 4n - n = n - 9 - n$ Subtract n from each side.

$12 + 3n = -9$ Simplify.

$12 + 3n - 12 = -9 - 12$ Subtract 12 from each side.

$3n = -21$ Simplify.

$\dfrac{3n}{3} = \dfrac{-21}{3}$ Divide each side by 3.

$n = -7$ Simplify.

Exercise - Solving Equations with Variables on Both Sides

1

If $7n + 3 = 2n - 12$, what is the value of $-n + 3$?

2

If $7(h - 5) - 3h = \dfrac{3}{2}h$, what is the value

of $\dfrac{1}{7}h$?

3

$$\dfrac{r}{3} + \dfrac{s}{11} = \dfrac{39}{33}$$

Given the above equation, if $s = 2$, what is the value of r?

4

If $\dfrac{9 - 2k}{3} = k - 2$, what is the value of k?

5

A $48 shirts costs $22 more than one half the cost of a pair of pants. How much does the pair of pants cost?

6

Twice a number n, increased by 11 is the same as six times the number decreased by 9. What is the value of n?

7

One half of a number increased by 3 is five less than two thirds of the number.

8

Four times the greatest of three consecutive odd integers exceeds three times the least by 31. What is the greatest of the three consecutive odd integers?

2-4. Equation with No Solution and Identity

It is possible that an equation may have no solution. That is, there is no value of the variable that will result in a true equation. It is also possible that an equation may be true for all values of the variable. Such an equation is called an **identity**.

Example 1 □ Solve each equation. If the equation has no solution or it is an identity, write no solution or identity.

    a. $2(1-x)+5x = 3(x+1)$

    b. $5w - 3(1-w) = -2(3-w)$

    c. $\dfrac{1}{2}(8y-6) = 5y-(y+3)$

Solution □ a. $2(1-x)+5x = 3(x+1)$

$2-2x+5x = 3x+3$	Distributive property
$2+3x = 3x+3$	Simplify.
$2+3x-3x = 3x+3-3x$	Subtract $3x$ from each side.
$2 = 3$	Simplify.

The given equation is equivalent to the false statement $2 = 3$.
Therefore the equation has no solution.

    b. $5w - 3(1-w) = -2(3-w)$

$5w-3+3w = -6+2w$	Distributive property
$8w-3 = -6+2w$	Simplify.
$8w-3-2w = -6+2w-2w$	Subtract $2w$ from each side.
$6w-3 = -6$	Simplify.
$6w-3+3 = -6+3$	Add 3 to each side.
$6w = -3$	Simplify.
$\dfrac{6w}{6} = \dfrac{-3}{6}$	Divide each side by 6.
$w = -\dfrac{1}{2}$	Simplify.

    c. $\dfrac{1}{2}(8y-6) = 5y-(y+3)$

$4y-3 = 5y-y-3$	Distributive property
$4y-3 = 4y-3$	Simplify.

The given equation is equivalent to $4y-3 = 4y-3$, which is true for all values of y.
This equation is an identity.

Exercise - Equation with No Solution and Identity

1

If $\frac{1}{3}(9-6x)=5-2x$, what is the value of x?

A) 3

B) 4

C) 5

D) The equation has no solution.

2

If $5(x-2)-3x=2(x-5)$, which of the following must be true?

A) x is 3.

B) x is 4.

C) x is 5.

D) The equation is true for all values of x.

3

$$\frac{1}{3}(15-6x)=5-ax$$

If the linear equation above is an identity, what is the value of a?

A) 2

B) 3

C) 4

D) 5

4

$$4x+13=7(x-2)+bx$$

If the linear equation above has no solution, which of the following could be the value of b?

A) −1

B) −2

C) −3

D) −4

5

What is the value of n
if $-\frac{7}{2}(2n-3)+4n=\frac{3}{2}(5+2n)$?

6

What is the value of k
if $\frac{13-7(k+1)}{3}=3k-2$?

7

What is the value of x
if $-2[3-(x-4)]+5x=2-x$?

8

What is the value of m
if $0.4(5m-9)=-5m-4(0.3-m)$?

2-5. Solving for a Specific Variable

A **formula** is an equation that states the relationship between two or more variables. Formulas and some equations contain more than one variable. It is often useful to solve formulas for one of the variables.

Example 1 □ Solve each equation or formula for the specified variable.

    a. $3x - a = kx + b$, for x b. $A = \dfrac{1}{2}(a+b)h$, for h

    c. $C = \dfrac{5}{9}(F - 32)$, for F

Solution □ a. $3x - a = kx + b$

       $3x - a - kx = kx + b - kx$ Subtract kx from each side.

       $3x - a - kx = b$ Simplify.

       $3x - a - kx + a = b + a$ Add a to each side.

       $3x - kx = b + a$ Simplify.

       $x(3 - k) = b + a$ Distributive property

       $\dfrac{x(3-k)}{3-k} = \dfrac{b+a}{3-k}$ Divide each side by $3 - k$.

       $x = \dfrac{b+a}{3-k}$ Simplify.

    b. $A = \dfrac{1}{2}(a+b)h$

       $2 \cdot A = 2 \cdot \dfrac{1}{2}(a+b)h$ Multiply each side by 2.

       $2A = (a+b)h$ Simplify.

       $\dfrac{2A}{a+b} = \dfrac{(a+b)}{a+b}h$ Divide each side by $a + b$.

       $h = \dfrac{2A}{a+b}$ Simplify.

    c. $C = \dfrac{5}{9}(F - 32)$

       $\dfrac{9}{5} \cdot C = \dfrac{9}{5} \cdot \dfrac{5}{9}(F - 32)$ Multiply each side by $\dfrac{9}{5}$.

       $\dfrac{9}{5}C = F - 32$ Simplify.

       $\dfrac{9}{5}C + 32 = F - 32 + 32$ Add 32 to each side.

       $F = \dfrac{9}{5}C + 32$ Simplify.

Exercise - Solving for a Specific Variable

1

If $2x + 3y = 18$, which of the following gives y in terms of x?

A) $y = 6 + \dfrac{2}{3}x$

B) $y = 6 - \dfrac{2}{3}x$

C) $y = 6 + \dfrac{3}{2}x$

D) $y = 6 - \dfrac{3}{2}x$

2

If $P = 2l + 2w$, which of the following gives w in terms of P and l?

A) $w = P - 2l$

B) $w = P - l$

C) $w = \dfrac{P}{2} - l$

D) $w = P - \dfrac{l}{2}$

3

If $c = \dfrac{a}{a+b}$, which of the following gives a in terms of b and c?

A) $a = \dfrac{bc}{1-c}$

B) $a = \dfrac{bc}{1+c}$

C) $a = \dfrac{bc}{b-c}$

D) $a = \dfrac{bc}{b+c}$

4

If $\dfrac{ab-1}{3} = c$, which of the following gives b in terms of the other variables?

A) $b = \dfrac{3c+1}{a}$

B) $b = \dfrac{3c-1}{a}$

C) $b = \dfrac{3c}{a} + 1$

D) $b = \dfrac{3c}{a} - 1$

5

If $gh - f = g - h$, which of the following gives g in terms of the other variables?

A) $g = \dfrac{f+h}{h-1}$

B) $g = \dfrac{f-h}{h+1}$

C) $g = \dfrac{f+h}{h+1}$

D) $g = \dfrac{f-h}{h-1}$

6

If $n = a + (k-1)d$, which of the following gives k in terms of the other variables?

A) $k = \dfrac{n-a+1}{d}$

B) $k = \dfrac{n+a-1}{d}$

C) $k = \dfrac{n-a-d}{d}$

D) $k = \dfrac{n-a+d}{d}$

Chapter 2 Practice Test

1

If $\dfrac{5}{6}x = \dfrac{4}{5}$, what is the value of x ?

A) $\dfrac{3}{2}$

B) $\dfrac{2}{3}$

C) $\dfrac{24}{25}$

D) $\dfrac{25}{24}$

2

When one half of the number n is decreased by 4, the result is -6. What is three times n added to 7?

A) -7

B) -5

C) -3

D) -1

3

If $4 - 7x$ is 5 less than 23, what is the value of $3x$?

A) -12

B) -9

C) -6

D) -3

4

$$P = F(\tfrac{1}{2}v^2 + 1)$$

The above equation gives pressure P, which is exerted by a fluid that is forced to stop moving. The pressure depends on the initial force, F, and the speed of the fluid, v. Which of the following expresses the square of the velocity in terms of the pressure and the force?

A) $v^2 = 2(P - F) - 1$

B) $v^2 = 2(P - F - 1)$

C) $v^2 = 2(\dfrac{P}{F}) - 1$

D) $v^2 = 2(\dfrac{P - F}{F})$

5

One half of the number n increased by 10 is the same as four less than twice the number.

Which of the following equations represents the statement above?

A) $\dfrac{1}{2}(n + 10) = 2(n - 4)$

B) $\dfrac{1}{2}n + 10 = 2(n - 4)$

C) $\dfrac{1}{2}n + 10 = 2n - 4$

D) $\dfrac{1}{2}(n + 10) = 2n - 4$

6

If a is b less than one-half of c, what is b in terms of a and c?

A) $\frac{1}{2}c - a$

B) $a - \frac{1}{2}c$

C) $2a - c$

D) $c - 2a$

7

If $x = 1 - y$ and $3x = 8 - 5y$, what is the value of x?

A) -2

B) $-\frac{3}{2}$

C) $-\frac{1}{2}$

D) $\frac{5}{2}$

8

The quotient of a number and five equals nine less than one half of the number. What is the number?

A) -20

B) -10

C) 20

D) 30

9

If $\frac{a}{b} = 1$, what is the value of $a - b$?

10

When an object is thrown from the ground into the air with an initial upward speed of v_0 meters per second, the speed v, in meters per second, is given by the equation $v = v_0 - 9.8t$, where t is the time in seconds. The speed of an object becomes 0 when the object reaches its maximum height. If an object is thrown upward with an initial speed of 14 m/sec, how many seconds does it taken an to reach its maximum height?
(Round your answer to the nearest hundredth of a second.)

11

When an object is dropped from a height of s feet above the ground, the height h of the object is given by the equation $h = -16t^2 + s$, where t is the time in seconds after the object has dropped. If an object is dropped from a height of 144 feet above the ground, how many seconds will it take to hit the ground?

Answer Key

Section 2-1

1. 107   2. 13.5   3. 12   4. 7   5. 77
6. A   7. A   8. C

Section 2-2

1. 29   2. 27   3. $\dfrac{5}{2}$ 4. 4   5. 136
6. B   7. C   8. C

Section 2-3

1. 6   2. 2   3. 3   4. 3   5. 52
6. 5   7. 48   8. 19

Section 2-4

1. D   2. D   3. A   4. C   5. $\dfrac{1}{2}$

6. $\dfrac{3}{4}$ 7. 2   8. 0.8

Section 2-5

1. B   2. C   3. A   4. A   5. D
6. D

Chapter 2 Practice Test

1. C   2. B   3. C   4. D   5. C
6. A   7. B   8. D   9. 0   10. 1.43
11. 3

Answers and Explanations

Section 2-1

1. 107

$$\underbrace{n+18}_{18\ \text{more than}\ n}=125$$
$$n=125-18=107$$

2. 13.5

$$20=\underbrace{2w-7}_{7\ \text{less than twice}\ w}$$

$20+7=2w-7+7$	Add 7 to each side.
$27=2w$	Simplify.
$\dfrac{27}{2}=\dfrac{2w}{2}$	Divide each side by 2.
$13.5=w$	Simplify.

3. 12

$$\underbrace{2x-9}_{9\ \text{less than twice}\ x}=\underbrace{x+3}_{3\ \text{more than}\ x}$$

$2x-9-x=x+3-x$	Subtract x from each side.
$x-9=3$	Simplify.
$x=12$	

4. 7

$$\underbrace{4c-8}_{8\ \text{less than 4 times}\ c}=20$$

$4c-8+8=20+8$	Add 8 to each side.
$4c=28$	Simplify.
$c=7$	

5. 77

Let $n=$ the smallest of four consecutive odd integers. Then,
$$n+(n+2)+(n+4)+(n+6)=296.$$
$$4n+12=296$$
$$4n=284$$
$$n=71$$
The greatest of the four consecutive odd integers is $n+6$. Therefore,

$$n+6=71+6=77$$

6. A

$$\underbrace{\dfrac{3}{4}a+24}_{\text{the sum of three fourths of}\ a\ \text{and 24}}=-9$$

$\dfrac{3}{4}a+24-24=-9-24$	Subtract 24 from each side.
$\dfrac{3}{4}a=-33$	Simplify.
$\dfrac{4}{3}\cdot\dfrac{3}{4}a=\dfrac{4}{3}(-33)$	Multiply each side by $\dfrac{4}{3}$.
$a=-44$	

7. A

$$\underbrace{(g-23)\dfrac{1}{2}}_{g\ \text{is decrease by 23 and then multiplied by}\ \frac{1}{2}.}=\underbrace{2g+8}_{8\ \text{more than twice}\ g}$$

$(g-23)\dfrac{1}{2}\cdot 2=(2g+8)2$	Multiply each side by 2.
$g-23=4g+16$	Simplify.
$g-23+23=4g+16+23$	Add 23 to each side.
$g=4g+39$	Simplify.
$g-4g=4g+39-4g$	Subtract $4g$.
$-3g=39$	Simplify.
$g=-13$	

8. C

$$\underbrace{\frac{p}{q}}_{\substack{\text{the quotient} \\ \text{of } p \text{ and } q}} \quad = \quad \underbrace{3(p+q)}_{\substack{\text{three times the} \\ \text{sum of } p \text{ and } q}} \quad \underbrace{-12}_{\text{twelve less than}}$$

Section 2-2

1. 29

   Given $-11 + x = 9$.
   $20 - (11 - x) = 20 - 11 + x = 20 + (-11 + x)$
   $ = 20 + 9 = 29$

2. 27

   $33 - a = a + 27 - 5a$
   $33 - a = 27 - 4a$ Simplify.
   $33 - a + 4a = 27 - 4a + 4a$ Add $4a$ to each side.
   $33 + 3a = 27$ Simplify.

3. $\dfrac{5}{2}$

   $$\frac{1}{2}x - 3 = \frac{3}{4} - x$$

   Multiply by 4 on both sides of the equation to simplify the given equation.
   $$4(\frac{1}{2}x - 3) = 4(\frac{3}{4} - x)$$
   $2x - 12 = 3 - 4x$ Distributive Property
   $2x - 12 + 4x = 3 - 4x + 4x$ Add $4x$ to each side.
   $6x - 12 = 3$ Simplify.
   $6x - 12 + 12 = 3 + 12$ Add 12 to each side.
   $6x = 15$ Simplify.
   $$x = \frac{15}{6} = \frac{5}{2}$$

4. 4

   $x - (3 - 2x) + (4 - 5x) = -7$
   $x - 3 + 2x + 4 - 5x = -7$ Simplify.
   $-2x + 1 = -7$ Simplify.
   $-2x + 1 - 1 = -7 - 1$ Subtract 1.
   $-2x = -8$ Simplify.
   $$x = \frac{-8}{-2} = 4$$

5. 136

   $$\underbrace{\frac{3}{4}x}_{\substack{\text{three quarters} \\ \text{of a number}}} \underbrace{-}_{\text{decreased by}} \underbrace{20}_{\text{twenty}} \underbrace{=}_{\text{equals}} \underbrace{82}_{\text{eighty two}}$$

$\dfrac{3}{4}x - 20 + 20 = 82 + 20$ Add 20 to each side.

$\dfrac{3}{4}x = 102$ Simplify.

$x = \dfrac{4}{3} \cdot 102 = 136$

6. B

   $$\underbrace{2\frac{3}{5}x}_{\substack{\text{two and three fifth} \\ \text{of a number}}} \underbrace{=}_{\text{equals}} \underbrace{-26}_{\text{negative twenty six}}$$

   $\dfrac{13}{5}x = -26$ $2\dfrac{3}{5} = \dfrac{13}{5}$

   $\dfrac{5}{13} \cdot \dfrac{13}{5}x = \dfrac{5}{13} \cdot -26$ Multiply each side by $\dfrac{5}{13}$.
   $x = -10$

7. C

   Let $x =$ the total students in the high school.
   Then $\dfrac{2}{9}x = 142$.

   $x = \dfrac{9}{2} \cdot 142 = 639$

8. C

   $820c + 380r = 4,360$
   Substitute 3 for c in the equation above since c represents the number of cups of cashews.

   $820(3) + 380r = 4,360$
   $2,460 + 380r = 4,360 \implies 380r = 1,900$
   $\implies r = 5$

Section 2-3

1. 6

   $7n + 3 = 2n - 12 \implies 5n = -15 \implies n = -3$
   Therefore, $-n + 3 = -(-3) + 3 = 3 + 3 = 6$.

2. 2

   $7(h - 5) - 3h = \dfrac{3}{2}h \implies 7h - 35 - 3h = \dfrac{3}{2}h$

   $\implies 4h - 35 = \dfrac{3}{2}h \implies 4h - \dfrac{3}{2}h = 35$

   $\implies \dfrac{5}{2}h = 35 \implies h = 35 \cdot \dfrac{2}{5} = 14$

   Therefore, $\dfrac{1}{7}h = \dfrac{1}{7}(14) = 2$.

3. 3

$\dfrac{r}{3}+\dfrac{s}{11}=\dfrac{39}{33}$ and $s=2$. $\Rightarrow \dfrac{r}{3}+\dfrac{2}{11}=\dfrac{39}{33}$

To simplify the equation, multiply both sides of the equation by 33, which is the LCD of 3 and 11.

$33(\dfrac{r}{3}+\dfrac{2}{11})=33\cdot\dfrac{39}{33} \Rightarrow 11r+6=39$

$\Rightarrow 11r=33 \Rightarrow r=3$

4. 3

$\dfrac{9-2k}{3}=k-2$

To simplify the equation, multiply both sides of the equation by 3.

$3(\dfrac{9-2k}{3})=3(k-2) \Rightarrow 9-2k=3k-6$

$\Rightarrow -2k-3k=-6-9 \Rightarrow -5k=-15$

$\Rightarrow k=3$

5. 52

Let $p=$ the cost of a pair of pants.

Since a \$48 shirts costs \$22 more than one half the cost of a pair of pants, you can set up the following equation.

$48=\dfrac{1}{2}p+22$

$\Rightarrow 26=\dfrac{1}{2}p \Rightarrow 52=p$

6. 5

$\underbrace{2n+11}_{\substack{\text{twice a number}\\\text{increased by 11}}} = \underbrace{6n-9}_{\substack{\text{six times the number}\\\text{decreased by 9}}}$

$2n+11=6n-9 \Rightarrow 20=4n \Rightarrow n=5$

7. 48

$\underbrace{\dfrac{1}{2}n+3}_{\substack{\text{one half of a number}\\\text{increased by three}}} = \underbrace{\dfrac{2}{3}n-5}_{\substack{\text{five less than two thirds}\\\text{of the number}}}$

To simplify the equation, multiply both sides of the equation by 6, which is the LCD of 2 and 3.

$6(\dfrac{1}{2}n+3)=6(\dfrac{2}{3}n-5)$

$3n+18=4n-30$

Solving for n yields $n=48$.

8. 19

Let n be the first of the three consecutive odd integers, so n, $n+2$, and $n+4$ are the three

consecutive odd integers.

$\underbrace{4(n+4)}_{\substack{\text{4 times the greatest of 3}\\\text{consecutive odd integers}}} = \underbrace{3n}_{\substack{\text{3 times the least of 3}\\\text{consecutive odd integers}}} \underbrace{+31}_{\substack{\text{exceeds}\\\text{by 31}}}$

$4(n+4)=3n+31$

$4n+16=3n+31 \Rightarrow n=15$

The greatest of the three consecutive odd integers is $n+4=15+4=19$.

Section 2-4

1. D

$\dfrac{1}{3}(9-6x)=5-2x$

$3-2x=5-2x$ Distributive Property

$3-2x+2x=5-2x+2x$ Add $2x$ to each side.

$3=5$

The given equation is equivalent to the false statement $3=5$. Therefore the equation has no solution.

2. D

$5(x-2)-3x=2(x-10)$

$5x-10-3x=2x-20$ Distributive Property

$2x-10=2x-10$ Simplify.

The given equation is equivalent to $2x-10=2x-10$, which is true for all values of x.

3. A

$\dfrac{1}{3}(15-6x)=5-ax$

$5-2x=5-ax$ Distributive Property

If the linear equation is an identity, the value of a is 2.

4. C

$4x+13=7(x-2)+bx$

$4x+13=7x-14+bx$

$4x+13=(7+b)x-14$

If $4=7+b$, the linear equation has no solution. Solving for b yields $b=-3$.

5. $\dfrac{1}{2}$

$-\dfrac{7}{2}(2n-3)+4n=\dfrac{3}{2}(5+2n)$

To simplify the equation, multiply both sides of the equation by 2.

$$2[-\frac{7}{2}(2n-3)+4n] = 2[\frac{3}{2}(5+2n)]$$

$-7(2n-3)+8n = 3(5+2n)$	Distributive Property
$-14n+21+8n = 15+6n$	Simplify.
$-6n+21 = 15+6n$	Simplify.
$-6n+21+6n = 15+6n+6n$	Add $6n$ to each side.
$21 = 15+12n$	
$21-15 = 15+12n-15$	Subtract 15.
$6 = 12n$ or $12n = 6$	Simplify.

$$n = \frac{6}{12} = \frac{1}{2}$$

6. $\dfrac{3}{4}$

$$\frac{13-7(k+1)}{3} = 3k-2$$

To simplify the equation, multiply both sides of the equation by 3.

$$3[\frac{13-7(k+1)}{3}] = 3[3k-2]$$

$13-7(k+1) = 9k-6$	Simplify.
$13-7k-7 = 9k-6$	Distributive Property
$6-7k = 9k-6$	Simplify.
$6-7k-6 = 9k-6-6$	Subtract 6.
$-7k = 9k-12$	Simplify.
$-7k-9k = 9k-12-9k$	Subtract $9k$.
$-16k = -12$	

$$k = \frac{-12}{-16} = \frac{3}{4}$$

7. 2

$$-2[3-(x-4)]+5x = 2-x$$
$$-2[3-x+4]+5x = 2-x$$
$$-2[7-x]+5x = 2-x$$
$$-14+2x+5x = 2-x$$
$$-14+7x = 2-x$$
$$8x = 16$$
$$x = 2$$

8. 0.8

$$0.4(5m-9) = -5m-4(0.3-m)$$
$$2m-3.6 = -5m-1.2+4m$$
$$2m-3.6 = -m-1.2$$
$$3m = 2.4$$
$$m = 0.8$$

Section 2-5

1. B

$2x+3y = 18$	
$2x+3y-2x = 18-2x$	Subtract $2x$ from each side.
$3y = 18-2x$	Simplify.
$\dfrac{3y}{3} = \dfrac{18}{3} - \dfrac{2x}{3}$	Divide each side by 3.
$y = 6 - \dfrac{2}{3}x$	Simplify.

2. C

$P = 2l+2w$	
$P-2l = 2l+2w-2l$	Subtract $2l$ from each side.
$P-2l = 2w$	Simplify.
$\dfrac{P}{2} - \dfrac{2l}{2} = \dfrac{2w}{2}$	Divide each side by 2.
$\dfrac{P}{2} - l = w$	Simplify.

3. A

$c = \dfrac{a}{a+b}$	
$(a+b)c = (a+b)\dfrac{a}{a+b}$	Multiply each side by $a+b$.
$ac+bc = a$	Simplify.
$ac+bc-ac = a-ac$	Subtract ac from each side.
$bc = a-ac$	Simplify.
$bc = a(1-c)$	Factor.
$\dfrac{bc}{1-c} = a$	Divide each side by $1-c$.

4. A

$\dfrac{ab-1}{3} = c$	
$3[\dfrac{ab-1}{3}] = 3c$	Multiply each side by 3.
$ab-1 = 3c$	Simplify.
$ab-1+1 = 3c+1$	Add 1 to each side.
$ab = 3c+1$	Simplify.
$\dfrac{ab}{a} = \dfrac{3c+1}{a}$	Divide each side by a.
$b = \dfrac{3c+1}{a}$	Simplify.

5. D

$$gh - f = g - h$$
$$gh - f + f = g - h + f \qquad \text{Add } f \text{ to each side.}$$
$$gh = g - h + f \qquad \text{Simplify.}$$
$$gh - g = g - h + f - g \qquad \text{Subtract } g \text{ from each side.}$$
$$gh - g = f - h \qquad \text{Simplify.}$$
$$g(h-1) = f - h \qquad \text{Factor.}$$
$$g = \frac{f-h}{h-1} \qquad \text{Divide each side by } h-1.$$

6. D

$$n = a + (k-1)d$$
$$n = a + kd - d \qquad \text{Distributive Property}$$
$$n - a + d = a + kd - d - a + d$$
$$\qquad \text{Add } -a + d \text{ to each side.}$$
$$n - a + d = kd \qquad \text{Simplify.}$$
$$\frac{n-a+d}{d} = k \qquad \text{Divide each side by } d.$$

Chapter 2 Practice Test

1. C

$$\frac{5}{6}x = \frac{4}{5}$$
$$\frac{6}{5} \cdot \frac{5}{6}x = \frac{6}{5} \cdot \frac{4}{5} \qquad \text{Multiply each side by } \frac{6}{5}.$$
$$x = \frac{24}{25}$$

2. B

$$\underbrace{\frac{1}{2}n}_{\frac{1}{2} \text{ of a number } n} \quad \underbrace{- \ 4}_{\text{decreased by 4}} \ = \ \underbrace{-6}_{\text{negative 6}}$$

$$\frac{1}{2}n - 4 + 4 = -6 + 4 \qquad \text{Add 4 to each side.}$$
$$\frac{1}{2}n = -2 \qquad \text{Simplify.}$$
$$2 \cdot \frac{1}{2}n = 2 \cdot -2 \qquad \text{Multiply each side by 2.}$$
$$n = -4 \qquad \text{Simplify.}$$

Three times n added to 7 is $3n + 7$.
$$3n + 7$$
$$= 3(-4) + 7 \qquad \text{Substitute } -4 \text{ for } n.$$
$$= -5$$

3. C

$$\underbrace{4 - 7x = 23 - 5}_{4-7x \text{ is 5 less than 23}}$$

$$4 - 7x = 18 \ \Rightarrow \ -7x = 14 \ \Rightarrow \ x = -2$$
$$3x = 3(-2) = -6$$

4. D

$$P = F\left(\frac{1}{2}v^2 + 1\right)$$
$$\frac{P}{F} = \frac{F}{F}\left(\frac{1}{2}v^2 + 1\right) \qquad \text{Divide each side by } F.$$
$$\frac{P}{F} = \frac{1}{2}v^2 + 1 \qquad \text{Simplify.}$$
$$\frac{P}{F} - 1 = \frac{1}{2}v^2 + 1 - 1 \qquad \text{Subtract 1 from each side.}$$
$$\frac{P}{F} - 1 = \frac{1}{2}v^2 \qquad \text{Simplify.}$$
$$2\left(\frac{P}{F} - 1\right) = 2 \cdot \frac{1}{2}v^2 \qquad \text{Multiply each side by 2.}$$
$$2\left(\frac{P}{F} - 1\right) = v^2 \qquad \text{Simplify.}$$
$$2\left(\frac{P}{F} - \frac{F}{F}\right) = v^2 \qquad \frac{F}{F} = 1$$
$$2\left(\frac{P-F}{F}\right) = v^2 \qquad \text{The common denominator is } F.$$
$$\qquad \text{Combine the numerators.}$$

5. C

$$\underbrace{\frac{1}{2}n + 10}_{\substack{\frac{1}{2} \text{ of the number } n \\ \text{increased by 10}}} \ = \ \underbrace{2n - 4}_{\substack{\text{four less than twice} \\ \text{the number}}}$$

6. A

$$\underbrace{a = \frac{1}{2}c - b}_{a \text{ is } b \text{ less than } \frac{1}{2} \text{ of } c}$$

$$a - \frac{1}{2}c = \frac{1}{2}c - b - \frac{1}{2}c \qquad \text{Add } -\frac{1}{2}c \text{ to each side.}$$
$$a - \frac{1}{2}c = -b \qquad \text{Simplify.}$$
$$(-1)\left[a - \frac{1}{2}c\right] = (-1)(-b) \qquad \text{Multiply each side by } -1.$$
$$-a + \frac{1}{2}c = b \ \text{ or } \ \frac{1}{2}c - a = b$$

7. B

$x = 1 - y$ First equation

$3x = 8 - 5y$ Second equation

Solving the first equation for y yields $y = 1 - x$.
Substitute $1 - x$ for y in the second equation.

$3x = 8 - 5(1 - x)$ Substitution

$3x = 8 - 5 + 5x$ Distributive property

$3x = 3 + 5x$ Simplify.

$3x - 5x = 3 + 5x - 5x$ Subtract $5x$ from each side.

$-2x = 3$ Simplify.

$\dfrac{-2x}{-2} = \dfrac{3}{-2}$ Divide each side by -2.

$x = -\dfrac{3}{2}$ Simplify.

8. D

$$\underbrace{\frac{x}{5}}_{\substack{\text{the quotient of}\\\text{of a number and 5}}} = \underbrace{\frac{1}{2}x - 9}_{\substack{\text{nine less than one}\\\text{half of the number}}}$$

$10(\dfrac{x}{5}) = 10(\dfrac{1}{2}x - 9)$ Multiply each side by 10.

$2x = 5x - 90$ Distributive Property

$2x - 5x = 5x - 90 - 5x$ Subtract $5x$ from each side.

$-3x = -90$ Simplify.

$\dfrac{-3x}{-3} = \dfrac{-90}{-3}$ Divide each side by -3.

$x = 30$ Simplify.

9. 0

$\dfrac{a}{b} = 1$

$b(\dfrac{a}{b}) = b(1)$ Multiply each side by b.

$a = b$ Simplify.

$a - b = b - b$ Subtract b from each side.

$a - b = 0$ Simplify.

10. 1.43

As the object moves upward, its speed decreases
continuously and becomes 0 as it reaches its
maximum height.
$v = v_0 - 9.8t$ is the given equation. Substituting
14 for v_0 and 0 for v gives $0 = 14 - 9.8t$.

Solving the equation for t gives $t = \dfrac{14}{9.8} = 1.428$

seconds, which is 1.43 to the nearest hundredth
of a second.

11. 3

When the object hits the ground, the height is 0.
Substitute 0 for h and 144 for s in the equation
$0 = -16t^2 + 144$. Solving the equation for t^2
gives $t^2 = \dfrac{144}{16} = 9$.
Therefore, $t = \sqrt{9} = 3$.

CHAPTER 3
Functions and Linear Equations

3-1. Relations and Functions

A **coordinate plane** is formed by the horizontal line called the **x- axis** and the vertical line called the **y- axis**, which meet at the **origin** $(0,0)$.

The axes divide the plane into four parts called **quadrants**.

An **ordered pair** gives the coordinates and location of a point. The ordered pairs $(2,1)$, $(-2,2)$, $(-4,-4)$, and $(3,-2)$ are located in Quadrant I, Quadrant II, Quadrant III, and Quadrant IV respectively.

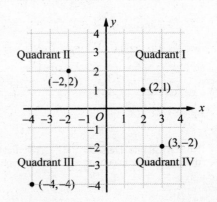

A **relation** is a set of ordered pairs. A relation can be represented by a graph, a table, or a **mapping**.

The **domain** of a relation is the set of all *x*- coordinates and the **range** of a relation is the set of all *y*- coordinates from the ordered pairs.

A **function** is a special type of relation in which each element of the domain is paired with exactly one element of the range.

Table   **Mapping**

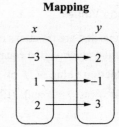

x	y
-3	2
1	-1
2	3

Example 1 □ Express each relation below as a set of ordered pairs and determine whether it is a function.

a.

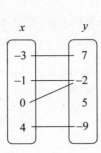

b.

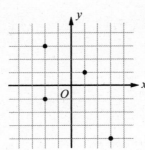

c.

x	y
1	-2
2	3
3	5
4	-2

Solution □ a. $\{(-3,7), (-1,-2), (0,-2), (4,-9)\}$
The mapping represents a function.

b. $\{(1,1), (-2,3), (-2,-1), (3,-4)\}$
The element -2 in the domain is paired with both 3 and -1 in the range. This relation does not represent a function.

c. $\{(1,-2), (2,3), (3,5), (4,-2)\}$
The table represents a function.

You can use the **vertical line test** to see if a graph represents a function. A relation is a function if and only if no vertical line intersects its graph more than once.

Function

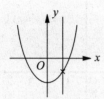

No vertical line intersects the graph more than once.

Not a Function

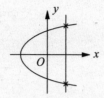

A vertical line intersects the graph at two points.

Function

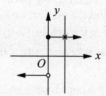

No vertical line intersects the graph more than once.

Function Values

Equations that are functions can be written in a form called **function notation**. In function notation, the equation $y = 2x + 3$ is written as $f(x) = 2x + 3$.

The **function value** of f at $x = c$ is denoted as $f(c)$. For instance, if $f(x) = 5x - 3$, $f(2)$ is the value of f at $x = 2$ and $f(2) = 5(2) - 3 = 7$.

Example 2 □ If $f(x) = 3x + 2$, find each value.

 a. $f(-2)$

 b. $f(c - 2)$

 c. $-2[f(-1)] + f(-2)$

 d. $f(-\frac{1}{2}x + 1)$

Solution □ a. $f(-2) = 3(-2) + 2$ 　　　　　Substitute -2 for x.

 $= -6 + 2 = -4$ 　　　　　Multiply and simplify.

 b. $f(c - 2) = 3(c - 2) + 2$ 　　　　　Substitute $c - 2$ for x.

 $= 3c - 6 + 2$ 　　　　　Multiply.

 $= 3c - 4$ 　　　　　Simplify.

 c. $-2[f(-1)] + f(-2)$

 $= -2[3(-1) + 2] + [3(-2) + 2]$ 　　　　　Substitute -1 for x and -2 for x.

 $= -2[-3 + 2] + [-6 + 2]$ 　　　　　Multiply.

 $= -2[-1] + [-4]$ 　　　　　Simplify.

 $= 2 - 4$ 　　　　　Simplify.

 $= -2$ 　　　　　Simplify.

 d. $f(-\frac{1}{2}x + 1) = 3(-\frac{1}{2}x + 1) + 2$ 　　　　　Substitute $-\frac{1}{2}x + 1$ for x.

 $= -\frac{3}{2}x + 3 + 2$ 　　　　　Multiply.

 $= -\frac{3}{2}x + 5$ 　　　　　Simplify.

Exercises - Relations and Functions

1

What is the domain of the function that contains points at $(-5, 2)$, $(-2, 1)$, $(0, 2)$, and $(4, -3)$?

A) $\{-3, 1, 2\}$

B) $\{-2, 1, 0\}$

C) $\{-5, -2, 1, 2\}$

D) $\{-5, -2, 0, 4\}$

2

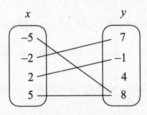

Which of the following relation is a correct representation of the mapping shown above?

A) $\{(-5, 7), (-2, -1), (2, 4), (5, 8)\}$

B) $\{(-5, 8), (-2, 7), (2, -1), (5, 8)\}$

C) $\{(7, -5), (-1, -2), (4, 2), (8, 5)\}$

D) $\{(8, -5), (7, -2), (-1, 2), (8, 5)\}$

3

If point $(7, b)$ is in Quadrant I and point $(a, -3)$ is in Quadrant III, in which Quadrant is the point (a, b) ?

A) Quadrant I

B) Quadrant II

C) Quadrant III

D) Quadrant IV

4

If $f(x) = -2x + 7$, what is $f(\frac{1}{2}x + 3)$ equal to?

A) $-x + 1$

B) $-x + 3$

C) $-x + 5$

D) $-x + 10$

5

$$g(x) = kx^3 + 3$$

For the function g defined above, k is a constant and $g(-1) = 5$. What is the value of $g(1)$?

A) -3

B) -1

C) 1

D) 3

6

If $f(x+1) = -\frac{1}{2}x + 6$, what is the value of $f(-3)$?

7

$$f(x) = x^2 - b$$

In the function above, b is a constant.
If $f(-2) = 7$, what is the value of $f(b)$?

3-2. Rate of Change and Slope

The **average rate of change** is a ratio that describes, on average, change in one quantity with respect to change in another quantity. If x is the independent variable and y is the dependent variable, then

$$\text{the average rate of change} = \frac{\text{change in } y}{\text{change in } x}.$$

Geometrically, the rate of change is the slope of the line through the points (x_1, y_1) and (x_2, y_2).

The **slope** m of a line through (x_1, y_1) and (x_2, y_2) is $m = \dfrac{y_2 - y_1}{x_2 - x_1} = \dfrac{\text{change in } y}{\text{change in } x} = \dfrac{\text{rise}}{\text{run}}$.

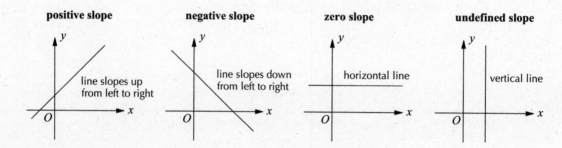

positive slope	negative slope	zero slope	undefined slope
line slopes up from left to right	line slopes down from left to right	horizontal line	vertical line

The **standard form** of a linear equation of a line is $Ax + By = C$, in which A, B, and C are integers.

The x-coordinate of the point at which the graph of an equation crosses the x-axis is called the **x-intercept**. To find the x-intercept, let $y = 0$ and solve the equation for x.

The y-coordinate of the point at which the graph of an equation crosses the y-axis is called the **y-intercept**. To find the y-intercept, let $x = 0$ and solve the equation for y.

The intercepts of a line provide a quick way to sketch the line.

Values of x for which $f(x) = 0$ are called **zeros** of the function f. A function's zero is its x-intercept.

Example 1 □ The table at the right shows Evan's height from age 12 to 18. Find the average rate of change in Evan's height from age 12 to 18.

Age (years)	12	14	16	18
Height (inches)	61	64	68	70

Solution □ Average rate of change $= \dfrac{\text{change in height}}{\text{change in years}}$

$$= \frac{70 - 61}{18 - 12} = \frac{9}{6} = 1.5 \text{ inches per year}$$

Example 2 □ Find the slope of the line that passes through $(3, -2)$ and $(-5, 4)$.

Solution □ $m = \dfrac{y_2 - y_1}{x_2 - x_1} = \dfrac{4 - (-2)}{-5 - 3} = \dfrac{6}{-8} = -\dfrac{3}{4}$

Example 3□ Find the x-intercept and y-intercept of $2x + 3y = 6$.

Solution □ To find the x-intercept, let $y = 0$.

$2x + 3(0) = 6 \implies x = 3$ The x-intercept is 3.

To find the y-intercept, let $x = 0$.

$2(0) + 3y = 6 \implies y = 2$ The y-intercept is 2.

Exercises - Rate of Change and Slope

1

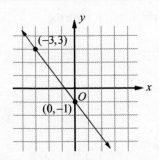

What is the rate of change shown in the graph of the line above?

A) $-\dfrac{4}{3}$

B) $-\dfrac{3}{4}$

C) $\dfrac{3}{4}$

D) $\dfrac{4}{3}$

2

x	-3	0	3	6
y	-1	1	3	5

What is the average rate of change for the relation shown in the table above?

A) $\dfrac{1}{3}$

B) $\dfrac{1}{2}$

C) $\dfrac{2}{3}$

D) $\dfrac{5}{6}$

3

The graph of the linear function f passes through the points $(a,1)$ and $(1,b)$ in the xy- plane. If the slope of the graph of f is 1, which of the following is true?

A) $a-b=1$

B) $a+b=1$

C) $a-b=2$

D) $a+b=2$

4

What is the slope of the line that passes through $(3,2)$ and $(-1,-8)$?

5

What is the value of r if the line that passes through $(4,3)$ and $(-5,r)$ has a slope of -1?

6

What is the value of a if the line that passes through $(a,7)$ and $(1,a)$ has a slope of $-\dfrac{5}{9}$?

7

$$-x+4y=6$$

What is the slope of the line in the equation above?

3-3. Slope-Intercept Form and Point-Slope Form

The **slope-intercept form** of the equation of a line is $y = mx + b$, in which m is the slope and b is the y-intercept.

The **point-slope form** of the equation of a line is $y - y_1 = m(x - x_1)$, in which (x_1, y_1) are the coordinates of a point on the line and m is the slope of the line.

Example 1   □   The graph of a linear equation is shown on the diagram at the right.

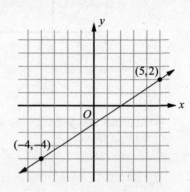

     a. Find the slope of the line on the graph.

     b. Write the equation of the line in point-slope form.

     c. Write the equation of the line in slope-intercept form and find the y-intercept.

     d. Write the equation of the line in standard form.

     e. Find the x-intercept on the graph.

Solution   □   a. $m = \dfrac{y_2 - y_1}{x_2 - x_1}$

         $= \dfrac{2 - (-4)}{5 - (-4)}$ $(x_1, y_1) = (-4, -4)$, $(x_2, y_2) = (5, 2)$

         $= \dfrac{6}{9} = \dfrac{2}{3}$ Simplify.

     b. $y - y_1 = m(x - x_1)$ Point-slope form

        $y - 2 = \dfrac{2}{3}(x - 5)$ $m = \dfrac{2}{3}$. Choose either point for (x_1, y_1).

     c. $y - 2 = \dfrac{2}{3}x - \dfrac{10}{3}$ Simplify point-slope form.

        $y = \dfrac{2}{3}x - \dfrac{4}{3}$ Add 2 to each side.

        The y-intercept is $-\dfrac{4}{3}$.

     d. $y = \dfrac{2}{3}x - \dfrac{4}{3}$ Slope-intercept form

        $3y = 3(\dfrac{2}{3}x - \dfrac{4}{3})$ Multiply each side by 3.

        $3y = 2x - 4$ Simplify.

        $-2x + 3y = -4$ or $2x - 3y = 4$ Subtract $2x$ from each side.

     e. $-2x + 3(0) = -4$ To find the x-intercept, let $y = 0$.

        $x = 2$

        The x-intercept is 2.

Exercises - Slope-Intercept Form and Point-Slope Form

Questions 1-3 refer to the following information.

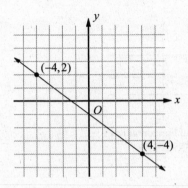

The graph of a linear equation is shown in the diagram above.

1

Which of the following is the equation of the line in point-slope form?

A) $y+4=-\dfrac{4}{3}(x-4)$

B) $y-4=-\dfrac{4}{3}(x+4)$

C) $y-2=-\dfrac{3}{4}(x+4)$

D) $y+2=-\dfrac{3}{4}(x-4)$

2

Which of the following is the equation of the line in slope-intercept form?

A) $y=-\dfrac{3}{4}x+1$

B) $y=-\dfrac{3}{4}x-1$

C) $y=-\dfrac{4}{3}x+1$

D) $y=-\dfrac{4}{3}x-1$

3

Which of the following is the equation of the line in standard form?

A) $4x-3y=-4$

B) $4x+3y=-4$

C) $3x-4y=-4$

D) $3x+4y=-4$

4

In 2005, 120 students at Lincoln High School had smart phones. By 2010, 345 students in the same school had smart phones. Which of the following best describes the annual rate of change in the number of smart phones students had from 2005 to 2010 at Lincoln High School?

A) The average increase in the number of smart phones per year is 40.

B) The average increase in the number of smart phones per year is 45.

C) The average increase in the number of smart phones per year is 50.

D) The average increase in the number of smart phones per year is 55.

5

Which of the following is the equation of the line that passes through point $(4,-1)$ and has slope -2?

A) $x+2y=2$

B) $x-2y=6$

C) $2x-y=9$

D) $2x+y=7$

3-4. Parallel and Perpendicular Lines

Lines in the same plane that do not intersect are called **parallel lines**. Parallel lines have the same slope. If two nonvertical lines have the same slope, then they are parallel.

Parallel Lines in a Coordinate Plane

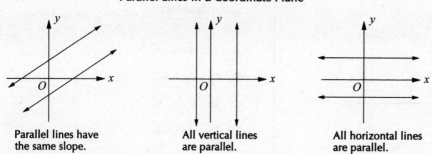

| Parallel lines have the same slope. | All vertical lines are parallel. | All horizontal lines are parallel. |

Lines that intersect at right angles are called **perpendicular lines**.
If the product of the slopes of two nonvertical lines is -1, then the lines are perpendicular.

Perpendicular Lines in a Coordinate Plane

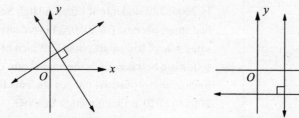

The slopes of perpendicular lines are negative reciprocals of each other.

Vertical lines and horizontal lines are perpendicular.

Example 1   □   Write the equation in point-slope form of the lines through point $(1,2)$ that are (a) parallel to (b) perpendicular to, $3x - y = -2$.

Solution   □   a.

$3x - y = -2$	Original equation
$3x - y - 3x = -2 - 3x$	Subtract $3x$ from each side.
$-y = -3x - 2$	Simplify.
$(-1)(-y) = (-1)(-3x - 2)$	Multiply each side by -1.
$y = 3x + 2$	Simplify.

Parallel lines have the same slope. Replace m with 3 and (x_1, y_1) with $(1,2)$ in point-slope form.

$y - y_1 = m(x - x_1)$	Point-slope form
$y - 2 = 3(x - 1)$	Substitution

b. The line perpendicular to $y = 3x + 2$ has a slope of $-\dfrac{1}{3}$, which is the negative reciprocal of 3. Replace m with $-\dfrac{1}{3}$ and (x_1, y_1) with $(1,2)$ in point-slope form.

$$y - 2 = -\frac{1}{3}(x - 1) \qquad\qquad m = -\frac{1}{3} \text{ and } (x_1, y_1) = (1,2)$$

Exercises - Parallel and Perpendicular Lines

1

Which of the following equations represents a line that is parallel to the line with equation $y = -\frac{1}{2}x + 5$ and contains the point $(-2, \frac{1}{2})$?

A) $x - 2y = -3$

B) $x + 2y = -1$

C) $2x - y = -5$

D) $2x + y = -3$

2

Which of the following equations represents a line that passes through $(7, 6)$ and is parallel to the x-axis?

A) $x = 6$

B) $y = 7$

C) $y = 7$

D) $y = 6$

3

Which of the following equations represents a line that passes through $(-5, 1)$ and is parallel to the y-axis?

A) $y = -5$

B) $y = 1$

C) $x = -5$

D) $x = 1$

4

A line passes through the points $(-1, 2)$ and $(5, b)$, and is parallel to the graph of the equation $4x - 2y = 13$. What is the value of b?

5

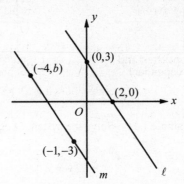

In the xy-plane above, line ℓ is parallel to line m. What is the value of b?

6

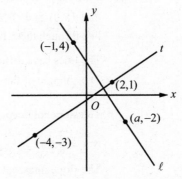

In the xy-plane above, if line ℓ is perpendicular to line t, what is the value of a?

3-5. Solving Systems of Linear Equations

A set of linear equations with the same two variables is called a **system of linear equations**.
A system of two linear equations can have no solution, one solution, or an infinite number of solutions.

Solving Linear Systems by Graphing

Three types of graphs of linear systems are illustrated below.

intersecting lines
exactly one solution

coinciding lines
infinitely many solutions

parallel lines
no solution

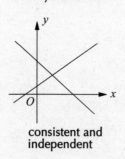   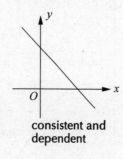   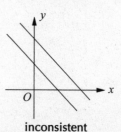

consistent and
independent

consistent and
dependent

inconsistent

Example 1   □   Solve the system of equations by graphing.

a. $y = 2x$

$x + 2y = 5$

b. $-9x + 6y = 12$

$3x - 2y = -4$

Solution   □   a. $y = 2x$ has the y-intercept 0 and the
slope 2. Graph $(0,0)$. From $(0,0)$,
move right 1 unit and up 2 units. Draw
a dot. Draw a line through the points.

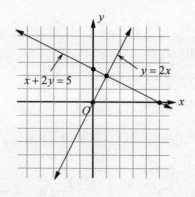

To find the x-intercept of $x + 2y = 5$,
let $y = 0$. $x + 2(0) = 5$ implies $x = 5$.
To find the y-intercept let $x = 0$.
$0 + 2y = 5$ implies $y = 2.5$.
Plot $(5,0)$ and $(0, 2.5)$. Then draw a
line through these two points.

The lines have different slopes and intersect at $(1, 2)$.
The solution of the system is $(1, 2)$.

b. The slope-intercept form of $-9x + 6y = 12$

is $y = \dfrac{3}{2}x + 2$.

The slope-intercept form of $3x - 2y = -4$

is $y = \dfrac{3}{2}x + 2$.

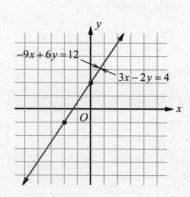

Since the equations are equivalent,
their graphs show the same line. Any
ordered pair representing a point on
that line will satisfy both equations.
So, there are infinitely many solutions
to this system.

Solving Linear Systems by Substitution

The basic steps in the substitution method are as follows:

1. Solve one of the equations for one of its variables.
2. Substitute the resulting expression into the other equation and solve.
3. Substitute the resulting value into either of the original equations and solve for the other variable.

Example 2 $\square$ Solve the linear system by substitution method.

$$y = x - 1$$
$$2x + y = 5$$

Solution $\square$

$2x + y = 3$	Second equation
$2x + (x - 1) = 5$	Since the first equation is $y = x - 1$, substitute $x - 1$ for y in the second equation.
$3x - 1 = 5$	Combine like terms.
$3x = 6$	Add 1 to each side.
$x = 2$	Divide each side by 3 and simplify.
$y = (2) - 1$	Substitute 2 for x in the first equation.
$= 1$	Simplify.

The solution is $(2, 1)$.

Solving Linear Systems by Elimination

The basic steps in the elimination method are as follows:

1. Arrange the equations with the like terms in columns.
2. Multiply one or both equations to obtain new coefficients for x (or y) that are opposites.
3. Add the equations and solve for the remaining variable.
4. Substitute this value into either of the original equations and solve for the other variable.

Example 3 $\square$ Solve the linear system by elimination method.

$$2x - 3y = 13$$
$$-3x + 2y = -12$$

Solution $\square$

$3(2x - 3y = 13)$	Multiply the first equation by 3.
$2(-3x + 2y = -12)$	Multiply the second equation by 2.

By multiplying the first equation by 3 and multiplying the second equation by 2, we obtain coefficients of x that are opposites.

$6x - 9y = 39$	First equation modified.
$-6x + 4y = -24$	Second equation modified.
$-5y = 15$	Sum of equations
$y = -3$	Simplify.
$2x - 3(-3) = 13$	Substitute -3 for y in the first equation.
$2x + 9 = 13$	Simplify.
$2x = 4$	Subtract 9 from each side.
$x = 2$	Divide each side by 2 and simplify.

The solution is $(2, -3)$.

Systems of Equations with No Solution and Infinitely Many Solutions

1. A system of equations has no solution if the two equations have the same slope but different y- intercepts.
2. A system of equations has infinitely many solutions if the two equations are equivalent. Therefore the two equations have the same slope and same y- intercepts.

When you are asked if a system of equations has no solution or infinitely many solutions, you need to change the equations into *slope-intercept form* and check the slopes and y- intercepts.

Example 4 □ For what value of c will the system of equations below have no solution?

$$cx - 2y = 6$$
$$3x + 4y = 4$$

Solution □ Change the equations into slope-intercept form.

$$y = \frac{c}{2}x - 3 \qquad \text{First equation in slope-intercept form}$$

$$y = -\frac{3}{4}x + 1 \qquad \text{Second equation in slope-intercept form}$$

If two equations have the same slope and different y- intercepts, the system has

no solution. So, let $\frac{c}{2} = -\frac{3}{4}$. Solving this equation for c gives $c = -\frac{3}{2}$.

Since the lines are parallel and the y- intercepts are -3 and 1, the two equations are

not identical. Therefore, when $c = -\frac{3}{2}$, the system of equations has no solution.

Example 5 □ For what value of b will the system of equations below have infinitely many
solutions?
$$-2x + y = 4$$
$$5x - by = -10$$

Solution □ $y = 2x + 4 \qquad \text{First equation in slope-intercept form}$

$$y = \frac{5}{b}x + \frac{10}{b} \qquad \text{Second equation in slope-intercept form}$$

If two equations have infinitely many solutions, they are equivalent .

Therefore, $2 = \frac{5}{b}$ or $4 = \frac{10}{b}$. Solving these equations for b gives $b = \frac{5}{2}$.

Example 6 □ Solve the linear system. $2x - 3y = 5$

$$y = \frac{2}{3}x + 2$$

Solution □ Substitute the expression for y from the second equation into the first equation.

$$2x - 3y = 5 \qquad \text{First equation}$$

$$2x - 3(\frac{2}{3}x + 2) = 5 \qquad \text{Substitute } \frac{2}{3}x + 2 \text{ for } y \text{ in the first equation.}$$

$$2x - 2x - 6 = 5 \qquad \text{Simplify.}$$

$$-6 = 5 \qquad \text{Simplify.}$$

Since $-6 = 5$ is false, the system has no solution.

Exercises - Solving Systems of Linear Equations

1

$$y = 2x + 4$$
$$x - y = -1$$

Which ordered pair (x, y) satisfies the system of equations shown above?

A) $(-2, -3)$

B) $(-3, -2)$

C) $(-1, 2)$

D) $(-2, 0)$

2

$$\frac{1}{2}x + y = 1$$
$$-2x - y = 5$$

If (x, y) is a solution to the system of equations above, what is the value of $x + y$?

A) -2

B) -1

C) 1

D) 2

3

$$2x - ky = 14$$
$$5x - 2y = 5$$

In the system of equations above, k is a constant and x and y are variables. For what values of k will the system of equations have no solution?

4

Which of the following systems of equations has infinitely many solutions?

A) $x + y = 1$

   $x - y = 1$

B) $-2x + y = 1$

   $-2x + y = 5$

C) $\frac{1}{2}x - \frac{1}{3}y = 1$

   $3x - 2y = 6$

D) $2x + 3y = 1$

   $3x - 2y = 1$

5

$$ax - y = 0$$
$$x - by = 1$$

In the system of equations above, a and b are constants and x and y are variables. If the system of equations above has no solution, what is the value of $a \cdot b$?

6

$$2x - \frac{1}{2}y = 15$$
$$ax - \frac{1}{3}y = 10$$

In the system of equations above, a is a constant and x and y are variables. For what values of a will the system of equations have infinitely many solution?

3-6. Absolute Value Equations

The **absolute value** of a number is the distance on a number line between the graph of the number and the origin.

The distance between -3 and the origin is 3. Thus $|-3| = 3$.

The distance between 3 and the origin is 3. Thus $|3| = 3$.

Therefore, if $|x| = 3$, then $x = 3$ or $x = -3$.

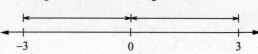

$|-3| = 3$, because the distance from the origin to -3 is 3. $|3| = 3$, because the distance from the origin to 3 is 3.

An **absolute value function** is a function written as $f(x) = |x|$, for all values of x.

An absolute function can be written using two or more expressions such as $f(x) = |x| = \begin{cases} -x \text{ if } x < 0 \\ x \text{ if } x \geq 0 \end{cases}$.

Example 1 □ Solve each absolute value equation.

  a. $|3x - 5| = 7$ b. $|x + 3| = 0$ c. $|x - 8| = -3$

Solution □ a. $|3x - 5| = 7$

  $3x - 5 = 7$ or $3x - 5 = -7$ If $|x| = a$, then $x = a$ or $x = -a$.

  $3x = 12$ or $3x = -2$ Add 5 to each side.

  $x = 4$ or $x = \dfrac{-2}{3}$ Divide each side by 3.

  b. $|x + 3| = 0$

  $x + 3 = 0$ If $|x| = 0$, then $x = 0$.

  $x = -3$ Subtract 3 from each side.

  c. $|x - 8| = -3$

  $|x - 8| = -3$ means that the distance between x and 8 is -3. Since distance cannot be negative, the equation has no solution.

To sketch the graph of $y = a|x + h| + k$, use the following steps.

1. Find the x- coordinate of the vertex by finding the value of x for which $x + h = 0$.
2. Make a table of values using the x- coordinate of the vertex. Find two x- values to its left and two to its right.
3. Plot the points from inside the table. If $a > 0$, the vertex will be the minimum point and if $a < 0$, the vertex will be the maximum point.

The graph of $y = |x|$

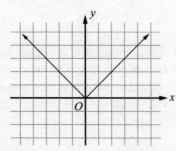

Table of values

x	$y = |x|$
-2	2
-1	1
0	0	← Vertex
1	1
2	2

Exercises - Absolute Value Equations

1

Which of the following expressions is equal to -1 for some values of x?

A) $|1-x|+6$

B) $|1-x|+4$

C) $|1-x|+2$

D) $|1-x|-2$

2

If $|2x+7|=5$, which of the following could be the value of x?

A) -6

B) -4

C) -2

D) 0

3

For what value of x is $|x-1|-1$ equal to 1?

A) -1

B) 0

C) 1

D) 2

4

For what value of x is $|3x-5|=-1$?

A) -2

B) -1

C) 0

D) There is no such value of x.

5

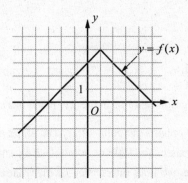

The graph of the function f is shown in the xy-plane above. For what value of x is the value of $f(x)$ at its maximum?

A) -3

B) -1

C) 1

D) 3

6

For what value of n is $3-|3-n|$ equal to 3?

Chapter 3 Practice Test

1

x	−4	0	6
$f(x)$	−4	−1	k

In the table above, if $f(x)$ is a linear function, what is the value of k?

A) 2.5

B) 3

C) 3.5

D) 4

2

The graph of a line in the xy- plane has slope $\dfrac{1}{3}$ and contains the point $(9,1)$. The graph of a second line passes through the points $(-2,4)$ and $(5,-3)$. If the two lines intersect at (a,b), what is the value of $a+b$?

A) −2

B) 2

C) 4

D) 6

3

Which of the following expressions is equal to 0 for some value of x?

A) $5+|x+5|$

B) $5+|x-5|$

C) $-5+|x+5|$

D) $-5-|x-5|$

4

Line ℓ in the xy- plane contains points from each of the Quadrants I, III, and IV, but no points from Quadrant II. Which of the following must be true?

A) The slope of line ℓ is zero.

B) The slope of line ℓ is undefined.

C) The slope of line ℓ is positive.

D) The slope of line ℓ is negative.

5

x	−3	−1	1	5
$f(x)$	9	5	1	−7

The table above shows some values of the linear function f. Which of the following defines f?

A) $f(x)=2x-3$

B) $f(x)=-2x+3$

C) $f(x)=2x-1$

D) $f(x)=-2x+1$

6

If $f(x)=-6x+1$, what is $f(\dfrac{1}{2}x-1)$ equal to?

A) $-3x+7$

B) $-3x-5$

C) $-3x+1$

D) $-3x-1$

Questions 7 and 8 refer to the following information.

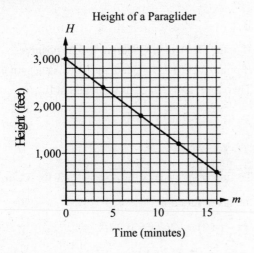

Height of a Paraglider

The graph above shows the relationship between the height of paraglider H, in feet, and time m, in minutes.

7

Which of the following represents the relationship between H and m?

A) $H = -100m + 3000$

B) $H = -150m + 3000$

C) $H = -175m + 3000$

D) $H = -225m + 3000$

8

If the height of the paraglider is 1,350 feet, which of the following best approximates the time the paraglider has been flying?

A) 10 minutes

B) 10 minutes and 30 seconds

C) 11 minutes

D) 11 minutes and 30 seconds

9

A line in the xy-plane passes through the point $(1,-2)$ and has a slope of $\frac{1}{3}$. Which of the following points lies on the line?

A) $(3,-2)$

B) $(2,-\frac{4}{3})$

C) $(0,-2)$

D) $(-1,-\frac{8}{3})$

10

$$f(x) = ax + 2$$

In the function above, a is a constant. If $f(-1) = 4$, what is the value of $f(-\frac{1}{2})$?

11

If the slope of the line in the xy-plane that passes through the points $(2,-4)$ and $(6,k)$ is $\frac{3}{2}$, what is the value of k?

12

$$\frac{1}{3}x - \frac{3}{4}y = -11$$

$$\frac{1}{2}x + \frac{1}{6}y = -1$$

If (x, y) is the solution to the system of equations above, what is the value of $x + y$?

Answer Key

Section 3-1

1. D   2. B   3. B   4. A   5. C
6. 8   7. 12

Section 3-2

1. A   2. C   3. D   4. $\dfrac{5}{2}$ or 2.5

5. 12   6. $\dfrac{29}{2}$ or 14.5   7. $\dfrac{1}{4}$ or 0.25

Section 3-3

1. C   2. B   3. D   4. B   5. D

Section 3-4

1. B   2. D   3. C   4. 14   5. $\dfrac{3}{2}$ or 1.5
6. 3

Section 3-5

1. B   2. B   3. $\dfrac{4}{5}$ or 0.8   4. C

5. 1   6. $\dfrac{4}{3}$ or 1.33

Section 3-6

1. D   2. A   3. A   4. D   5. C
6. 3

Chapter 3 Practice Test

1. C   2. B   3. C   4. C   5. B
6. A   7. B   8. C   9. D   10. 3
11. 2   12. 6

Answers and Explanations

Section 3-1

1. D

    The domain of a function is the set of all
    x-coordinates. Therefore, $\{-5, -2, 0, 4\}$ is
    the domain of the given function.

2. B

    The ordered pairs $\{(-5,8),\ (-2,7),\ (2,-1),\ (5,8)\}$
    is a correct representation of the mapping shown.

3. B

    If point $(7, b)$ is in Quadrant I, b is positive.
    If point $(a, -3)$ is in Quadrant III, a is negative.
    Therefore, point (a, b) is in Quadrant II.

4. A

    $f(x) = -2x + 7$

    To find $f(\frac{1}{2}x + 3)$, substitute $\frac{1}{2}x + 3$ for x, in
    the given function.
    $f(\frac{1}{2}x + 3) = -2(\frac{1}{2}x + 3) + 7$
    $= -x - 6 + 7 = -x + 1$

5. C

    $g(x) = kx^3 + 3$
    $g(-1) = k(-1)^3 + 3 = 5 \qquad g(-1) = 5$
    $-k + 3 = 5 \qquad\qquad\qquad$ Simplify.
    $k = -2 \qquad\qquad\qquad\quad$ Solve for k.

    Substitute -2 for k in the given function.
    $g(x) = kx^3 + 3 = -2x^3 + 3$
    $g(1) = -2(1)^3 + 3 = 1$

6. 8

    $f(x + 1) = -\dfrac{1}{2}x + 6$

    To find $f(-3)$, first solve $x + 1 = -3$.
    $x + 1 = -3 \ \Rightarrow\ x = -4$.
    Substitute -4 for x in the given function.
    $f(-3) = -\dfrac{1}{2}(-4) + 6 = 8$.

7. 12

    $f(x) = x^2 - b$
    $f(-2) = 7 \ \Rightarrow\ (-2)^2 - b = 7$
    $\Rightarrow\ 4 - b = 7 \ \Rightarrow\ b = -3$
    Therefore, $f(x) = x^2 + 3$.
    $f(b) = f(-3) = (-3)^2 + 3 = 12$

Section 3-2

1. A

   Rate of change $= \dfrac{\text{change in } y}{\text{change in } x} = \dfrac{-1-3}{0-(-3)} = \dfrac{-4}{3}$

2. C

   Pick any two points from the table.
   Let's pick $(-3,-1)$ and $(6,5)$.

   Average rate of change $= \dfrac{\text{change in } y}{\text{change in } x}$

   $= \dfrac{5-(-1)}{6-(-3)} = \dfrac{6}{9} = \dfrac{2}{3}$

3. D

   $\text{slope} = \dfrac{y_2 - y_1}{x_2 - x_1} = \dfrac{b-1}{1-a} = 1$

   $\Rightarrow b-1 = 1-a \quad \Rightarrow a+b=2$

4. $\dfrac{5}{2}$ or 2.5

   $\text{slope} = \dfrac{y_2 - y_1}{x_2 - x_1} = \dfrac{-8-2}{-1-3} = \dfrac{-10}{-4} = \dfrac{5}{2}$

5. 12

   $\text{slope} = \dfrac{y_2 - y_1}{x_2 - x_1} = \dfrac{r-3}{-5-4} = \dfrac{r-3}{-9} = -1$

   $\Rightarrow r-3 = 9 \Rightarrow r = 12$

6. $\dfrac{29}{2}$ or 14.5

   $\text{slope} = \dfrac{y_2 - y_1}{x_2 - x_1} = \dfrac{a-7}{1-a} = -\dfrac{5}{9}$

   $\Rightarrow 9(a-7) = -5(1-a)$

   $\Rightarrow 9a-63 = -5+5a$

   $\Rightarrow 4a = 58 \Rightarrow a = \dfrac{58}{4} = \dfrac{29}{2}$

7. $\dfrac{1}{4}$ or 0.25

   $-x+4y = 6$

   Write the equation in slope-intercept form.

   $-x+4y=6 \Rightarrow 4y = x+6 \Rightarrow y = \dfrac{x}{4} + \dfrac{6}{4}$

   The slope of the line is $\dfrac{1}{4}$.

Section 3-3

1. C

   . Since the points $(-4,2)$ and $(4,-4)$ lie on the line,

   the slope of the line is $\dfrac{2-(-4)}{-4-4} = \dfrac{6}{-8} = -\dfrac{3}{4}$.

   If we use the point $(4,-4)$ and the slope $m = -\dfrac{3}{4}$,

   the point-slope form of the line is

   $y-(-4) = -\dfrac{3}{4}(x-4)$ or $y+4 = -\dfrac{3}{4}(x-4)$.

   If we use the point $(-4,2)$ and the slope $m = -\dfrac{3}{4}$,

   the point-slope form of the line is

   $y-2 = -\dfrac{3}{4}(x-(-4))$ or $y-2 = -\dfrac{3}{4}(x+4)$.

   Choice C is correct.

2. B

$y-2 = -\dfrac{3}{4}(x+4)$	Point-slope form of the line.
$y-2 = -\dfrac{3}{4}x-3$	Distributive Property
$y = -\dfrac{3}{4}x-1$	Add 2 to each side and simplify.

3. D

$y = -\dfrac{3}{4}x-1$	Slope-intercept form
$4y = 4(-\dfrac{3}{4}x-1)$	Multiply each side by 4.
$4y = -3x-4$	Simplify.
$4y+3x = -3x-4+3x$	Add $3x$ to each side.
$3x+4y = -4$	Simplify.

4. B

   Average rate of change

   $= \dfrac{\text{change in number of smart phones}}{\text{change in years}}$

   $= \dfrac{345-120}{2010-2005} = \dfrac{225}{5} = 45$

   The increase in the average number of smart phones is 45 each year.

5. D

Since the line passes through point $(4,-1)$ and has slope -2, the point-slope form of the line is $y-(-1)=-2(x-4)$.

$y+1=-2(x-4)$ Point-slope form simplified.

$y+1=-2x+8$ Distributive Property

$2x+y=7$ $2x-1$ is added to each side.

Section 3-4

1. B

Lines that are parallel have the same slope. So, we need to find the equation of a line with the slope $-\frac{1}{2}$ and the point $(-2,\frac{1}{2})$.

The point-slope form of this line is

$y-\frac{1}{2}=-\frac{1}{2}(x-(-2))$.

$y-\frac{1}{2}=-\frac{1}{2}x-1$ Simplified.

$2(y-\frac{1}{2})=2(-\frac{1}{2}x-1)$ Multiply each side by 2.

$2y-1=-x-2$ Simplify.

$x+2y=-1$ $x+1$ is added to each side.

2. D

A line parallel to the x-axis has slope 0.

$y-y_1=m(x-x_1)$ Point-slope form

$y-6=0(x-7)$ $m=0$, $x_1=7$, and $y_1=6$

$y-6=0$ Simplify.

$y=6$

3. C

If a line is parallel to the y-axis, it is a vertical line and the equation is given in the form $x=a$, in which a is the x-coordinate of the point the line passes through. Therefore, the equation of the vertical line that passes through $(-5,1)$ is $x=-5$.

4. 14

$4x-2y=13$ can be rewritten as $y=2x-\frac{13}{2}$.

The line has slope 2. Lines that are parallel have the same slope. Therefore, $2=\frac{b-2}{5+1}$.

Solving the equation for b gives $b=14$.

5. $\frac{3}{2}$ or 1.5

Since lines ℓ and m are parallel, the two lines have the same slope. Therefore,

$\frac{0-3}{2-0}=\frac{-3-b}{-1-(-4)}$.

$\frac{-3}{2}=\frac{-3-b}{3}$ Simplified.

$-9=-6-2b$ Cross Multiplication

$-3=-2b$ Add 6 to each side.

$\frac{3}{2}=b$ Divide each side by -2.

6. 3

The slope of line t is $\frac{1-(-3)}{2-(-4)}$, or $\frac{2}{3}$. So, the slope of the line perpendicular to line t is the negative reciprocal of $\frac{2}{3}$, or $-\frac{3}{2}$. Therefore,

$-\frac{3}{2}=\frac{-2-4}{a+1}$ $\Rightarrow$ $-3(a+1)=2(-6)$

$\Rightarrow$ $-3a-3=-12$

$\Rightarrow$ $-3a=-9$ $\Rightarrow$ $a=3$

Section 3-5

1. B

$y=2x+4$ First equation

$x-y=-1$ Second equation

Substituting $2x+4$ for y in the second equation gives $x-(2x+4)=-1$.

$x-(2x+4)=-1$ $\Rightarrow$ $x-2x-4=-1$

$\Rightarrow$ $-x-4=-1$ $\Rightarrow$ $-x=3$ or $x=-3$

Substituting -3 for x in the first equation gives $y=2(-3)+4=-2$. Therefore, the solution (x,y) to the given system of equations is $(-3,-2)$.

2. B

$\frac{1}{2}x+y=1$ First equation

$-2x-y=5$ Second equation

$-\frac{3}{2}x\ \ \ \ \ =6$ Add the equations.

$-\frac{2}{3}(-\frac{3}{2}x)=-\frac{2}{3}(6)$ Multiply each side by $-\frac{2}{3}$

$x = -4$ Simplify.

$\frac{1}{2}(-4) + y = 1$ Substitute –4 for x in the first equation.

$-2 + y = 1$ Simplify.

$y = 3$ Add 2 to each side.

Therefore, $x + y = -4 + 3 = -1$

3. $\frac{4}{5}$

If a system of two linear equations has no solution, then the lines represented by the equations in the coordinate plane are parallel. So, the slopes of the line are equal.

$2x - ky = 14$ 1st equation

$y = \frac{2}{k}x - \frac{14}{k}$ 1st equation in slope-intercept form

$5x - 2y = 5$ 2nd equation

$y = \frac{5}{2}x - \frac{5}{2}$ 2nd equation in slope-intercept form

The system of equations will have no solution

if $\frac{2}{k} = \frac{5}{2}$. Solving for k yields $k = \frac{4}{5}$.

If $k = \frac{4}{5}$, the y- intercept of the first equation is

$-\frac{35}{2}$, and the y- intercept of the second equation

is $-\frac{5}{2}$. Therefore, the lines are parallel, but not

identical.

4. C

In order for a system of two linear equations to have infinitely many solutions, the two equations must be equivalent. The two equations in the answer choice A have different slopes. The two equations in the answer choice B have different y- intercepts. For answer choice C, multiply by 6 on each side of the first equation.

$6(\frac{1}{2}x - \frac{1}{3}y) = 6(1) \Rightarrow 3x - 2y = 6$.

The result is identical to the second equation. Therefore, the two equations are equivalent. The two equations in answer choice D have different slopes,

5. 1

Change the two equations into slope-intercept form.

$ax - y = 0 \Rightarrow y = ax$

$x - by = 1 \Rightarrow y = \frac{1}{b}x - \frac{1}{b}$

If $a = \frac{1}{b}$, the system of equations will have no

solution. Therefore, $a \cdot b = 1$

6. $\frac{4}{3}$

In order for a system of two linear equations to have infinitely many solutions, the two equations

must be equivalent. The equation $2x - \frac{1}{2}y = 15$

can be rewritten as $y = 4x - 30$ and the equation

$ax - \frac{1}{3}y = 10$ can be rewritten as $y = 3ax - 30$.

If two equations are equivalent, then $4x = 3ax$

or $a = \frac{4}{3}$.

Section 3-6

1. D

By definition, the absolute value of any expression is a nonnegative number. Therefore, $|1-x| + 6 > 0$,

$|1-x| + 4 > 0$, and $|1-x| + 2 > 0$. Only $|1-x| - 2$

could be a negative number.

$|1-x| - 2 = -1 \Rightarrow |1-x| = 1 \Rightarrow x = 2$ or $x = 0$.

2. A

$|2x + 7| = 5$

$2x + 7 = 5$ or $2x + 7 = -5$

$2x = -2$ or $2x = -12$

$x = -1$ or $x = -6$

3. A

$|x-1| - 1 = 1$

$|x-1| = 2$ Add 1 to each side.

$x - 1 = 2$ or $x - 1 = -2$ The expression can be 2 or –2.

$x = 3$ or $x = -1$ Add 1 to each side.

4. D

The expression $|3x - 5|$ is the absolute value

of $3x - 5$, and the absolute value can never be

a negative number. Thus $|3x - 5| = -1$ has no

solution

5. C

The maximum value of the function corresponds to the y- coordinate of the point on the graph, which is highest along the vertical axis. The highest point along the y- axis has coordinates $(1,4)$. Therefore, the value of x at the maximum of $f(x)$ is 1.

6. 3

$$3-|3-n|=3$$
$$-|3-n|=0 \qquad \text{Subtract 3 from each side.}$$
If $-|3-n|=0$ or $|3-n|=0$, then $3-n=0$,
Thus $n=3$.

Chapter 3 Practice Test

1. C

Use the slope formula to find the slope of the function. Since $f(x)$ is a linear function, the slope between $(-4,-4)$ and $(0,-1)$ equals the slope between $(0,-1)$ and $(6,k)$.

Therefore, $\dfrac{-1-(-4)}{0-(-4)}=\dfrac{k-(-1)}{6-0}$.

$\dfrac{3}{4}=\dfrac{k+1}{6}$ \qquad Simplify.

$4(k+1)=18$ \qquad Cross Multiplication

$4k+4=18$ \qquad Distributive Property

$4k=14$ \qquad Subtract 4 from each side.

$k=\dfrac{7}{2}$ or 3.5 \qquad Divide each side by 4.

2. B

The equation of the line with slope $\dfrac{1}{3}$ and point $(9,1)$ is $y-1=\dfrac{1}{3}(x-9)$ or $y=\dfrac{1}{3}x-2$.

The slope of the second line is $\dfrac{-3-4}{5-(-2)}$ or -1.

The equation of the second line is $y-4=-1(x+2)$ or $y=-x+2$. To find the point of intersection, substitute $\dfrac{1}{3}x-2$ for y in the second equation and solve for x.

$$\dfrac{1}{3}x-2=-x+2$$

Solving for x yields $x=3$. Substituting 3 for x in the equation of the second line yields $y=-1$. Therefore, $(a,b)=(3,-1)$ and $a+b=3-1=2$.

3. C

The expressions $|x+5|$ or $|x-5|$ can never be a negative number. Thus $5+|x+5|$ or $5+|x-5|$ can not equal zero. The expression $-|x-5|$ can never be a positive number. Thus $-5-|x-5|$ can not equal zero. If $-5+|x+5|=0$, then $|x+5|=5$, when $x=0$.

4. C

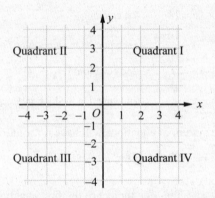

If the slope of a line is positive, it is possible that the line contains no points from Quadrant II or from Quadrant IV. If the slope of a line is negative, it is possible that the line contains no points from Quadrant I or from Quadrant III. Since the line ℓ contains points from each of the Quadrants I, III, and IV, but no points from Quadrant II, the slope of line ℓ must be positive.

5. B

x	-3	-1	1	5
$f(x)$	9	5	1	-7

First, find the slope of the linear function f. We can choose any two points from the table. Let's use $(1,1)$ and $(-1,5)$ to find the slope m of f. $m=\dfrac{5-1}{-1-1}=\dfrac{4}{-2}=-2$. Thus the slope intercept form of f can be written as $f(x)=-2x+b$. From the table we know $f(1)=1$. $f(1)=-2(1)+b=1$ implies $b=3$. Thus f is defined as $f(x)=-2x+3$.

6. A

$$f(x) = -6x + 1$$

$f(\frac{1}{2}x - 1) = -6(\frac{1}{2}x - 1) + 1$ Substitute $\frac{1}{2}x - 1$ for x.

$\qquad = -3x + 6 + 1$ Distributive Property

$\qquad = -3x + 7$ Simplify.

7. B

Since the points $(0, 3000)$ and $(4, 2400)$ lie on the line, the slope of the line is $\frac{2400 - 3000}{4 - 0} = -150$.

The H-intercept of the line is 3,000. Therefore the relationship between H and m can be represented by $H = -150m + 3000$, the slope-intercept form of the line.

8. C

$H = -150m + 3000$ Equation of the line

$1350 = -150m + 3000$ Substitute 1350 for H.

Solving for m yields $m = 11$.

9. D

The point-slope form of the line that passes through the point $(1, -2)$ and has a slope of $\frac{1}{3}$

is $y + 2 = \frac{1}{3}(x - 1)$. The slope-intercept form of

the line is $y = \frac{1}{3}x - \frac{7}{3}$. We can replace $f(x)$ for

y to get the function form. Thus, $f(x) = \frac{1}{3}x - \frac{7}{3}$.

Now check each answer choices.

A) $(3, -2)$ $f(3) = \frac{1}{3}(3) - \frac{7}{3} = -\frac{4}{3} \neq -2$

B) $(2, -\frac{4}{3})$ $f(2) = \frac{1}{3}(2) - \frac{7}{3} = -\frac{5}{3} \neq -\frac{4}{3}$

C) $(0, -2)$ $f(0) = \frac{1}{3}(0) - \frac{7}{3} = -\frac{7}{3} \neq -2$

D) $(-1, -\frac{8}{3})$ $f(-1) = \frac{1}{3}(-1) - \frac{7}{3} = -\frac{8}{3}$

Choice D is correct.

10. 3

$$f(x) = ax + 2$$

If $f(-1) = 4$, then $f(-1) = a(-1) + 2 = 4$.

Solving for a yields $a = -2$.

Thus $f(x) = -2x + 2$ and

$$f(-\frac{1}{2}) = -2(-\frac{1}{2}) + 2 = 3.$$

11. 2

Use the slope formula.

Slope $= \frac{k - (-4)}{6 - 2} = \frac{3}{2}$.

$\frac{k + 4}{4} = \frac{3}{2}$ Simplify.

$2(k + 4) = 3 \cdot 4$ Cross Product

$2k + 8 = 12$ Distributive Property

Solving for k yields $k = 2$.

12. 6

$\frac{1}{3}x - \frac{3}{4}y = -11$ $\overset{\text{Multiply by 3}}{\Longrightarrow}$ $x - \frac{9}{4}y = -33$

$\frac{1}{2}x + \frac{1}{6}y = -1$ $\overset{\text{Multiply by } -2}{\Longrightarrow}$ $-x - \frac{1}{3}y = 2$

Add the equations and we get $-\frac{9}{4}y - \frac{1}{3}y = -31$.

$12(-\frac{9}{4}y - \frac{1}{3}y) = 12(-31)$ Multiply each side by 12.

$-27y - 4y = -372$ Distributive Property

$-31y = -372$ Simplify.

$\frac{-31y}{-31} = \frac{-372}{-31}$ Divide each side by -31.

$y = 12$ Simplify.

$\frac{1}{3}x - \frac{3}{4}y = -11$ First equation

$\frac{1}{3}x - \frac{3}{4}(12) = -11$ $y = 12$

$\frac{1}{3}x - 9 = -11$ Simplify.

$\frac{1}{3}x - 9 + 9 = -11 + 9$ Add 9 to each side.

$\frac{1}{3}x = -2$ Simplify.

$3(\frac{1}{3}x) = 3(-2)$ Multiply each side by -2.

$x = -6$ Simplify.

Therefore, $x + y = -6 + 12 = 6$.

CHAPTER 4
Linear Inequalities and Graphs

4-1. Solving Inequalities

An inequality is a mathematical sentence that contains inequality symbols such as $>$, $<$, $\geq$, $\leq$. between numerical or variable expressions. Four types of simple inequalities and their graphs are shown below.

Verbal Expressions	Inequality	Graph
All real numbers **less than** 4.	$x < 4$	
All real numbers **greater than** -3.	$x > -3$	
All real numbers **less than or equal to** 2. All real numbers **at most** 2. All real numbers **no greater than** 2.	$x \leq 2$	
All real numbers **greater than or equal to** -1. All real numbers **at least** -1. All real numbers **no less than** -1.	$x \geq -1$	

Notice on the graphs that we use an open dot for $>$ or $<$ and a solid dot for $\geq$ or $\leq$.

Properties of Inequalities

For all real numbers a, b, and c, the following are true.

Transitive Property If $a < b$ and $b < c$, then $a < c$.

Addition and Subtraction Properties If $a < b$, then $a + b < a + c$ and $a - c < b - c$.

Multiplication and Division Properties If $a < b$ and c is positive, then $ac < bc$ and $\dfrac{a}{c} < \dfrac{b}{c}$.

If $a < b$ and c is negative, then $ac > bc$ and $\dfrac{a}{c} > \dfrac{b}{c}$.

Example 1 □ Write each statement as an inequality.

    a. The number x is no greater than -2.

    b. The amount of calories n meet or exceed 1,200.

Solution □ a. $x \leq -2$

    b. $n \geq 1,200$

Example 2 □ Solve $4n - 9 \geq 12 - 3n$.

Solution □
$4n - 9 \geq 12 - 3n$

$4n - 9 + 3n \geq 12 - 3n + 3n$ Add $3n$ to each side.

$7n - 9 \geq 12$ Simplify.

$7n - 9 + 9 \geq 12 + 9$ Add 9 to each side.

$7n \geq 21$ Simplify.

$\dfrac{7n}{7} \geq \dfrac{21}{7}$ Divide each side by 7.

$n \geq 3$ Simplify.

Exercises - Translating Words into Inequalities

1

If $-3 + n \le 25$, which inequality represents the possible range of values for $4n - 12$?

A) $4n - 12 \le -100$

B) $4n - 12 \le 100$

C) $4n - 12 \ge -100$

D) $4n - 12 \ge 100$

2

Which of the following numbers is NOT a solution to the inequality $\frac{1}{2}x - \frac{1}{3} > \frac{7}{9} + \frac{5}{2}x$?

A) $-\frac{7}{2}$

B) $-\frac{5}{2}$

C) $-\frac{3}{2}$

D) $-\frac{1}{2}$

3

If $-3a + 7 \ge 5a - 17$, what is the greatest possible value of $3a + 7$?

A) 16

B) 14

C) 12

D) 10

4

Nine is not more than the sum of a number and 17.

Which of the following inequalities represents the statement above?

A) $9 \ge 17n$

B) $9 \ge n + 17$

C) $9 \le 17n$

D) $9 \le n + 17$

5

The product of 7 and number n is no less than 91.

Which of the following inequalities represents the statement above?

A) $7n \le 91$

B) $7n < 91$

C) $7n \ge 91$

D) $7n > 91$

6

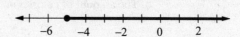

Which of the following inequalities represents the graph above?

A) $n \le -5$

B) $n < -5$

C) $n \ge -5$

D) $n > -5$

4-2. Compound and Absolute Value Inequalities

Two or more inequalities that are connected by the words *and* or *or* are called a **compound inequality**. A compound inequality containing *and* is true only if both inequalities are true. Its graph is the **intersection** of the graphs of the two inequalities. A compound inequality containing *or* is true if one or more of the inequalities is true. Its graph is the **union** of the graphs of the two inequalities.

Since the absolute value of any number x is its distance from zero on a number line, $|x| < 1$ means that the distance from zero to x is less than 1 unit and $|x| > 1$ means that the distance from zero to x is greater than 1 unit. Therefore the inequality $|x| < 1$ is equivalent to $-1 < x < 1$ and $|x| > 1$ is equivalent to $x < -1$ or $x > 1$.

Graph of $|x| < 1$

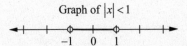

The distance between x and 0 is less than 1.

Graph of $|x| > 1$

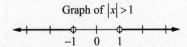

The distance between x and 0 is greater than 1.

To translate more general absolute value inequalities into compound inequalities, use the following properties.

1. The inequality $|ax + b| < c$ is equivalent to $-c < ax + b < c$, in which $0 \le c$.

2. The inequality $|ax + b| > c$ is equivalent to $ax + b < -c$ or $ax + b > c$, in which $0 \le c$.

In the statements above, $<$ could be replaced by $\le$ and $>$ could be replaced by $\ge$.

Example 1 □ Solve $7 - 2x > 15$ and $10 + 3x > -11$

Solution □ $7 - 2x > 15$ and $10 + 3x > -11$
$7 - 2x - 7 > 15 - 7$ and $10 + 3x - 10 > -11 - 10$
$-2x > 8$ and $3x > -21$
$\dfrac{-2x}{-2} < \dfrac{8}{-2}$ and $\dfrac{3x}{3} > \dfrac{-21}{3}$
$x < -4$ and $x > -7$

Example 2 □ Solve each inequality.

     a. $|2x - 3| \le 7$ b. $|n - 4| > 3$

Solution □   a. $|2x - 3| \le 7$

$-7 \le 2x - 3 \le 7$ $|ax + b| < c$ is equivalent to $-c < ax + b < c$.

$-7 + 3 \le 2x - 3 + 3 \le 7 + 3$ Add 3 to each expression.
$-4 \le 2x \le 10$ Simplify.

$\dfrac{-4}{2} \le \dfrac{2x}{2} \le \dfrac{10}{2}$ Divide each expression by 2.

$-2 \le x \le 5$ Simplify.

   b. $|n - 4| > 3$

$n - 4 < -3$ or $n - 4 > 3$ $|ax + b| > c$ is equivalent to $ax + b < -c$ or
                               $ax + b > c$.

$n - 4 + 4 < -3 + 4$ or $n - 4 > 3 + 4$ Add 4 to each side.

$n < 1$ or $n > 7$ Simplify.

Exercises - Compound and Absolute Value Inequalities

1

Which of the following numbers is NOT a solution to the inequality $3 - n < -2$ or $2n + 3 \le -1$?

A) -6

B) -2

C) 2

D) 6

2

Which of the following numbers is a solution to the inequality $5w + 7 > 2$ and $6w - 15 \le 3(-1 + w)$?

A) -1

B) 2

C) 5

D) 8

3

Which of the following is the graph of
$-x \le 5$ and $7 - \dfrac{1}{2}x > x + 1$?

A) ◄━━━━━●━━━━━━━━━━━►
　　　　　　-5

B) ◄━━━━━━━━━━━○━━━━►
　　　　　　　　　　4

C) ◄━━━●━━━━━━━○━━━►
　　　　-5　　　　4

D) ◄━━━●━━━━━━━○━━━►
　　　　-5　　　　4

4

If $-2 < n < -1$, what is the value of $7 + \dfrac{1}{2}n$
rounded to the nearest whole number?

5

Which of the following numbers is NOT a solution to the inequality $\left| \dfrac{1}{2}x - 1 \right| \le 1$?

A) 0

B) 2

C) 4

D) 6

6

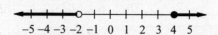

Which of the following is the compound inequality for the graph above?

A) $x < -2$ or $4 \le x$

B) $x \le -2$ or $4 < x$

C) $-2 < x \le 4$

D) $-2 \le x < 4$

7

If $\dfrac{1}{4}x - 1 \le -x + 5$, what is the greatest possible value of x?

8

If $\left| \dfrac{3}{4}n - 2 \right| < 1$ and n is an integer, what is one possible value of n?

4-3. Graphing Inequalities in Two Variables

A **linear inequality** in x and y is an inequality that can be written in one of the following forms.

$ax + by < c$, $ax + by \leq c$, $ax + by > c$, $ax + by \geq c$

An ordered pair (a,b) is a **solution** to a linear inequality in x and y if the inequality is true when a and b are substituted for x and y, respectively.

Sketching the Graph of a Linear Inequality

1. Sketch the graph of the corresponding linear equation. Use a dashed line for inequalities with $<$ or $>$ and a solid line for inequalities with $\leq$ or $\geq$. This line divides the coordinate plane into two **half planes**.
2. Test a point in one of the half planes to find whether it is a solution of the inequality.
3. If the test point is a solution, shade its half plane. If not, shade the other half plane.

Example 1 □ Graph each inequality.
a. $2y + x \leq 4$ b. $3x - 2y > 2$

Solution □ a. The corresponding equation is $2y + x = 4$.

Write the equation in slope-intercept form.

$y = -\dfrac{1}{2}x + 2$ Slope-intercept form of the corresponding equation.

Graph the line that has a slope of $-\dfrac{1}{2}$ and a y-intercept of 2. The boundary should be drawn as a solid line.

Select a point in one of the half planes and test it. Let's use $(0,0)$.

$2y + x \leq 4$ Original inequality

$2(0) + 0 \leq 4$ $x = 0$, $y = 0$

$0 \leq 4$ True

Since the statement is true, shade the half plane containing the origin.

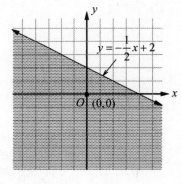

b. The corresponding equation is $3x - 2y = 2$.

Write the equation in slope-intercept form.

$y = \dfrac{3}{2}x - 1$ Slope-intercept form of the corresponding equation.

Graph the line that has a slope of $\dfrac{3}{2}$ and a y-intercept of -1. The boundary should be drawn as a dashed line.

Select a point in one of the half planes and test it. Let's use $(0,0)$.

$3x - 2y > 2$ Original inequality

$3(0) - 2(0) > 2$ $x = 0$, $y = 0$

$0 > 2$ False

Since the statement is false, shade the other half plane not containing the origin.

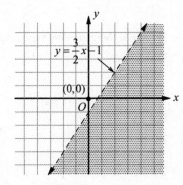

Exercises - Graphing Inequalities in Two Variables

1

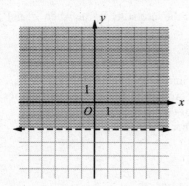

Which of the following inequalities represents the graph above?

A) $x > -2$

B) $x < -2$

C) $y > -2$

D) $y < -2$

2

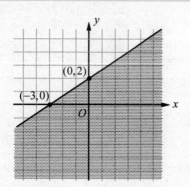

Which of the following inequalities represents the graph above?

A) $2y - 3x \geq 6$

B) $2y - 3x \leq 6$

C) $3y - 2x \geq 6$

D) $3y - 2x \leq 6$

3

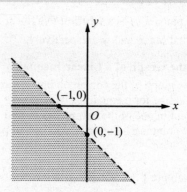

Which of the following inequalities represents the graph above?

A) $x + y < -1$

B) $x + y > -1$

C) $x + y \leq -1$

D) $x + y \geq -1$

4

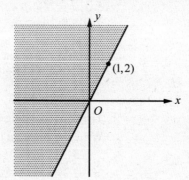

Which of the following inequalities represents the graph above?

A) $2x - y \geq 0$

B) $2x - y \leq 0$

C) $x - 2y \geq 0$

D) $x - 2y \leq 0$

4-4. Graphing Systems of Inequalities

A **system of inequalities** is a set of two or more inequalities with the same variables. The ordered pairs that satisfy all inequalities is a solution to the system. The solution set is represented by the intersection, or overlap, of the graphs.

Example 1 □ Solve each system of inequalities by graphing.

a. $x > -2$ b. $y \le 3x - 1$
    $y \le 3$ $y > -2x$
    $y > x - 1$

Solution □ a. The corresponding equations are
$x = -2$, $y = 3$, and $y = x - 1$.

Use a dashed line for inequalities with < or >
and a solid line for inequalities with ≤ or ≥.

Select $(0, 0)$ as a test point for each inequality.

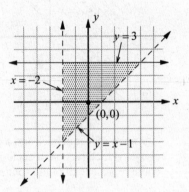

$0 > -2$	True
$0 \le 3$	True
$0 > 0 - 1$	True

The graph of the first inequality is the half
plane right of the vertical line. The graph of
the second inequality is the half plane on and
below the horizontal line. The graph of the third inequality is the half plane above
the line $y = x - 1$. The graph of the system is the shaded region shown above.

b. The corresponding equations are
$y = 3x - 1$ and $y = -2x$.

Use a dashed line for inequalities with < or >
and a solid line for inequalities with ≤ or ≥.

Select $(0, 0)$ as a test point for the inequality
$y \le 3x - 1$.

$0 \le 3(0) - 1$ False

The point $(0, 0)$ is not part of the solution.
Shade the half plane on or below the line
$y = 3x - 1$.

We cannot select $(0, 0)$ as a test point for the
inequality $y > -2x$, because $(0, 0)$ is on the boundary line. Let's use $(0, 1)$ as
a test point.

$y > -2x$.

$1 > -2(0)$ True

The point $(0, 1)$ is part of the solution. Shade the half plane above the line $y = -2x$.
The graph of the system is the shaded region shown above.

Exercises - Graphing Systems of Inequalities

1

$$\begin{cases} y - x \ge 1 \\ y \le -2x \end{cases}$$

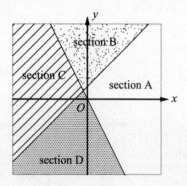

A system of inequalities and a graph are shown above. Which section or sections of the graph could represent all of the solutions to the system?

A) Section A

B) Section B

C) Section C

D) Section D

2

Which of the following ordered pairs (x, y) is a solution to the system of inequalities $y > x - 4$ and $x + y < 5$?

A) $(4, -2)$

B) $(0, 2)$

C) $(5, 3)$

D) $(0, -5)$

3

$$\begin{cases} x - 2y \le -2 \\ y < -x + 2 \end{cases}$$

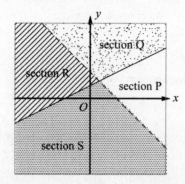

A system of inequalities and a graph are shown above. Which section or sections of the graph could represent all of the solutions to the system?

A) Section P

B) Section Q

C) Section R

D) Section S

4

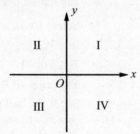

If the system of inequalities $2 - y < 2x$ and $-x \le 4 - y$ is graphed on the xy- plane above, which quadrant contains no solutions to the system?

A) Quadrant II

B) Quadrant III

C) Quadrant IV

D) There are solutions in all four quadrants.

Chapter 4 Practice Test

1

The sum of $120k$ and $215j$ does not exceed 2,500.

Which of the following inequalities represents the statement above?

A) $120k + 215j < 2,500$

B) $120k + 215j > 2,500$

C) $120k + 215j \leq 2,500$

D) $120k + 215j \geq 2,500$

2

One half of a number decreased by 3 is at most -5.

Which of the following inequalities represents the statement above?

A) $\dfrac{1}{2}n - 3 \leq -5$

B) $3 - \dfrac{1}{2}n \leq -5$

C) $\dfrac{1}{2}n - 3 < -5$

D) $3 - \dfrac{1}{2}n < -5$

3

Which of the following numbers is NOT a solution to the inequality $\dfrac{3b+5}{-2} \geq b - 8$?

A) 0

B) 1

C) 2

D) 3

4

Which of the following inequalities is equivalent to $0.6(k-7) - 0.3k > 1.8 + 0.9k$?

A) $k < 10$

B) $k < -10$

C) $k > 10$

D) $k > -10$

5

$4m - 3 \leq 2(m+1)$ or $7m + 23 < 15 + 9m$

Which of the following numbers is a solution to the compound inequality above?

A) 2

B) 3

C) 4

D) 5

6

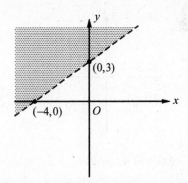

Which of the following inequalities represents the graph above?

A) $4y - 3x > 12$

B) $4y - 3x < 12$

C) $3y - 4x > 12$

D) $3y - 4x < 12$

7

$$\begin{cases} 2y - 3x \le 6 \\ y > 1 - x \end{cases}$$

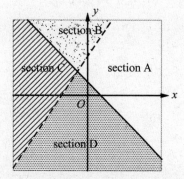

A system of inequalities and a graph are shown above. Which section or sections of the graph could represent all of the solutions to the system?

A) Section A

B) Section B

C) Section C

D) Section D

8

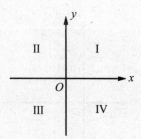

If the system of inequalities $3 \ge x$ and $-1 \le y$ is graphed in the xy-plane above, which quadrant contains no solutions to the system?

A) Quadrant II

B) Quadrant III

C) Quadrant IV

D) All four quadrants contain solutions.

9

$$\begin{cases} y < ax + 1 \\ y > bx - 1 \end{cases}$$

In the xy-plane, if $(1, 0)$ is a solution to the system of inequalities above, which of the following must be true?

I. $a > -1$

II. $a + b = 0$

III. $b < 1$

A) I only

B) I and II only

C) I and III only

D) I, II, and III

10

$$\begin{cases} y \ge 12x + 600 \\ y \ge -6x + 330 \end{cases}$$

In the xy-plane, if (x, y) lies in the solution set of the system of inequalities above, what is the minimum possible value of y?

11

If $-6 \le 3 - 2x \le 9$, what is the greatest possible value of $x - 1$?

12

For what integer value of x is $4x - 2 > 17$ and $3x + 5 < 24$?

Answer Key

Section 4-1

1. B   2. D   3. A   4. D   5. C
6. C

Section 4-2

1. B   2. B   3. D   4. 6   5. D

6. A   7. $\frac{24}{5}$ 8. 2 or 3

Section 4-3

1. C   2. D   3. A   4. B

Section 4-4

1. C   2. B   3. C   4. B

Chapter 4 Practice Test

1. C   2. A   3.D   4. B   5. A
6. A   7. A   8. D   9. C   10. 420

11. $\frac{7}{2}$ or 3.5   12. 5 or 6

Answers and Explanations

Section 4-1

1. **B**

$$-3+n \le 25$$
$$-3+n+3 \le 25+3 \qquad \text{Add 3 to each side.}$$
$$n \le 28 \qquad \text{Simplify.}$$
$$4n \le 4 \cdot 28 \qquad \text{Multiply each side by 4.}$$
$$4n \le 112 \qquad \text{Simplify.}$$
$$4n-12 \le 112-12 \qquad \text{Subtract 12 from each side.}$$
$$4n-12 \le 100 \qquad \text{Simplify.}$$

2. **D**

$$\frac{1}{2}x - \frac{1}{3} > \frac{7}{9} + \frac{5}{2}x$$

$$\frac{1}{2}x - \frac{1}{3} - \frac{5}{2}x > \frac{7}{9} + \frac{5}{2}x - \frac{5}{2}x \qquad \text{Subtract } \frac{5}{2}x \text{ from each side.}$$

$$-2x - \frac{1}{3} > \frac{7}{9} \qquad \text{Simplify.}$$

$$-2x - \frac{1}{3} + \frac{1}{3} > \frac{7}{9} + \frac{1}{3} \qquad \text{Add } \frac{1}{3} \text{ to each side.}$$

$$-2x > \frac{10}{9} \qquad \text{Simplify.}$$

$$-\frac{1}{2}(-2x) < -\frac{1}{2}\left(\frac{10}{9}\right) \qquad \text{Multiply each side by } -\frac{1}{2} \text{ and change > to <.}$$

$$x < -\frac{5}{9} \qquad \text{Simplify.}$$

Therefore, $-\frac{1}{2}$ is not a solution to the inequality.

3. **A**

$$-3a+7 \ge 5a-17$$
Add $-5a-7$ to each side of the inequality.
$$-3a+7+(-5a-7) \ge 5a-17+(-5a-7)$$

$$-8a \ge -24 \qquad \text{Simplify.}$$
$$(-8a) \div (-8) \le (-24) \div (-8) \qquad \text{Divide each side by } -8 \text{ and change } \ge \text{ to } \le.$$
$$a \le 3 \qquad \text{Simplify.}$$
$$3a \le 3(3) \qquad \text{Multiply each side by 3.}$$
$$3a \le 9 \qquad \text{Simplify.}$$
$$3a+7 \le 9+7 \qquad \text{Add 7 to each side.}$$
$$3a+7 \le 16 \qquad \text{Simplify.}$$

Therefore, the greatest possible value of $3a+7$ is 16.

4. **D**

$$\underset{\text{nine}}{9} \quad \underset{\text{is not more than}}{\le} \quad \underset{\text{the sum of a number and 17}}{n+17}$$

5. **C**

$$\underset{\substack{\text{the product of 7} \\ \text{and a number } n}}{7n} \quad \underset{\text{is no less than}}{\ge} \quad \underset{91}{91}$$

6. **C**

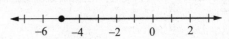

The solution set is $n \ge -5$.

Section 4-2

1. **B**

$$3-n < -2 \qquad \text{or} \quad 2n+3 \le -1$$
$$3-n-3 < -2-3 \qquad \text{or} \quad 2n+3-3 \le -1-3$$
$$-n < -5 \qquad \text{or} \quad 2n \le -4$$
$$n > 5 \qquad \text{or} \quad n \le -2$$

$-6 \le -2$, $-2 \le -2$, and $6 > 5$ are true. 2 is not a solution to the given compound inequality.

2. B

$$5w + 7 > 2 \qquad \text{and} \qquad 6w - 15 \le 3(-1 + w)$$
$$5w + 7 - 7 > 2 - 7 \qquad \text{and} \qquad 6w - 15 \le -3 + 3w$$
$$5w > -5 \qquad \text{and} \qquad 3w \le 12$$
$$w > -1 \qquad \text{and} \qquad w \le 4$$

Thus, 2 is a solution to the inequality.

3. D

$-x \le 5$	First inequality
$(-1)(-x) \ge (-1)(5)$	Multiply each side by -1 and change $\ge$ to $\le$.
$x \ge -5$	First inequality simplified.
$7 - \dfrac{1}{2}x > x + 1$	Second inequality
$7 - \dfrac{1}{2}x - 7 > x + 1 - 7$	Subtract 7 from each side.
$-\dfrac{1}{2}x > x - 6$	Simplify.
$-\dfrac{1}{2}x - x > x - 6 - x$	Subtract x from each side.
$-\dfrac{3}{2}x > -6$	Simplify.
$\left(-\dfrac{2}{3}\right)\left(-\dfrac{3}{2}x\right) < \left(-\dfrac{2}{3}\right)(-6)$	Multiply each side by $-\dfrac{2}{3}$ and change $>$ to $<$.
$x < 4$	Simplify.

The inequality can be written as $-5 \le x < 4$, so answer choice D is correct.

4. 6

$-2 < n < -1$	
$\left(\dfrac{1}{2}\right)(-2) < \left(\dfrac{1}{2}\right)n < \left(\dfrac{1}{2}\right)(-1)$	Multiply each side by $\dfrac{1}{2}$.
$-1 < \dfrac{1}{2}n < -\dfrac{1}{2}$	Simplify.
$7 - 1 < 7 + \dfrac{1}{2}n < 7 - \dfrac{1}{2}$	Add 7 to each side.
$6 < 7 + \dfrac{1}{2}n < 6.5$	Simplify

Thus, $7 + \dfrac{1}{2}n$ rounded to the nearest whole number is 6.

5. D

$\left|\dfrac{1}{2}x - 1\right| \le 1$ is equivalent to $-1 \le \dfrac{1}{2}x - 1 \le 1$.

$-1 + 1 \le \dfrac{1}{2}x - 1 + 1 \le 1 + 1$	Add 1 to each side.
$0 \le \dfrac{1}{2}x \le 2$	Simplify.
$2 \cdot 0 \le 2 \cdot \dfrac{1}{2}x \le 2 \cdot 2$	Multiply each side by 2.
$0 \le x \le 4$	Simplify.

Thus, 6 is not a solution of the given inequality.

6. A

The compound inequality $x < -2$ or $4 \le x$ represents the graph above.

7. $\dfrac{24}{5}$

$$\frac{1}{4}x - 1 \le -x + 5$$

Add $x + 1$ to each side of the inequality.

$$\frac{1}{4}x - 1 + (x + 1) \le -x + 5 + (x + 1)$$

$\dfrac{5}{4}x \le 6$	Simplify.
$\dfrac{4}{5}\left(\dfrac{5}{4}x\right) \le \dfrac{4}{5}(6)$	Multiply each side by $\dfrac{4}{5}$.
$x \le \dfrac{24}{5}$	Simplify.

The greatest possible value of x is $\dfrac{24}{5}$.

8. 2 or 3

$\left|\dfrac{3}{4}n - 2\right| < 1$ is equivalent to $-1 < \dfrac{3}{4}n - 2 < 1$.

$-1 + 2 < \dfrac{3}{4}n - 2 + 2 < 1 + 2$	Add 2 to each side.
$1 < \dfrac{3}{4}n < 3$	Simplify.
$\dfrac{4}{3} \cdot 1 < \dfrac{4}{3} \cdot \dfrac{3}{4}n < \dfrac{4}{3} \cdot 3$	Multiply each side by $\dfrac{4}{3}$.
$\dfrac{4}{3} < n < 4$	Simplify.

Since n is an integer, the possible values of n are 2 and 3.

Section 4-3

1. C

    The equation of the boundary line is $y = -2$. Any point above that horizontal has a y-coordinate that satisfies $y > -2$. Since the boundary line is drawn as a dashed line, the inequality should not include an equal sign.

2. D

    The slope-intercept form of the boundary line is $y = \dfrac{2}{3}x + 2$. The standard form of the line is $3y - 2x = 6$. Since the boundary line is drawn as a solid line, the inequality should include an equal sign. Select a point in the plane which is not on the boundary line and test the inequalities in the answer choices. Let's use $(0,0)$.

    C) $3y - 2x \geq 6$
    $3(0) - 2(0) \geq 6$ $x = 0,\ y = 0$
    $0 \geq 6$ false

    D) $3y - 2x \leq 6$
    $3(0) - 2(0) \leq 6$ $x = 0,\ y = 0$
    $0 \leq 6$ true

    Since the half-plane containing the origin is shaded, the test point $(0,0)$ should give a true statement. Answer choice D is correct. Choices A and B are incorrect because the equations of the boundary lines are not correct.

3. A

    The slope-intercept form of the boundary line is $y = -x - 1$. The standard form of the line is $x + y = -1$. Since the boundary line is drawn as a dashed line, the inequality should not include an equal sign. Select a point in the plane which is is not on the boundary line and test the inequalities in the answer choices. Let's use $(0,0)$.

    A) $x + y < -1$
    $0 + 0 < -1$ $x = 0,\ y = 0$
    $0 < -1$ false

    Since the half-plane containing the origin is not shaded, the test point $(0,0)$ should give a false statement. Answer choice A is correct. Choices C and D are incorrect because the inequalities include equal signs.

4. B

    The slope-intercept form of the boundary line is $y = 2x$. The standard form of the line is $2x - y = 0$. Since the boundary line is drawn as a solid line, the inequality should include an equal sign. Select a point in the plane which is not on the boundary line and test the inequalities in the answer choices. We cannot use $(0,0)$ for this question because $(0,0)$ is on the boundary line. Let's use $(0,1)$.

    A) $2x - y \geq 0$
    $2(0) - (1) \geq 0$ $x = 0,\ y = 1$
    $-1 \geq 0$ false

    B) $2x - y \leq 0$
    $2(0) - (1) \leq 0$ $x = 0,\ y = 1$
    $-1 \leq 0$ true

    Since the half-plane containing the $(0,1)$ is shaded, the test point $(0,1)$ should give a true statement. Answer choice B is correct. Choices C and D are incorrect because the equations of the boundary lines are not correct.

Section 4-4

1. C

    $y - x \geq 1$
    $y \leq -2x$

    Select a point from each section, then test them on the inequalities. Let's use $(3,0)$, $(0,3)$, $(-3,0)$, and $(0,-3)$, from each section as test points.

    $0 - 3 \geq 1$ $x = 3,\ y = 0$ is false.
    $0 \leq -2(3)$ $x = 3,\ y = 0$ is false.

    $3 - 0 \geq 1$ $x = 0,\ y = 3$ is true.
    $3 \leq -2(0)$ $x = 0,\ y = 3$ is false.

    $0 - (-3) \geq 1$ $x = -3,\ y = 0$ is true.
    $0 \leq -2(-3)$ $x = -3,\ y = 0$ is true.

    Since $x = -3$ and $y = 0$ are true for both inequalities, section C represents all of the solutions to the system.

2. **B**

$$y > x - 4$$
$$x + y < 5$$

Check each answer choice, to determine which ordered pair (x, y) is a solution to the system of inequalities.

A) $(4, -2)$

$-2 > 4 - 4$ $x = 4, y = -2$ is false.

$4 + (-2) < 5$ $x = 4, y = -2$ is true.

B) $(0, 2)$

$2 > 0 - 4$ $x = 0, y = 2$ is true.

$0 + 2 < 5$ $x = 0, y = 2$ is true.

$(0, 2)$ is a solution to the system of inequalities because the ordered pair gives a true statement for both pairs of inequalities.

3. **C**

$$x - 2y \le -2$$
$$y < -x + 2$$

Select a point from each section, then test them on the inequalities. Let's use $(3, 0)$, $(0, 3)$, $(-3, 0)$, and $(0, -3)$, from each section as test points.

$3 - 2(0) \le -2$ $x = 3, y = 0$ is false.

If the first statement is false, we don't need to check the second statement because the ordered pair must give a true statement for both pairs of the inequalities.

$0 - 2(3) \le -2$ $x = 0, y = 3$ is true.

$3 < -(0) + 2$ $x = 0, y = 3$ is false.

$-3 - 2(0) \le -2$ $x = -3, y = 0$ is true.

$0 < -(-3) + 2$ $x = -3, y = 0$ is true.

Since $x = -3$ and $y = 0$ are true for both inequalities, section R represents all of the solutions to the system.

4. **B**

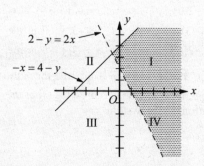

To determine which quadrant does not contain any solution to the system of inequalities, graph the inequalities. It is easier to use x-intercept and y-intercept to graph the boundary line. Graph the inequality $2 - y < 2x$ by drawing a dashed line through the x-intercept $(1, 0)$ and y-intercept $(0, 2)$. Graph the inequality $-x \ge 4 - y$ by drawing a solid line through the x-intercept $(-4, 0)$ and y-intercept $(0, 4)$. The solution to the system of inequalities is the shaded region as shown in the graph above. It can be seen that the solutions only include points in quadrants I, II, and IV and do not include any points in quadrant III.

Chapter 4 Practice Test

1. **C**

$$\underbrace{120k + 215j}_{\substack{\text{the sum of} \\ 120k \text{ and } 215j}} \quad \underbrace{\le}_{\text{does not exceed}} \quad \underbrace{2,500}_{2,500}$$

2. **A**

$$\underbrace{\frac{1}{2}n}_{\substack{\text{one half of} \\ \text{a number}}} \quad \underbrace{-3}_{\text{decreased by 3}} \quad \underbrace{\le}_{\text{is at most}} \quad \underbrace{-5}_{-5}$$

3. **D**

$$\frac{3b + 5}{-2} \ge b - 8$$

$-2(\frac{3b + 5}{-2}) \le -2(b - 8)$ Multiply each side by -2

                           and change $\ge$ to $\le$.

$3b + 5 \le -2b + 16$ Simplify.

$3b + 5 + 2b \le -2b + 16 + 2b$ Add $2b$ to each side.

$5b + 5 \le 16$ Simplify.

$5b + 5 - 5 \le 16 - 5$ Subtract 5.

$5b \le 11$ Simplify.

$\frac{5b}{5} \le \frac{11}{5}$ Divide each side by 5.

$b \le \frac{11}{5}$ Simplify.

So, 3 is not a solution to the inequality.

4. **B**

$$0.6(k - 7) - 0.3k > 1.8 + 0.9k$$
$$\Rightarrow \quad 0.6k - 4.2 - 0.3k > 1.8 + 0.9k$$
$$\Rightarrow \quad 0.3k - 4.2 > 1.8 + 0.9k$$

$\Rightarrow \quad 0.3k - 4.2 - 0.9k > 1.8 + 0.9k - 0.9k$

$\Rightarrow \quad -0.6k - 4.2 > 1.8 \quad \Rightarrow \quad -0.6k > 6$

$\Rightarrow \quad \dfrac{-0.6k}{-0.6} < \dfrac{6}{-0.6} \quad \Rightarrow \quad k < -10$

5. A

$4m - 3 \le 2(m+1)$ or $\quad 7m + 25 < 15 + 9m$
$4m - 3 \le 2m + 2$ or $\quad -2m + 25 < 15$
$2m \le 5$ $\qquad$ or $\quad -2m < -10$

$m \le \dfrac{5}{2}$ $\qquad$ or $\quad m > 5$

Thus, among the answer choices, 2 is the only solution to the compound inequality.

6. A

Slope m of the boundary line is

$m = \dfrac{3-0}{0-(-4)} = \dfrac{3}{4}$. The y-intercept is 3. So, the

slope-intercept form of the line is $y = \dfrac{3}{4}x + 3$.

The standard form of the line is $4y - 3x = 12$.
Select a point in the shaded region and test each inequality.
Let's use $(0, 4)$, as a test point.

A) $4y - 3x > 12$

$\quad 4(4) - 3(0) > 12 \qquad\qquad x = 0, \ y = 4$

$\quad 16 > 12 \qquad\qquad\qquad$ true

Since the half-plane containing $(0, 4)$ is shaded, the test point $(0, 4)$ should give a true statement. Answer choice A is correct.
Choices C and D are incorrect because the equations of the boundary lines are not correct.

7. A

Let's check $(3, 0)$, which is in section A.

$2(0) - 3(3) \le 6 \qquad\qquad x = 3, \ y = 0$ is true.

$0 > 1 - 3 \qquad\qquad\qquad x = 3, \ y = 0$ is true.

Since $x = 3$ and $y = 0$ are true for both inequalities, section A represents all of the solutions to the system.

8. D

To determine which quadrant does not contain any solution to the system of inequalities, graph the inequalities.

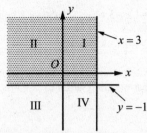

The solution to the system of inequalities is the shaded region shown in the graph above. Its solutions include points in all four quadrants. D is correct answer.

9. C

$y < ax + 1$ and $y > bx - 1$

Since $(1, 0)$ is a solution to the system of inequalities, substitute $x = 1$ and $y = 0$ in the given inequalities.

$0 < a(1) + 1$ and $\quad 0 > b(1) - 1 \qquad x = 1, \ y = 0$

$-1 < a \qquad$ and $\quad 1 > b \qquad\qquad$ Simplify.

Statements I and III are true. But we do not know the exact value of a or b, so statement II is not true.

10. 420

$y \ge 12x + 600 \qquad\qquad$ First inequality

$y \ge -6x + 330 \qquad\qquad$ Second inequality

Multiply each side of the second inequality by 2 and then add it to the first inequality.

$\quad 2y \ge -12x + 660 \qquad$ 2nd inequality multiplied by2.

$+\underline{\quad y \ge 12x + 600 \quad} \qquad$ First inequality

$\quad 3y \ge 1260 \qquad\qquad$ Sum of two inequalities

$\quad \dfrac{3y}{3} \ge \dfrac{1260}{3} \qquad\qquad$ Divide each side by 3.

$\quad y \ge 420 \qquad\qquad\quad$ Simplify.

Therefore, the minimum possible value of y is 420.

11. $\dfrac{7}{2}$ or 3.5

$-6 \le 3 - 2x \le 9$

$-6 - 3 \le 3 - 2x - 3 \le 9 - 3 \quad$ Subtract 3 from each side.

$-9 \le -2x \le 6 \qquad\qquad$ Simplify.

$\dfrac{-9}{-2} \ge \dfrac{-2x}{-2} \ge \dfrac{6}{-2} \qquad\qquad$ Divide each side by -2

$\qquad\qquad\qquad\qquad\qquad$ and change $\le$ to $\ge$.

$\dfrac{9}{2} \ge x \ge -3 \qquad\qquad$ Simplify.

$$\frac{9}{2} - 1 \geq x - 1 \geq -3 - 1 \qquad \text{Subtract 1 from each side.}$$

$$\frac{7}{2} \geq x - 1 \geq -4 \qquad\qquad \text{Simplify.}$$

The greatest possible value of $x - 1$ is $\frac{7}{2}$.

12. 5 or 6

$$4x - 2 > 17 \quad \text{and} \quad 3x + 5 < 24$$
$$4x > 19 \quad \text{and} \quad 3x < 19$$
$$x > \frac{19}{4} \quad \text{and} \quad x < \frac{19}{3}$$

Since x is between $\frac{19}{4} (= 4.75)$ and $\frac{19}{3} (\approx 6.33)$, the integer value of x is 5 or 6.

CHAPTER 5
Word Problems in Real-Life Situation

5-1. Solving Word Problems Using Linear Models

In SAT verbal problems, the construction of mathematical models that represent real-world scenarios is a critical skill. Linear equations can be used to model many types of real life situation word problems, such as cost, profit, speed, distance and time problems. To solve the verbal problems, you need to interpret the situation described in the problem into an equation, then solve the problem by solving the equation.

Plan for Solving a Word Problem

1. **Find out what numbers are asked** for from the given information.
2. **Choose a variable** to represent the number(s) described in the problem. Sketch or a chart may be helpful.
3. **Write an equation** that represents relationships among the numbers in the problem.
4. **Solve the equation** and find the required numbers.
5. **Answer** the original question. **Check** that your answer is reasonable.

A **linear function** $y = mx + b$ can be used as a model for many types of real life word problems which involve a constant rate of change.

Example 1 □ A person travels home from work at a constant speed. Ten minutes after leaving work he is 20 miles from home, and 20 minutes after leaving work he is 12 miles from home. If he continues to travel at the same speed, how long will it take him to arrive home from work?

Solution □ 1. The problem asks for the number of minutes it takes to travel from work to home.

2. Start with the linear equation $y = mx + b$, in which y is the distance in miles from home, and x is the time in minutes.

3. When $x = 10$, $y = 20$.
   When $x = 20$, $y = 12$.

4. $20 = 10m + b$ First equation
   $12 = 20m + b$ Second equation

   By subtracting the second equation from the first equation we get
   $8 = -10m$.

   $$\frac{8}{-10} = \frac{-10m}{-10}$$ Divide each side by -10.

   $$m = -\frac{4}{5}$$ Simplify.

   $$20 = 10(-\frac{4}{5}) + b$$ Substitute $m = -\frac{4}{5}$ into the first equation.

   $20 = -8 + b$ Simplify.

   $b = 28$ Simplify.

   $$y = -\frac{4}{5}x + 28$$ Replace m with $-\frac{4}{5}$ and b with 48.

   $$0 = -\frac{4}{5}x + 28$$ When he arrives home, $y = 0$.

   $x = 35$ Solve for x.

5. It takes 35 minutes from work to home.

Exercises - Problem Solving Using Linear Models

1

At the beginning of a trip, the tank of Chloe's car was filled with 12 gallons of gas. When she travels constantly on the highway 60 miles per hour, the car consumes 1 gallon of gas per 35 miles. If she traveled 5 hours and 15 minutes on the highway with a constant speed of 60 miles per hour, how many gallons of gas are left in the tank?

A) 3

B) 4

C) 5

D) 6

2

A rock climber is climbing up a 450 feet high cliff. By 9:30 AM. the climber reached 90 feet up the cliff and by 11:00 AM he has reached 210 feet up the cliff. If he climbs with a constant speed, by what time will he reach the top of the cliff?

A) 1:45 PM

B) 2:00 PM

C) 2:15 PM

D) 2:30 PM

3

In 2005 a house was purchased for $280,000 and in 2013 it was sold at $334,000. Assuming that the value of the house increased at a constant annual rate what will be the price of the house in the year 2018?

A) $354,250

B) $361,000

C) $367,750

D) $374,500

4

To join Eastlake Country Club one must pay d dollars for a one time membership fee and pay w dollars for a monthly fee. If the first month is free for the club, what is the total amount, y, x months after a person joined the club, in terms of d, w, and x?

A) $y = wx - 1 + d$

B) $y = w(x-1) + d$

C) $y = d(x-1) + w$

D) $y = dx - 1 + w$

5

From 1990 to 2000 The population of city A rose from 12,000 to 28,000 and the population of city B rose from 18,000 to 24,000. If the population of the two cities increased at a constant rate, in what year was the population of both cities the same?

6

An empty 1,200 gallon tank is filled with water at a rate of 6 gallons of water per minute. At the same time, another 1,200 gallon tank full of water is being drained at a rate of 9 gallons per minute. How many minutes will it take for the amount of water in both tanks to become the same?

5-2. Solving Word Problems Using Equations

Cost, Profit, and Value Problems

Total value = number of items × value per item

Profit = selling cost − buying cost

Example 1 □ A music store owner purchased x compact discs for $6.50 each. He sold all but 19 of them for $12.00 each. If he made a profit of $564.00 from the compact discs, what is the value of x?

Solution □ 1. The problem asks for the value of x.

2. x is given as the number of compact discs purchased.

3. Selling cost = number of items sold × value per item = $(x-19) \times 12$

Buying cost = number of items bought × value per item = $x \times 6.50$

Profit = selling cost − buying cost = $(x-19) \times 12 - 6.5x$

4. $564 = (x-19) \times 12 - 6.5x$

$564 = 12x - 228 - 6.5x = 5.5x - 228$

$792 = 5.5x$

$x = 144$

5. The number of compact discs purchased is 144.

Distance, Rate, and Time Problems

Distance = rate × time, $d = rt$ **Average speed** = $\dfrac{\text{total distance}}{\text{total time}}$, $r = \dfrac{d}{t}$ **Average time** = $\dfrac{\text{total distance}}{\text{average speed}}$, $t = \dfrac{d}{r}$

Example 2 □ Carl drove from his home to the beach at a speed of 50 mph and returned home along the same route at a speed of 30mph. If his total driving time for the trip was two hours, how many minutes did it take him to drive from his home to the beach?

Solution □ 1. The problem asks for the time it took for Carl to drive to the beach.

2. Let t = the time in hours it took for Carl to drive to the beach.
Then $2 - t$ = the time spent for the return trip.
Make a chart and a sketch showing the given facts.

	Rate	× Time	= Distance
Going out	50	t	$50t$
Returning	30	$2-t$	$30(2-t)$

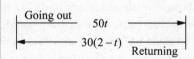

3. $50t = 30(2-t)$ The distance going out = the distance returning.

$50t = 60 - 30t$ Distributive Property

$80t = 60$ Add $30t$ on each side.

4. $t = \dfrac{60}{80} = \dfrac{3}{4}$ hours   Solve for t.

5. It took Carl $\dfrac{3}{4}$ hours, or $\dfrac{3}{4} \times 60 = 45$ minutes, to drive from his home to the beach.

Exercises - Problem Solving with Equations

1

	Distance to Finish Line (meters)
Jason	$-8t + 200$
Mary	$-7.5t + 200$

Jason and Mary are running on a 200 meter track. The expressions in the table above show the distance to the finish line t seconds after they started the race. How many meters will Mary have left to finish the race when Jason is on the finish line?

A) 10.5 meters

B) 11.5 meters

C) 12.5 meters

D) 13.5 meters

2

At a bagel shop the first 6 bagels purchased cost 55 cents apiece, and additional bagels cost c cents apiece. If a customer paid $5.70 for 12 bagels, what is the value of c?

A) 25

B) 30

C) 35

D) 40

3

Manny bought c candies at a price of 70 cents each. He sold all but k candies at a price of $1.25, and made a profit of p dollars. Which of the following represents p in terms of c and k?

A) $p = 1.25(c - k) - 0.7c$

B) $p = 1.25c - 0.7k$

C) $p = 1.25c - 0.7(c - k)$

D) $p = 1.25(c - k) - 0.7k$

4

David used $\frac{1}{10}$ of his monthly salary for groceries and $\frac{3}{18}$ of his remaining money for his car payment. He also paid twice as much money for rent as for his car payment. If David has $1,620 left after paying for groceries, car payment, and rent, how much is his monthly salary?

A) $3,240

B) $3,320

C) $3,480

D) $3,600

5

In a school election, 680 students voted for one of two candidates for president. If the winner received 120 more votes than the loser, how many votes did the winner receive?

6

If a gas tank contains 15 liters of gas and is $\frac{3}{8}$ full, how many additional liters of gas are needed to fill up the tank?

5-3. Solving Word Problems Using Systems of Equations

A problem involving two unknown quantities can be solved by using a system of equations.

Example 1 □ At a museum, Elly bought 3 student tickets and 2 adult tickets for $29.00. At the same museum Samantha bought 5 student tickets and 4 adult tickets for $54.00. How much does one student ticket and one adult ticket cost?

Solution □ 1. The problem asks for the cost of one student ticket plus one adult ticket.

2. Let s = the price of student ticket and
   and a = the price of adult ticket.

3. $\left\{\begin{array}{c}\text{number of}\\\text{student ticket}\end{array}\right\} \cdot \left\{\begin{array}{c}\text{price of}\\\text{student ticket}\end{array}\right\} + \left\{\begin{array}{c}\text{number of}\\\text{adult ticket}\end{array}\right\} \cdot \left\{\begin{array}{c}\text{price of}\\\text{adult ticket}\end{array}\right\} = \text{total cost}$

   $3s + 2a = 29$ First equation
   $5s + 4a = 54$ Second equation

4. $-6s - 4a = -58$ First equation multiplied by -2.
   $5s + 4a = 54$ Second equation

   By adding the two equations we get $-s = -4$ or $s = 4$.
   Substitute $s = 4$ in the first equation.

   $3(4) + 2a = 29$

   $12 + 2a = 29$

   $2a = 17$

   $a = 8.5$

5. $s + a = 4 + 8.5 = 12.5$

   The cost of one student ticket and one adult ticket is $12.50.

Example 2 □ On the second weekend of July, Eric hiked 10 less than twice the number of miles that he hiked on the first weekend of July. In these two weeks he hiked a total of 38 miles. How many miles did he hike on the first weekend?

Solution □ 1. The problem asks for the number of miles Eric hiked on the first week of July.

2. Let f = the number of miles Eric hiked on the first week
   and s = the number of miles Eric hiked on the second week.

3. $\left\{\begin{array}{c}\text{number of miles hiked}\\\text{on the second weekend}\end{array}\right\} = \left\{\begin{array}{c}\text{10 miles less than twice the number}\\\text{of miles he hiked on the first weekend}\end{array}\right\}$

   $\{\text{total number of miles hiked in the two weekends}\} = 38$

   $s = 2f - 10$ First equation

   $f + s = 38$ Second equation

4. $f + (2f - 10) = 38$ $s = 2f - 10$ is substituted to the
                                           second equation.

   $3f - 10 = 38$ Simplify.

   $3f - 10 + 10 = 38 + 10$ Add 10 to each side.

   $3f = 48$ Simplify.

   $f = 16$ Divide each side by 3.

5. Eric hiked 16 miles on the first weekend.

Exercises - Solving Word problems Using Systems of Equations

1

Adam and Betty purchased a printer together for $258. If Adam paid $18 less than twice Betty, how much money did Adam pay for the printer?

A) 172

B) 166

C) 158

D) 146

2

There are 28 tables for customers at Mesa Grill Restaurant. The tables are either two-seat tables or four-seat tables. When all the tables are full, there will be 90 customers in the restaurant. How many two-seat tables are at the restaurant?

A) 11

B) 13

C) 15

D) 17

3

In a basketball, a field goal is either 2 or 3 points. In a college basketball tournament, Jim made 73 more 2-point field goals than 3-point field goals. If he scored a total of 216 goals in the tournament how many 3-point field goals did he make?

A) 12

B) 14

C) 16

D) 18

4

In a car dealership, all of the vehicles are either a sedan or a SUV. If 36 sedans are sold and 36 SUVs are added, there will be an equal number of sedans and SUVs. If 8 SUVs are sold and 8 sedans are added, there will be twice as many sedans as SUVs. How many sedans were at the dealership before any vehicle was sold?

A) 132

B) 144

C) 156

D) 168

5

At a coffee shop, a 16 ounce bag of coffee is on sale at $5.25 less than the regular price. The cost of 4 bags of coffee at regular price is the same as the cost of 6 bags of coffee at sale price. Let r be the regular price of coffee and s be the sale price of coffee. Which of the following systems of equations can be used to find the values of variables r and s ?

A) $\begin{cases} s = r - 16 \\ r = 6s \end{cases}$

B) $\begin{cases} s = r - 5.25 \\ 4r = 16 \end{cases}$

C) $\begin{cases} s = r - 5.25 \\ 4r = 6s \end{cases}$

D) $\begin{cases} s = r + 5.25 \\ 4r = 6s \end{cases}$

5-4. Solving Word Problems Using Inequalities

Many of the real-life word problems can be solved algebraically by translating the given information into an inequality and then solving the inequality.

Example 1 □ Apex Car Rental charges a flat fee of $40.00 per day plus $0.54 per mile to rent a car. Jason Car Rental charges a flat fee of $65.00 per day plus $0.36 per mile to rent a car. If a car is rented for three days, at least how many miles would you have to drive, to the nearest mile, to make the Jason Car Rental company the better option?

Solution □ 1. The problem asks for how many miles you would have to drive to make Jason Car Rental the better option.

2. Let x = the number of miles of driving which would make Jason Car Rental the better option.

3. $\left\{\begin{array}{l}\text{Apex Car Rental's} \\ \text{rental charge for 3 days}\end{array}\right\} > \left\{\begin{array}{l}\text{Jason Car Rental's} \\ \text{rental charge for 3 days}\end{array}\right\}$

$40 \cdot 3 + 0.54x > 65 \cdot 3 + 0.36x$

4. $120 + 0.54x > 195 + 0.36x$ Simplify.

$120 + 0.54x - 0.36x > 195 + 0.36x - 0.36x$ Subtract $0.36x$ from each side.

$120 + 0.18x > 195$ Simplify.

$120 + 0.18x - 120 > 195 - 120$ Subtract 120 from each side.

$0.18x > 75$ Simplify.

$\dfrac{0.18x}{0.18} > \dfrac{75}{0.18}$ Divide each side by 0.18.

$x > 416.67$ Simplify.

5. You need to drive 417 miles or more to make Jason Car Rental the better option.

Example 2 □ A 38 inch long wire is cut into two pieces. The longer piece has to be at least 3 inches longer than twice the shorter piece. What is the maximum length of the shorter piece, to the nearest inch?

Solution □ 1. The problem asks for the maximum length of the shorter piece, to the nearest inch.

2. Let x = the length of the shorter piece, and $38 - x$ = the length of the longer piece.

3. {The longer piece is at least 3 inches longer than twice the shorter piece.}

$38 - x \geq 2x + 3$

4. $38 - x + x \geq 2x + 3 + x$ Add x to each side.

$38 \geq 3x + 3$ Simplify.

$38 - 3 \geq 3x + 3 - 3$ Subtract 3 from each side.

$35 \geq 3x$ Simplify.

$\dfrac{35}{3} (\approx 11.66) \geq x$ Divide each side by 3.

5. The maximum length of the shorter piece, to the nearest inch, is 11.

Exercises - Solving Word Problems Using Inequalities

1

Tom wants to rent a truck for two days and pay no more than $300. How far can he drive the truck if the truck rental cost $49 a day plus $0.40 a mile?

A) 490

B) 505

C) 520

D) 535

2

Tim has 140 paperback and hard cover copies in his book shelf. If the hard cover copies do not exceed one sixth the number of paperback copies, what is the minimum number of paperback copies in Tim's book shelf?

A) 114

B) 116

C) 118

D) 120

3

The number of students in a geometry class is four fifths the number of students in a Spanish class. The total number of students in both classes does not exceed 54. What is the greatest possible number of students in the Spanish class?

A) 30

B) 32

C) 34

D) 36

4

At a sporting goods store, Jay paid $172 for a pair of shoes and a pair of pants. The pants cost less than two thirds of what the shoes cost. What is the minimum price of the shoes to the nearest dollar?

5

Ty earns $14 an hour working on weekdays and $21 an hour working on weekends. If he wants to make at least $600 by working a total of 36 hours in a week, to the nearest hour, at least how many hours does he need work on the weekends?

Chapter 5 Practice Test

Questions 1 - 3 refer to the following information.

The manager of an apartment building needs an electrician to repair the power generator for the building. The table below shows the fixed amount for a time service call and hourly charges for two different companies.

Company	Fixed amount for a service call	Hourly Rate
A	$40	$55
B	$75	$48

1

Which of the following equations gives the total cost, y, of repairing the power generator in terms of the total number of hours, x, from company A?

A) $y = 48x + 75$

B) $y = 75x + 48$

C) $y = 40x + 55$

D) $y = 55x + 40$

2

For what number of hours, x, will the total cost of repairing the generator for company B be less than or equal to the total cost of repairing the generator for company A?

A) $x \geq \dfrac{5}{2}$

B) $x \leq \dfrac{5}{2}$

C) $x \geq 5$

D) $x \leq 5$

3

Company B's total cost, y, is the fixed amount for a service call plus the hourly rates. If the relationship between Company B's total cost, y, and the number of hours, x, is graphed in the xy- plane, what does the slope of the line represent?

A) Fixed amount for a service call

B) Hourly Rate

C) Total amount for one day

D) Total amount for repairing the power generator

4

Apex Car Rental company charges a flat fee of $40.00 per day plus $0.75 per mile to rent a car. Jason Car Rental company charges a flat fee of $64.00 per day plus $0.60 per mile to rent a car. If a car is rented for three days, at how many miles would the rental charges of the two companies be the same?

A) 480

B) 450

C) 420

D) 380

5

It took Sara a total of 42 minutes to jog from home to the park and back again, by the same path. If she averaged 8 miles per hour going to the park and 6 miles per hour coming back, what is the distance from her home to the park?

A) 2.4 miles

B) 2.8 miles

C) 3.2 miles

D) 3.6 miles

6

Carl drove from his home to the beach at an average speed of 50 mph and returned home along the same route at an average speed of 30 mph. His total driving time for the trip was 2 hours. Solving which of the following systems of equations yields, x, the time it took for Carl to drive to the beach and, y, the time spent for the return trip?

A) $x = y + 2$
   $50x = 30y$

B) $x + y = 2$
   $30x = 50y$

C) $x + y = 2$
   $50x = 30y$

D) $y = x + 2$
   $30x = 50y$

7

To join Ace Gym, one must pay a $180 membership fee plus dues of $35 per month. To join Best Gym, one must pay a $300 membership fee plus dues of $23 per month. At how many months would the total cost of either gym be the same?

A) 7

B) 8

C) 9

D) 10

8

At a county fair the admission is $8.00 and each ride costs $1.25. If you go to the fair with $20.00, what is the maximum number of rides you can go on?

A) 8

B) 9

C) 10

D) 11

9

A car averages 18 miles per gallon of gas for city driving and 27 miles per gallon of gas for highway driving. What is the total number of gallons of gas needed to drive $6x$ miles in the city and $18x$ miles on the highway?

A) x

B) $2x$

C) $3.5x$

D) $4.5x$

10

One section of a grocery store display only water bottles. The water bottles are in either 6-bottle packages or 8-bottle packages. Let x represent the number of 6-bottle packages and y represent the number of 8-bottle packages. The total number of packages displayed are 270 and the total number of bottles are 1,860. To find the values of variables x and y, which of the following systems of equations can be used?

A) $\begin{cases} x + y = 1,860 \\ 6x + 8y = 270 \end{cases}$

B) $\begin{cases} 6x + 8y = 1,860 \\ x + y = 270 \end{cases}$

C) $\begin{cases} 8x + 6y = 1,860 \\ x + y = 270 \end{cases}$

D) $\begin{cases} x + y = 1,860 \\ 8x + 6y = 270 \end{cases}$

Answer Key

Section 5-1

1. A   2. B   3. C   4. B   5. 1996
6. 80

Section 5-2

1. C   2. D   3. A   4. D   5. 400
6. 25

Section 5-3

1. B   2. A   3. B   4. D   5. C

Section 5-4

1. B   2. D   3. A   4. 104   5. 14

Chapter 5 Practice Test

1. D   2. C   3. B   4. A   5. A
6. C   7. D   8. B   9. A   10. B

Answers and Explanations

Section 5-1

1. A

Distance traveled

$$= \text{speed} \times \text{time} = \frac{60 \text{ miles}}{1 \text{ hour}} \times 5\frac{1}{4} \text{ hours} = 315 \text{ miles}$$

Number of gallons of gas used

$$= \frac{1 \text{ gallon}}{35 \text{ miles}} \times 315 \text{ miles} = 9 \text{ gallons}$$

Since the tank of Chloe's car was filled with 12 gallons of gas at the beginning, $12-9$,or 3 gallons of gas are left in the tank.

2. B

Average rate of climbing per hour

$$= \frac{\text{height gained}}{\text{time}} = \frac{210-90}{11-9.5} = \frac{120}{1.5}$$
$$= 80 \text{ feet / hour}$$

By 11:00 AM he has reached 210 feet up the cliff, so, the remaining height is $450-210$, or 240 feet. Since he is climbing up 80 feet per hour, it will take him $\frac{240}{80}$, or 3 more hours to reach the top of the cliff. Three hour later from 11:00 am is 2 pm.

3. C

Average rate of change in the price of the house

$$= \frac{334,000-280,000}{2013-2005} = \frac{54,000}{8}$$
$$= 6,750 / \text{year}$$

The purchase price of the house in the year 2018 will be $334,000+5\times6,750$, or $367,750.

4. B

Since the first month is free for the club, the amount of monthly fee x months after a person joined the club will be $w\times(x-1)$, and the total amount including the one time membership fee will be $w\times(x-1)+d$.

Choice B is the correct.

5. 1996

Average rate of change in the population of city A

$$= \frac{28,000-12,000}{2000-1990} = \frac{16,000}{10}$$
$$= 1,600 / \text{year}$$

Average rate of change in the population of city B

$$= \frac{24,000-18,000}{2000-1990} = \frac{6,000}{10}$$
$$= 600 / \text{year}$$

Let $x=$ the number of years from 1990, and let $y=$ the population after 1990.

The population of city A after 1990 will be $y=1600x+12,000$ and the population of city B after 1990 will be $y=600x+18,000$.

To find the year the population of both cities were the same, let the two equations be equal.
$1600x+12,000 = 600x+18,000$

Solving the equation for x yields $x=6$.
The correct answer is 1996.

6. 80

Let $x=$ the time in minutes it takes for the amount of water in both tanks to become the same. During x minutes, $6x$ gallons of water filled in the empty tank and $9x$ gallons of water were drained from the 1,200 gallon tank. If the amount of water in the two tanks are the same, $6x=1200-9x$.

Solving the equation for x gives $x=80$.

Section 5-2

1. C

   To find out the time it took for Jason to reach the finish line, solve the equation $-8t + 200 = 0$ for t. Solving the equation for t gives $t = 25$. Substitute 25 for t in the expression $-7.5t + 200$.

   $-7.5(25) + 200 = 12.5$

   Therefore, Mary has 12.5 meters left to finish when Jason is on the finish line.

2. D

   First 6 bagels cost 55 cents each and the additional bagels cost c cents each. The total for 12 bagels is $5.70. So, the other 6 bagels cost c cents each.

   $6 \times 0.55 + 6c = 5.70$
   $3.3 + 6c = 5.70$
   $6c = 2.4$
   $c = 0.4$

   The value of c is 40 cents.

3. A

   Buying cost of candies $= 0.7c$
   Number of candies sold $= c - k$
   Selling price $= 1.25(c - k)$
   Profit $=$ selling price $-$ buying cost
   $\quad = 1.25(c - k) - 0.7c$

4. D

   Let $x =$ David's monthly salary, then

   $\dfrac{1}{10}x =$ grocery cost,

   $\dfrac{9}{10}x =$ remaining salary,

   $\dfrac{3}{18} \cdot \dfrac{9}{10}x =$ car payment,

   $2 \cdot \dfrac{3}{18} \cdot \dfrac{9}{10}x =$ rent.

   David's monthly salary x is equal to the sum of his grocery, car payment, rent, and $1,620.

   $x = \dfrac{1}{10}x + \dfrac{3}{18} \cdot \dfrac{9}{10}x + 2 \cdot \dfrac{3}{18} \cdot \dfrac{9}{10}x + 1620$

   $x = \dfrac{99}{180}x + 1440 \;\Rightarrow\; x - \dfrac{99}{180}x = 1620$

   $\Rightarrow\; x - \dfrac{99}{180}x = 1440 \;\Rightarrow\; \dfrac{81}{180}x = 1620$

   $\Rightarrow\; x = 1620 \cdot \dfrac{180}{81} = 3600$

5. 400

   Let $x =$ the number of votes the winner received, then $x - 120 =$ the number of votes the loser received. The sum of the votes both the winner and the loser received equals 680.

   $x + (x - 120) = 680$
   $2x - 120 = 680$
   $2x = 800$
   $x = 400$

6. 25

   Let $x =$ the total capacity of the gas tank in liters.

   Since $\dfrac{3}{8}$ of the gas tank is equivalent to 15 liters,

   $\dfrac{3}{8}x = 15$.

   $\dfrac{3}{8}x = 15 \;\Rightarrow\; x = 15 \cdot \dfrac{8}{3} = 40$

   Since the gas tank is $\dfrac{3}{8}$ full, we need $\dfrac{5}{8}x$ more liters to fill up the gas tank.

   $\dfrac{5}{8}x = \dfrac{5}{8}(40) = 25$ liters

Section 5-3

1. B

   Let $x =$ the amount Betty paid for the printer, then $2x - 18 =$ the amount Adam paid for the printer. Total amount they paid together is $258.

   $$\underbrace{(2x - 18)}_{\text{amount Adam paid}} + \underbrace{x}_{\text{amount Betty paid}} = 258$$

   $\Rightarrow\; 3x - 18 = 258 \;\Rightarrow\; 3x = 276 \;\Rightarrow\; x = 92$

   The amount Adam paid
   $= 2x - 18 = 2(92) - 18 = 166$

2. A

   Let $x =$ the number of two-seat tables, then $28 - x =$ the number of four-seat tables. When all the tables are full, there will be 90 customers in the restaurant. Therefore,

   $2x + 4(28 - x) = 90$
   $\Rightarrow\; 2x + 112 - 4x = 90 \;\Rightarrow\; -2x + 112 = 90$
   $\Rightarrow\; -2x = -22 \;\Rightarrow\; x = 11$

   There are 11 two-seat tables.

3. B

Let $x =$ the number of 3-point field goals,
then $x + 73 =$ the number of 2-point field goals.
He scored a total of 216 goals in the tournament.

$$\underbrace{3x}_{\substack{\text{number of points made} \\ \text{through 3-point field goal}}} + \underbrace{2(x + 73)}_{\substack{\text{number of points made} \\ \text{through 2-point field goal}}} = \underbrace{216}_{\substack{\text{total number} \\ \text{of points}}}$$

$3x + 2(x + 73) = 216 \Rightarrow 3x + 2x + 146 = 216$
$\Rightarrow 5x + 146 = 216 \Rightarrow 5x = 70 \Rightarrow x = 14$

4. D

Let $x =$ the original number of sedans.
Then $x - 36 =$ the number of sedans left after 36
of them are sold and $x + 8 =$ the number of sedans
after 8 are added.
Let $y =$ the original number of SUVs.
Then $y + 36 =$ the number of SUVs after 36 of
them are added and $y - 8 =$ the number of SUVs
after 8 of them are sold.

If 36 sedans are sold and 36 SUV are added then
there will be an equal number of sedans and SUVs,
and if 8 SUV are sold and 8 sedans are added then
there will be twice as many sedans as SUVs.
The equations that represent these relationships
are $x - 36 = y + 36$ and $x + 8 = 2(y - 8)$.

Solving the first equation for y gives $y = x - 72$.
Substituting $x - 72$ for y in the second equation
yields $x + 8 = 2(x - 72 - 8)$.

$x + 8 = 2(x - 72 - 8) \Rightarrow x + 8 = 2(x - 80)$
$\Rightarrow x + 8 = 2x - 160 \Rightarrow 168 = x$

Choice D is correct.

5. C

The sale price of coffee, s, is \$5.25 less than the
regular price, r. The equation that represents this
relationship is $s = r - 5.25$.
The cost of 4 bags of coffee at regular price is the
same as the cost of 6 bags of coffee at sale price.
The equation that represents this relationship is
$4r = 6s$.

Choice C is correct.

Section 5-4

1. B

The truck rental cost \$49 a day, so for two days
it will cost $2 \times \$49$, or \$98. In addition, it cost

\$0.40 per mile. If Tom drives m miles the total
cost will be $98 + 0.4m$ dollars. This cost will not
be more than \$300 if $98 + 0.4m \leq 300$.

$98 + 0.4m \leq 300 \Rightarrow 0.4m \leq 202$
$\Rightarrow m \leq \dfrac{202}{0.4} \Rightarrow m \leq 505$

2. D

Let $p =$ the number of paperback copies and
let $h =$ the number of hard cover copies.

$p + h = 140$ There are 140 paperback and hard
              cover copies.

$h \leq \dfrac{1}{6}p$ Hard cover copies do not exceed one
              sixth the number of paperback copies,

Solving the equation for h gives $h = 140 - p$.
Substitute $140 - p$ for h in the inequality.

$140 - p \leq \dfrac{1}{6}p \Rightarrow 140 - p + p \leq \dfrac{1}{6}p + p$

$\Rightarrow 140 \leq \dfrac{7}{6}p \Rightarrow \dfrac{6}{7} \cdot 140 \leq \dfrac{6}{7} \cdot \dfrac{7}{6}p$

$\Rightarrow 120 \leq p$

Therefore, the minimum number of paperback
copies in Tim's book shelf is 120.

3. A

Let $g =$ the number of students in geometry class
and let $s =$ the number of students in Spanish class.

$g = \dfrac{4}{5}s$ The number of students in a geometry
              class is four fifths the number of
              students in a Spanish class.

$g + s \leq 54$ The total number of students in both
              classes does not exceed 54.

Substitute $\dfrac{4}{5}s$ for g into the inequality.

$\dfrac{4}{5}s + s \leq 54 \Rightarrow \dfrac{9}{5}s \leq 54$

$\Rightarrow \dfrac{5}{9} \cdot \dfrac{9}{5}s \leq \dfrac{5}{9} \cdot 54$

$\Rightarrow s \leq 30$

Therefore, the greatest possible number of students
in the Spanish class is 30.

4. 104

Let $s =$ the price of shoes and
let $p =$ the price of pants.

$s + p = 172$ Jay paid \$172 for a pair of shoes and a pair of pants.

$p < \dfrac{2}{3}s$ The pants cost less than two thirds of what the shoes cost.

Solving the equation for p gives $p = 172 - s$.
Substitute $172 - s$ for p in the inequality.

$172 - s < \dfrac{2}{3}s \implies 172 - s + s < \dfrac{2}{3}s + s$

$\implies 172 < \dfrac{5}{3}s \implies \dfrac{3}{5} \cdot 172 < \dfrac{3}{5} \cdot \dfrac{5}{3}s$

$\implies 103.2 < s$

Therefore, the minimum price of the shoes to the nearest dollar is \$104.

5. **14**

Let $e =$ the number of hours Ty needs to work on weekends, then $36 - e =$ the number of hours Ty works on weekdays.
Ty earns \$14 an hour working on weekdays and \$21 an hour working on weekends and he wants to make at least \$600. The inequality that represents this relationship is $14(36 - e) + 21e \geq 600$.

$14(36 - e) + 21e \geq 600 \implies 504 - 14e + 21e \geq 600$

$\implies 504 + 7e \geq 600 \implies 7e \geq 96$

$\implies e \geq \dfrac{96}{7} (\approx 13.7)$

Therefore, he needs to work at least 14 hours on the weekends.

Chapter 5 Practice Test

1. **D**

If the apartment manager hires an electrician from company A, he needs to pay 55 dollars per hour. So for x hours, he has to pay $55x$ dollars plus 40 dollars for a service call. Therefore, the total cost, y, of repairing the power generator will be $y = 55x + 40$.

2. **C**

The total cost, y, of repairing the generator for company B will be $y = 48x + 75$. If the cost of repairing the generator for company B is less than or equal to the total cost of repairing the generator for company A, then $48x + 75 \leq 55x + 40$.

$48x + 75 \leq 55x + 40$

$\implies 48x + 75 - 48x \leq 55x + 40 - 48x$

$\implies 75 \leq 7x + 40 \implies 75 - 40 \leq 7x + 40 - 40$

$\implies 35 \leq 7x \implies 5 \leq x$

Choice C is correct.

3. **B**

The total cost, y, for a service call and hourly charge from company B is given by the equation $y = 48x + 75$. If the relationship is graphed on the xy-plane, the slope of the graph is 48, which is the hourly rate for company B.

Choice B is correct.

4. **A**

If a car is rented for three days and driven for x miles, the rental charges of Apex Car Rental will be $3 \times 40 + 0.75x$ and the rental charges of Jason Car Rental will be $3 \times 64 + 0.6x$.
The two company's charges will be the same if

$3 \times 40 + 0.75x = 3 \times 64 + 0.6x$.
$120 + 0.75x = 192 + 0.6x$
$120 + 0.75x - 0.6x = 192 + 0.6x - 0.6x$
$120 + 0.15x = 192$
$120 + 0.15x - 120 = 192 - 120$
$0.15x = 72$
$x = 480$

5. **A**

Let $d =$ the distance in miles from Sara's home to the park. Since average time $= \dfrac{\text{total distance}}{\text{average speed}}$,

the time it took to jog from home to the park $= \dfrac{d}{8}$ and the time it took to jog from the park to her home $= \dfrac{d}{6}$. Since the total time for the round trip was 42 minute, or $\dfrac{42}{60}$ hours, $\dfrac{d}{8} + \dfrac{d}{6} = \dfrac{42}{60}$.

By multiplying each side of the equation by 120, we have $120(\dfrac{d}{8} + \dfrac{d}{6}) = 120(\dfrac{42}{60})$.

$\implies 15d + 20d = 84 \implies 35d = 84$

$\implies d = \dfrac{84}{35} = 2.4$

6. **C**

The time it took for Carl to drive to the beach plus the time spent for the return trip equals 2 hours. Therefore $x + y = 2$.
Also the distance of going to the beach equals the returning distance. Use the formula $d = rt$.

The distance to the beach equals to $50x$ and the returning distance equals $30y$. Thus $50x = 30y$. Choice C is correct.

7. **D**

Let $x =$ number of months at which both gyms cost the same.

The total cost x months after joining Ace Gym is $180 + 35x$ and the total cost x months after joining Best Gym is $300 + 23x$. If $180 + 35x = 300 + 23x$ the total cost of either gym will be the same.

$180 + 35x - 23x = 300 + 23x - 23x$
$180 + 12x = 300$
$180 + 12x - 180 = 300 - 180$
$12x = 120$
$x = 10$

8. **B**

If you pay for admission and take r rides, the total cost will be $\$(8 + 1.25r)$.

The total cost does not exceed $20 if $8 + 1.25r \le 20$.

$8 + 1.25r \le 20 \Rightarrow 8 + 1.25r - 8 \le 20 - 8$

$\Rightarrow 1.25r \le 12 \Rightarrow r \le \dfrac{12}{1.25} \Rightarrow r \le 9.6$

Therefore, the maximum number of rides you can go on is 9.

9. **A**

The number of gallons of gas needed to drive $6x$ miles in the city $= \dfrac{6x}{18} = \dfrac{1}{3}x$.

The number of gallons of gas needed to drive $18x$ miles on the highway $= \dfrac{18x}{27} = \dfrac{2}{3}x$.

Total number of gallons of gas needed equals $\dfrac{1}{3}x + \dfrac{2}{3}x$, or x.

10. **B**

If x represents the number of 6-bottle packages and y represents the number of 8-bottle packages, then $x + y$ represents the total number of packages. Thus, $x + y = 270$.

If x is the number of 6-bottle packages, then there are $6x$ water bottles and if y is the number of 8-bottle packages, then there are $8y$ water bottles. Thus, $6x + 8y = 1860$.

Choice B is correct.

II. Statistics and Data Analysis

CHAPTER 6
Ratios, Rates, and Proportions

6-1 Ratios and Rates

A **ratio** is a comparison of two quantities by division.

The ratio of a to b can be written in three different ways: a to b, $a:b$, and $\frac{a}{b}$.

If two quantities are in the ratio of a to b, then the two numbers can be expressed as **ax** and **bx**, in which x is a positive integer.

A **rate** is a ratio of two measurements having different units of measure. For example, a price of $2.59 per gallon of gasoline, an income of $750 in 3 days, and a speed of 60 miles per hour are all rates.

A **unit rate** is a rate that has a denominator of 1. Some examples of unit rates are defined as follows.

$$\text{Unit Price} = \frac{\text{Price of Package}}{\text{Number of Units in the Package}}$$

$$\text{Gas Mileage} = \frac{\text{Number of Miles Traveled}}{\text{Number of Gallons of Gas Used}}$$

$$\text{Speed (Miles per Hour)} = \frac{\text{Number of Miles Traveled}}{\text{Number of Hours}}$$

$$\text{Density} = \frac{\text{Mass}}{\text{Volume}}$$

Example 1 □ Express each ratio as a unit rate.

    a. 1360 grams of coffee cost $17.68. What is the unit price of the coffee?

    b. A car travels 322 miles on 11.5 gallons of gas. What is the car's gas mileage?

    c. A driver traveled $485\frac{1}{3}$ miles in $8\frac{2}{3}$ hours. What is his speed?

    d. A volume of 46 cm^3 of silver has a mass of 483 grams. What is the density of silver?

Solution □ a. $\dfrac{\$17.68}{1360 \text{ grams}} = \dfrac{1768 \text{ cents}}{1360 \text{ grams}} = 1.3 \text{ cents / gram}$

    b. $\dfrac{322 \text{ mi}}{11.5 \text{ gal}} = 28 \text{ miles / gallon}$.

    c. $\dfrac{485\frac{1}{3} \text{ mi}}{8\frac{2}{3} \text{ hr}} = \dfrac{(485\frac{1}{3} \text{ mi}) \cdot 3}{(8\frac{2}{3} \text{ hr}) \cdot 3} = \dfrac{1456 \text{ mi}}{26 \text{ hr}} = 56 \text{ mph}$

    d. $\text{density} = \dfrac{\text{mass}}{\text{volume}} = \dfrac{483 \text{ grams}}{46 \text{ cm}^3} = 10.5 \text{ grams/cm}^3$

Example 2 □ 3 angles of a triangle are in the ratio of $3:5:7$. What is the measure of each angle?

Solution □ The measure of each angle of the triangle can be represented as $3x$, $5x$, and $7x$.

    $3x + 5x + 7x = 180$ The angle sum in a triangle is 180.

    $15x = 180$ Simplify.

    $x = 12$ Simplify.

    The measure of the 3 angles are $3x = 3 \cdot 12 = 36$, $5x = 5 \cdot 12 = 60$, and $7x = 7 \cdot 12 = 84$.

Exercises - Ratios and Rates

1

The ratio of $1\frac{3}{4}$ to $2\frac{1}{2}$ is equal to the ratio of 14 to what number?

A) 18

B) 20

C) 22

D) 24

2

The sum of two numbers is 14 and the ratio of the two numbers is -3. What is the product of the two numbers?

A) -105

B) -119

C) -133

D) -147

3

If $2(x-y) = 3y$, what is the ratio $\frac{x}{y}$?

A) $\frac{2}{5}$

B) $\frac{4}{3}$

C) $\frac{5}{2}$

D) $\frac{8}{3}$

4

The ratio of length to width of a rectangular garden is $6:7$. If the perimeter of the rectangle is 78 meters, what is the area of the garden in square meters?

A) 274

B) 326

C) 352

D) 378

5

A car travels 218.5 miles on 9.5 gallons of gas. What is the car's gas mileage?

6

At a grocery store, 20 fl oz of brand A vitamin water is sold for $0.95. What is the unit price of the vitamin water per ounce, to the nearest cents?

7

The density of aluminum is 2.7 grams per cm^3. How many grams does 12 cm^3 of aluminum weigh?

6-2 Proportions

A **proportion** is an equation stating that two ratios are equal.

The proportions $\dfrac{a}{b} = \dfrac{c}{d}$ is read "a is to b as c is to d." The numbers a and d are called the **extremes** of the proportion. The numbers b and c are called the **means** of the proportion.

In a proportion, the product of the extremes is equal to the product of the means.

If $\dfrac{a}{b} = \dfrac{c}{d}$, then $ad = bc$. The products ad and bc are called the **cross products** of the proportion $\dfrac{a}{b} = \dfrac{c}{d}$.

Example 1   □   Determine whether each pair of ratios forms a proportion.

     a. $\dfrac{0.4}{1.5}, \dfrac{1.6}{6}$ b. $\dfrac{12}{25}, \dfrac{7}{15}$

Solution   □   a. $\dfrac{0.4}{1.5} \overset{?}{=} \dfrac{1.6}{6}$ Write a proportion.

           $0.4 \times 6 \overset{?}{=} 1.5 \times 1.6$ Find the cross products.
           $2.4 = 2.4$ Simplify.

The cross products are equal, so the ratios form a proportion.

     b. $\dfrac{12}{25} \overset{?}{=} \dfrac{7}{15}$ Write a proportion.

           $12 \times 15 \overset{?}{=} 25 \times 7$ Find the cross products.
           $180 \neq 175$ Simplify.

The cross products are not equal, so the ratios do not form a proportion.

Example 2   □   Solve the proportion $\dfrac{3}{7} = \dfrac{6}{x-4}$.

Solution   □ $\dfrac{3}{7} = \dfrac{6}{x-4}$

           $3(x-4) = 7(6)$ Find the cross products.
           $3x - 12 = 42$ Distributive Property
           $3x = 54$ Add 12 to each side.
           $x = 18$ Divide each side by 3.

Example 3   □   Carter's SUV requires 8 gallons of gasoline to travel 148 miles. How much gasoline, to the nearest gallon, will he need for a 500 mile trip?

Solution   □   a. Let g = the number of gallons of gas needed for a 500 mile trip.

     miles → $\dfrac{148}{8} = \dfrac{500}{g}$ ← miles
     gallons →   ← gallons   Write a proportion.

     $148g = 8 \times 500$ Find the cross products.

     $g = \dfrac{8 \times 500}{148} \approx 27.03$ Divide each side by 148.

Carter's needs 27 gallons of gas for a 500 mile trip.

Exercises - Proportions

1

On a map, 1 inch represents 5 miles. If a certain state is represented on a map by a rectangle 10 inches by 7.2 inches, what is the area of the state in square miles?

A) 360 mi^2

B) 720 mi^2

C) 1,080 mi^2

D) 1,800 mi^2

2

Together there are 754 students and teachers in the meeting. If the ratio of students to teachers is $27:2$, how many teachers are there?

A) 46

B) 52

C) 58

D) 64

3

Concrete is made by mixing cement, sand, and gravel in the ratio 5 : 9 : 13. How much cement is needed to make 324 ft^3 of concrete?

A) 54 ft^3

B) 60 ft^3

C) 84 ft^3

D) 108 ft^3

4

If Andy drove 84 miles in 1 hour 45 minutes, how many miles can he drive in 5 hours?

5

A collection of quarters, dimes, and nickels is worth $5.00. If the ratio of quarters to dimes to nickels is $2:4:7$, how many quarters are there?

6

If $\dfrac{5x}{3} = \dfrac{x+14}{2}$, what is the value of x?

7

A trail mix contains raisin, peanut, and chocolate. The ratio of raisin to peanut is $2:3$ and the ratio of peanut to chocolate is $5:8$. What is the ratio of raisin to chocolate?

6-3   Ratios, Rates, and Proportions Word Problems

You can use conversion factors to convert a unit of measure from one system to another.
Sometimes you may need to use two or more conversion factors.

Example 1   □   A model car is scaled so that 1 inch of the model equals 6 feet of the actual

car. If the model is $1\frac{2}{3}$ inch long, how long is the actual car?

Solution   □   Let $x =$ the length of actual car.

$$\text{model} \rightarrow \frac{1 \text{ in}}{6 \text{ ft}} = \frac{1\frac{2}{3} \text{ in}}{x \text{ ft}} \begin{array}{l} \leftarrow \text{model} \\ \leftarrow \text{actual} \end{array}$$ Set up a proportion.

$$x = 6 \times 1\frac{2}{3} = 10$$ Cross product

The length of the actual car is 10 feet.

Example 2   □   A car is traveling at a constant rate of 54 miles per hour. How many kilometers
will the car travel in 5 minutes? (1 mile = 1.6 kilometers)

Solution   □ $54 \text{ miles} = 54 \text{ mi} \times \dfrac{1.6 \text{ km}}{1 \text{ mi}} = 86.4 \text{ km}$

$$\frac{54 \text{ mi}}{1 \text{ hr}} = \frac{86.4 \text{ km}}{60 \text{ min}}$$ 54 miles = 86.4 km and 1 hour = 60 min

$$\frac{86.4 \text{ km}}{60 \text{ min}} = \frac{x \text{ km}}{5 \text{ min}}$$ Set up a proportion.

$$86.4 \times 5 = 60x$$ Cross Products

$$x = \frac{86.4 \times 5}{60}$$ Divide.

$$= 7.2 \text{ km}$$

Example 3   □   The ratio of males to females in an office is $6 : 7$. If there are 42 males in the office,
what is the total number of people in the office?

Solution   □   Let $f =$ the number of females in the office.

$$\begin{array}{l} \text{male} \rightarrow \\ \text{female} \rightarrow \end{array} \frac{6}{7} = \frac{42}{f}$$ The ratio of males to females is 6 to 7.

$$6f = 7 \cdot 42 = 294$$ Cross products

$$f = \frac{294}{6} = 49$$ Divide.

The total number of people in the office is
$42 + 49$, or 91.

Exercises - Ratios, Rates, and Proportions Word Problems

1

If 20 machines produce 1,240 printers in a day, how many more machines are needed to produce 1,984 printers in a day?

A) 12

B) 20

C) 24

D) 32

2

If $\dfrac{3}{4}$ quart of lemonade concentrate is mixed with $6\dfrac{2}{3}$ quarts of water to make lemonade for 40 people, how many quarts of lemonade concentrate are needed to make the lemonade for 24 people?

A) $\dfrac{3}{10}$

B) $\dfrac{7}{20}$

C) $\dfrac{2}{5}$

D) $\dfrac{9}{20}$

3

A machine produced 735 tapes in $5\dfrac{1}{4}$ hours. What fraction of the 735 tapes was produced in one hour?

A) $\dfrac{1}{7}$

B) $\dfrac{4}{21}$

C) $\dfrac{5}{21}$

D) $\dfrac{2}{7}$

4

A 32-acre field yields 768 bushels of corn each year. How many more acres are needed to yield 960 bushels of corn each year?

A) 6

B) 8

C) 10

D) 12

5

The length of a rectangle is 8 inches longer than the width. If the ratio of the length to perimeter is $5:16$, what is the area of the rectangle?

A) 160 in^2

B) 180 in^2

C) 240 in^2

D) 280 in^2

6

If 12 grams of coffee costs x dollars and each gram makes y cups of coffee, what is the cost of one cup of coffee in terms of x and y?

A) $\dfrac{12y}{x}$

B) $\dfrac{y}{12x}$

C) $\dfrac{12x}{y}$

D) $\dfrac{x}{12y}$

Chapter 6 Practice Test

1

The density of an object is equal to the mass of the object divided by the volume of the object. What is the mass, in grams, of an object with a volume of 0.01 m^3 and a density of 4.54 grams per cubic centimeters? ($1 \text{ m} = 100 \text{ cm}$)

A) 454

B) 4,540

C) 45,400

D) 454,000

2

Jason and Donny painted a house and received $1,200. To complete the painting job Jason painted 4 hours 25 minutes and Donny spent 2 hours and 15 minutes. If they split the $1,200 in proportion to the amount of time each spent painting, how much did Donny receive?

A) $405.00

B) $443.00

C) $472.00

D) $492.00

3

The tennis balls in a bag are either white or yellow. If the ratio of white balls to yellow balls is $\dfrac{3}{10}$, which of the following could not be the number of balls in the bag?

A) 26

B) 39

C) 42

D) 52

4

A car is traveling at a constant rate of x miles per hour. How many miles will the car travel in y minutes?

A) $60xy$

B) $\dfrac{60x}{y}$

C) $\dfrac{xy}{60}$

D) $\dfrac{y}{60x}$

5

A tree is 8 feet tall and grows 8 inches each year. In how many years will the tree reach a height of 30 feet?

A) 27

B) 33

C) 45

D) 52

6

Aaron reads x pages of a science fiction book in m minutes. If he continues reading at this rate, what will be the number of pages he reads in $20\,m$ seconds?

A) $\dfrac{1}{3}x$

B) $\dfrac{1}{2}x$

C) $\dfrac{2}{3}x$

D) $2x$

7

If $\dfrac{x}{y} = 1$, what is the value of $x - y - 1$?

A) −1

B) 0

C) 1

D) The value cannot be determined from the information given.

8

In a certain room the ratio of males to females is 4 to 5. After 8 males enter the room, the ratio of males to females is 6 to 5. What is the total number of people in the room before the additional males enter the room?

A) 27

B) 36

C) 45

D) 54

9

A person is born every 5 seconds and a person dies every 12 seconds. How many seconds does it take for the population to grow by one person?

A) 7 sec

B) $8\dfrac{4}{7}$ sec

C) 10.5 sec

D) $10\dfrac{5}{7}$ sec

10

Steve is going to paint a wall that measures 9 feet by 12 feet. If one gallon of paint is needed for each s square foot of wall and each gallon costs g dollars, in terms of s and g how much does it cost to paint the entire wall?

A) $\dfrac{108}{gs}$

B) $\dfrac{gs}{108}$

C) $\dfrac{108s}{g}$

D) $\dfrac{108g}{s}$

11

If 2 inches are equivalent to 5 centimeters, how many square centimeters are in one square inch?

12

A large painting has a length of 18 inches and a width of 12 inches. If each dimension is reduced by x inches to make the ratio of length to width 5 to 3, what is the value of x?

Answer Key

Section 6-1

1. B   2. D   3. C   4. D   5. 23
6. 5   7. 32.4

Section 6-2

1. D   2. B   3. B   4. 240   5. 8
6. 6   7. $\dfrac{5}{12}$

Section 6-3

1. A   2. D   3. B   4. B   5. C
6. D

Chapter 6 Practice Test

1. C   2. A   3. C   4. C   5. B
6. A   7. A   8. B   9. B   10. D

11. $\dfrac{25}{4}$ or 6.25   12. 3

Answers and Explanations

Section 6-1

1. B

$$\dfrac{1\dfrac{3}{4}}{2\dfrac{1}{2}} = \dfrac{14}{x}$$ The ratio of $1\dfrac{3}{4}$ to $2\dfrac{1}{2}$ is equal
to the ratio of 14 to x.

$1\dfrac{3}{4} \cdot x = 14 \cdot 2\dfrac{1}{2}$ Cross Products

$\dfrac{7}{4}x = 14 \cdot \dfrac{5}{2}$ Simplify.

$\dfrac{7}{4}x = 35$ Simplify.

$\dfrac{4}{7} \cdot \dfrac{7}{4}x = \dfrac{4}{7} \cdot 35$ Multiply each side by $\dfrac{4}{7}$.

$x = 20$ Simplify.

2. D

Let x and y be the two numbers.

$x + y = 14$ The sum of two numbers is 14.

$\dfrac{x}{y} = -3$.   The ratio of the two numbers is -3.

$\dfrac{x}{y} = -3 \Rightarrow x = -3y$

$x + y = 14$ First equation
$(-3y) + y = 14$ Substitute $-3y$ for x.
$-2y = 14$ Simplify.
$y = -7$

Substitute $y = -7$ in the first equation.

$x + (-7) = 14 \Rightarrow x = 21$

Therefore the product of the two numbers is
$x \cdot y = 21 \cdot (-7) = -147$.

3. C

$2(x - y) = 3y$
$2x - 2y = 3y$ Distributive property
$2x = 5y$ Add $2y$ to each side.

$\dfrac{2x}{2} = \dfrac{5y}{2}$ Divide each side by 2.

$x = \dfrac{5}{2}y$ Simplify.

$\dfrac{x}{y} = \dfrac{\dfrac{5}{2}y}{y}$ Divide each side by y.

$\dfrac{x}{y} = \dfrac{5}{2}$ Simplify.

4. D

Let $6x =$ the length and $7x =$ the width of the
rectangle.

$P = 2\ell + 2w$ Perimeter of a rectangle.
$78 = 2(6x) + 2(7x)$ $P = 78$, $\ell = 6x$, and $w = 7x$
$78 = 26x$ Simplify.
$3 = x$ Divide each side by 26.

Therefore, the length of the rectangle is $6 \cdot 3$
or 18, and the width of the rectangle is $7 \cdot 3$
or 21. The area of the rectangle is $18 \cdot 21$ or 378.

5. 23

$\text{Gas Mileage} = \dfrac{\text{Number of Miles Traveled}}{\text{Number of Gallons of Gas Used}}$

$= \dfrac{218.5}{9.5} = 23$

The car's gas mileage is 23 miles per gallon.

6. 5

$\text{Unit Price} = \dfrac{\text{Price of Package}}{\text{Number of Units in the Package}}$

$= \dfrac{0.95}{20} = 0.0475$

The unit price of the vitamin water to the nearest
cent is 5.

7. 32.4

$$\text{Density} = \frac{\text{mass}}{\text{volume}}$$

$$\frac{2.7 \text{ grams}}{1 \text{ cm}^3} = \frac{x \text{ grams}}{12 \text{ cm}^3}$$

$$x = 2.7 \times 12 = 32.4 \text{ grams}$$

Section 6-2

1. D

Set up a proportion.

$$\frac{1 \text{ inch}}{5 \text{ miles}} = \frac{10 \text{ inches}}{x \text{ miles}} \Rightarrow x = 50 \text{ miles}$$

$$\frac{1 \text{ inch}}{5 \text{ miles}} = \frac{7.2 \text{ inches}}{y \text{ miles}} \Rightarrow y = 7.2 \times 5 = 36 \text{ miles}$$

The area of the state is 50×36, or $1,800 \text{ mi}^2$.

2. B

Let the number of students $= 27x$ and let the number of teachers $= 2x$. Then, there will be $27x + 2x$, or $29x$ students and teachers who are in the meeting. Now set up a proportion.

$$\frac{\text{total in the meeting}}{\text{number of teachers}} = \frac{29x}{2x} \Rightarrow$$

$$\frac{754}{\text{number of teachers}} = \frac{29\cancel{x}}{2\cancel{x}} \Rightarrow$$

$$\text{number of teachers} = \frac{754 \times 2}{29} = 52$$

3. B

Let $5x =$ the volume of cement, $9x =$ the volume of sand, and $13x =$ the volume of gravel. Thus the total volume of concrete is $5x + 9x + 13x$, or $27x$, which is equal to 324 ft^3.

$27x = 324 \Rightarrow x = 12$
Therefore, the amount of cement is $5x = 5 \cdot 12 = 60$.

4. 240

$$1 \text{ hour } 45 \text{ minutes} = 1\frac{3}{4} \text{ hours}$$

Set up a proportion.

$$\frac{84 \text{ miles}}{1\frac{3}{4} \text{ hours}} = \frac{x \text{ miles}}{5 \text{ hours}}$$

$$1\frac{3}{4}x = 84 \cdot 5 \qquad \text{Cross Products}$$

$$\frac{7}{4}x = 420 \qquad \text{Simplify.}$$

$$\frac{4}{7} \cdot \frac{7}{4}x = \frac{4}{7} \cdot 420 \qquad \text{Multiply each side by } \frac{4}{7}.$$

$$x = 240$$

He can drive 240 miles in 5 hours.

5. 8

Let $2x =$ the number of quarters, $4x =$ the number of dimes, and $7x =$ the number of nickels. Then the total amount in terms of x, $2x(0.25) + 4x(0.1) + 7x(0.05)$, is equal to \$5.00.

$$2x(0.25) + 4x(0.1) + 7x(0.05) = 5.00$$
$$0.5x + 0.4x + 0.35x = 5$$
$$1.25x = 5$$
$$x = 4$$

There are $2x = 2 \cdot 4$, or 8 quarters.

6. 6

$$\frac{5x}{3} = \frac{x+14}{2}$$
$$2(5x) = 3(x+14) \qquad \text{Cross Products}$$
$$10x = 3x + 42$$
$$7x = 42$$
$$x = 6$$

7. $\dfrac{5}{12}$

Let $r =$ the amount of raisin, $p =$ the amount of peanut, and $c =$ the amount of chocolate. Then

$$\frac{r}{p} = \frac{2}{3} \qquad \text{The ratio of raisin to peanut is } 2:3.$$
$$3r = 2p \qquad \text{Cross Products}$$
$$p = \frac{3}{2}r \qquad \text{Solve for } p.$$
$$\frac{p}{c} = \frac{5}{8} \qquad \text{The ratio of peanut to chocolate is } 5:8.$$
$$8p = 5c \qquad \text{Cross Products}$$
$$p = \frac{5}{8}c \qquad \text{Solve for } p.$$

Equate the two equations solved for p.

$$\frac{3}{2}r = \frac{5}{8}c \Rightarrow \frac{2}{3} \cdot \frac{3}{2}r = \frac{2}{3} \cdot \frac{5}{8}c$$

$$\Rightarrow r = \frac{5}{12}c \Rightarrow \frac{r}{c} = \frac{5}{12}$$

Section 6-3

1. A

Set up a proportion.

$$\frac{20}{1240} = \frac{x}{1984} \quad \begin{array}{l} \leftarrow \text{ number of machines} \\ \leftarrow \text{ number of printers} \end{array}$$

$$1240x = 20 \cdot 1984 \qquad \text{Cross Products}$$

$$x = \frac{20 \cdot 1984}{1240} = 32$$

Altogether we need 32 machines, therefore we need $32 - 20$, or 12, more machines.

2 D

Let $x =$ the number of quarts of lemonade concentrate needed for 24 people.

In this question " $6\frac{2}{3}$ quarts of water" was unnecessary information.

$$\frac{\frac{3}{4}}{40} = \frac{x}{24} \quad \begin{array}{l} \leftarrow \text{ quarts} \\ \leftarrow \text{ people} \end{array}$$

$$40x = 24 \cdot \frac{3}{4} \qquad \text{Cross products}$$

$$x = 24 \cdot \frac{3}{4} \cdot \frac{1}{40} = \frac{9}{20}$$

3. B

The number of tapes produced in one hour is equal to $735 \div 5\frac{1}{4}$, or 140.

The fraction of 735 tapes produced in one hour is $\frac{140}{735}$, or $\frac{4}{21}$.

4. B

Set up a proportion.

$$\frac{32}{768} = \frac{x}{960} \quad \begin{array}{l} \leftarrow \text{ number of acres} \\ \leftarrow \text{ number of bushels} \end{array}$$

$$768x = 32 \cdot 960 \qquad \text{Cross products}$$

$$x = \frac{32 \cdot 960}{768} = 40$$

Altogether we need 40 acres, therefore we need $40 - 32$, or 8, more acres.

5. C

Let $x =$ the width of the rectangle, then $x + 8 =$ the length of the rectangle.

$$P = 2\ell + 2w \qquad \text{Perimeter of a rectangle.}$$

$$P = 2(x + 8) + 2(x) \qquad \ell = x + 8 \text{, and } w = x$$

$$P = 4x + 16 \qquad \text{Simplify.}$$

$$\frac{\text{length}}{\text{perimeter}} = \frac{x + 8}{4x + 16} = \frac{5}{16}$$

$$16(x + 8) = 5(4x + 16) \qquad \text{Cross Products}$$

$$16x + 128 = 20x + 80$$

$$48 = 4x$$

$$12 = x$$

The length of the rectangle is $12 + 8$, or 20 and the width of the rectangle is 12.

The area of the rectangle is $20 \cdot 12$, or 240.

6. D

If 12 grams of coffee cost x dollars, the cost of each gram of coffee is $\frac{x}{12}$ dollars. Let one cup of coffee cost d dollars, and set up a proportion to find the cost of one cup of coffee.

$$\frac{\frac{x}{12}}{y} = \frac{d}{1} \quad \begin{array}{l} \leftarrow \text{ cost in dollars} \\ \leftarrow \text{ number of cups} \end{array}$$

$$y \cdot d = \frac{x}{12} \qquad \text{Cross Products}$$

$$d = \frac{x}{12y}$$

Chapter 6 Practice Test

1. C

$$1 \text{ m} = 100 \text{ cm}$$

$$1 \text{ m}^3 = (100 \text{ cm})^3 = 1,000,000 \text{ cm}^3$$

$$0.01 \text{ m}^3 = 0.01 \times 1,000,000 \text{ cm}^3 = 10,000 \text{ cm}^3$$

$$\text{Density} = \frac{\text{Mass}}{\text{Volume}}$$

$$4.54 \text{ grams} / \text{cm}^3 = \frac{\text{Mass}}{0.01 \text{ m}^3} = \frac{\text{Mass}}{10,000 \text{ cm}^3}$$

$$\text{Mass} = 4.54 \frac{\text{grams}}{\text{cm}^3} \cdot 10,000 \text{ cm}^3$$

$$= 45,400 \text{ grams}$$

2. A

$$\text{Total time} = \text{Jason's time} + \text{Donny's time}$$

$$= 4 \text{ hour } 25 \text{ min} + 2 \text{ hour } 15 \text{ min}$$

$$= 4\frac{5}{12} \text{ hour} + 2\frac{1}{4} \text{ hour} = 6\frac{2}{3} \text{ hour}$$

The amount Donny received

$$= 1,200 \times \frac{2\frac{1}{4} \text{ hour}}{6\frac{2}{3} \text{ hour}} = 1,200 \cdot \frac{\frac{9}{4}}{\frac{20}{3}} = 1,200 \cdot \frac{9}{4} \cdot \frac{3}{20}$$

$$= 405$$

3. C

If the ratio of white balls to yellow balls is $\frac{3}{10}$,

$3n$ represents the number of white balls and
$10n$ represents the number of yellow balls
(n is a positive integer).
Since the total number of balls in the bag is
$3n+10n$, or $13n$, and n is a positive integer,
the number of balls will be a multiple of 13.

Choice C is correct, because 42 is not a multiple
of 13.

4. C

Let $m =$ the number of miles traveled
in y minutes. Substitute 60 minutes for 1 hour
and set up a proportion.

$$\frac{x}{60} = \frac{m}{y} \quad \begin{array}{l} \leftarrow \text{ number of miles} \\ \leftarrow \text{ number of minutes} \end{array}$$

$60m = xy$ Cross Products

$$m = \frac{xy}{60}$$

5. B

Let $x =$ the number of years it will take the tree
to reach a height of 30 feet.

Also, 8 inches $= \frac{8}{12}$ feet .

$8 + \frac{8}{12}x = 30$ The tree is 8 feet tall and will

$\frac{8}{12}x = 22$ grow $\frac{8}{12}x$ feet in x years.

$x = 22 \cdot \frac{12}{8} = 33$

6. A

m minutes $= 60m$ seconds
Let $p =$ the number of pages he reads in $20m$
seconds.
Set up a proportion.

$$\frac{x}{60m} = \frac{p}{20m} \quad \begin{array}{l} \leftarrow \text{ number of pages} \\ \leftarrow \text{ number of seconds} \end{array}$$

$60m \cdot p = 20m \cdot x$ Cross Products

$$p = \frac{20m \cdot x}{60m} = \frac{1}{3}x$$

7. A

$$\frac{x}{y} = 1$$

$y \cdot \dfrac{x}{y} = y \cdot 1$ Multiply each side by y.

$x = y$ Simplify.

$x - y = y - y$ Subtract y from each side.

$x - y = 0$ Simplify.

$x - y - 1 = 0 - 1$ Subtract 1 from each side.

$x - y - 1 = -1$ Simplify.

8. B

Let $m =$ the number of males in the room and
let $f =$ the number of females in the room.

$\dfrac{m}{f} = \dfrac{4}{5}$ The ratio of males to females is 4 to 5.

$5m = 4f$ Cross Products

$\dfrac{m+8}{f} = \dfrac{6}{5}$ After 8 males enter the room, the ratio of males to females is 6 to 5.

$5(m+8) = 6f$ Cross Products

$5m + 40 = 6f$ Simplify.

$4f + 40 = 6f$ Substitute $4f$ for $5m$.

$40 = 2f$ Subtract $2f$ from each side.

$20 = f$ Divide each side by 2.

Substituting 20 for f in the equation $5m = 4f$
gives $5m = 4 \cdot 20$. Solving for m yields $m = 16$.

The total number of people in the room before
the additional males enter the room is
$m + f = 16 + 20 = 36$.

9. B

If a person is born every 5 seconds, 12 people
are born per minute. If a person dies every 12
seconds, 5 people die per minute. Every minute
the population grows by $12 - 5$, or 7, people.

Therefore, it takes $\dfrac{60}{7}$ seconds, or $8\dfrac{4}{7}$ seconds,

for the population to grow by one person.

10. D

Total area of the wall $= 9 \times 12 = 108 \text{ ft}^2$.

Let it take p gallons of paint to paint 108 ft^2.

Set up a proportion.

$\dfrac{1}{s} = \dfrac{p}{108} \quad\begin{array}{l}\leftarrow \text{ number of gallons} \\ \leftarrow \text{ number of square feet}\end{array}$

$sp = 108 \qquad\qquad$ Cross Products

$p = \dfrac{108}{s}$

It takes $\dfrac{108}{s}$ gallons of paint to paint 108 ft^2.

Since each gallon costs g dollars, the total cost will be $\dfrac{108}{s} \cdot g$ dollars.

11. $\dfrac{25}{4}$ or 6.25

$2 \text{ in} = 5 \text{ cm}$

$1 \text{ in} = \dfrac{5}{2} \text{ cm} \qquad$ Divide each side by 2.

$(1 \text{ in})^2 = (\dfrac{5}{2} \text{ cm})^2 \quad$ Square both sides.

$1 \text{ in}^2 = \dfrac{25}{4} \text{ cm}^2 \qquad$ Simplify.

There are $\dfrac{25}{4}$ square centimeters in 1 square inch.

12. 3

The reduced length of the painting is $18 - x$ and the reduced width of the painting is $12 - x$.

$\dfrac{18 - x}{12 - x} = \dfrac{5}{3} \qquad$ The new ratio is 5 to 3.

$3(18 - x) = 5(12 - x) \quad$ Cross Products

$54 - 3x = 60 - 5x \qquad$ Distributive Property

$54 + 2x = 60 \qquad$ Add $5x$ to each side.

$2x = 6 \qquad$ Subtract 54 from each side.

$x = 3 \qquad$ Divide each side by 2.

CHAPTER 7
Percents

7-1. Percent of Change

The word **percent** means *hundredth* or *out of every hundred*.

To write a decimal or a fraction as a percent, multiply the decimal or the fraction by 100 and add the % sign. Convert the fraction to decimal.

To write a percent as a decimal or a fraction, multiply the percent by $\dfrac{1}{100}$, and drop the % sign.

Simplify the fraction.

Example 1 □ Write each decimal or fraction as a percent.

a. 0.65   b. $\dfrac{3}{16}$

Solution □ a. $0.65 = 0.65 \times 100\% = 65\%$ Multiply the decimal by 100 and add the % sign.

c. $\dfrac{3}{16} = \dfrac{3}{16} \times 100\% = \dfrac{300}{16}\% = 18.75\%$ Multiply the fraction by 100 and add the % sign. Convert the fraction to decimal.

Example 2 □ Write 175% as a decimal and a fraction.

Solution □ $175\% = 175 \times \dfrac{1}{100} = \dfrac{175}{100} = 1.75$ Multiply the amount of percent by $\dfrac{1}{100}$, and drop the % sign. Simplify the fraction.

$175\% = 175 \times \dfrac{1}{100} = \dfrac{175}{100} = \dfrac{7}{4}$

The percent a quantity increases or decreases from its original amount is the **percent of change**.

percent increase $= \dfrac{\text{amount of increase}}{\text{original amount}}$ **percent decrease** $= \dfrac{\text{amount of decrease}}{\text{original amount}}$

Example 3 □ a. A $300 tablet is on sale for $234. What is the percent of discount?

b. The population of Sunny Hills increased from 12,000 to 15,840 in ten years. What is the percent increase of the population?

Solution □ a. percent discount $= \dfrac{\text{amount of discount}}{\text{original amount}}$

$= \dfrac{300 - 234}{300} = \dfrac{66}{300} = 0.22$

There was a 22% discount.

b. percent increase $= \dfrac{\text{number of increase}}{\text{original number}}$

$= \dfrac{15,840 - 12,000}{12,000} = \dfrac{3,840}{12,000} = 0.32$

There was a 32% increase in population.

Exercises - Percent of Change

1

Which of the following is equivalent to 0.03 % of 4?

A) 0.12

B) 0.012

C) 0.0012

D) 0.00012

2

$\dfrac{1}{400} =$

A) 0.25%

B) 0.025%

C) 0.0025%

D) 0.00025%

3

The quantities x and y are positive. If x is decreased by 20 percent and y is increased by 20 percent, then the product of x and y is

A) unchanged

B) decreased by 4%

C) increased by 5%

D) decreased by 6%

4

By what percent is 4.5×10^5 greater than 9×10^4?

A) 200%

B) 400%

C) 500%

D) 600%

5

The temperature increased from $60°\text{F}$ to $72°\text{F}$. What is the percent increase in temperature?

A) 15%

B) $\dfrac{50}{3}\%$

C) 20%

D) $\dfrac{70}{3}\%$

6

This year's enrollment in Mesa School District is 6,000, which is 20 percent higher than last year's. What was last year's enrollment in Mesa School District?

7

If 125% of x is 80 and x is $n\%$ of 400, what is the value of n?

7-2. Percents and Equations

You can solve a percent problem by writing and solving an equation or a proportion.
Three types of percent equations and corresponding verbal phrases are illustrated below.

	Verbal Phrase	**Algebraic Expression**	**Equation or Proportion**
1. Finding the Part	What is 15% of 72?	$n = 0.15 \times 72$	Write an equation.
		$\dfrac{15}{100} = \dfrac{n}{72}$	Write a proportion.
2. Finding the Percent	What percent of 20 is 6?	$\dfrac{n}{100} \times 20 = 6$	Write an equation.
		$\dfrac{n}{100} = \dfrac{6}{20}$	Write a proportion.
3. Finding the Whole	17 is 25% of what number?	$17 = 0.25 \times n$	Write an equation.
		$\dfrac{25}{100} = \dfrac{17}{n}$	Write a proportion.

Example 1 □ Translate each verbal phrase into an algebraic equation and a proportion.
Then solve.

a. What is 0.3% of 4?
b. What percent of 30 is 5?
c. 64 is 250% of what number?

Solution □ a. $x = 0.003 \times 4 = 0.012$ Write an equation.

$\dfrac{x}{4} = \dfrac{0.3}{100}$ Write a proportion.

$100x = 0.3 \times 4$ Cross products

$x = 1.2 \div 100 = 0.012$ Divide by 100 and solve.

b. $\dfrac{p}{100} \times 30 = 5$ Write an equation.

$p = 5 \times \dfrac{100}{30} = \dfrac{50}{3}$ Multiply both sides by $\dfrac{100}{30}$ and simplify.

$\dfrac{p}{100} = \dfrac{5}{30}$ Write a proportion.

$30p = 500$ Cross products

$p = \dfrac{500}{30} = \dfrac{50}{3}$ Divide by 30 and simplify.

c. $64 = 2.5 \times n$ Write an equation. $250\% = 2.5$

$n = \dfrac{64}{2.5} = 25.6$ Divide each side by 2.5.

$\dfrac{250}{100} = \dfrac{64}{n}$ Write a proportion.

$250n = 6400$ Cross products

$n = \dfrac{6400}{250} = 25.6$ Divide each side by 250.

Exercises - Percents and Equations

1

28% of what number is 7?

2

3.6 is 240% of what number?

3

$\frac{1}{2}$% of 180 is what number?

4

$3\frac{1}{3}$% of what number is 2.5?

5

26.4 is 0.55% of what number?

6

What percent of 12 is 8?

A) 60%

B) $66\frac{2}{3}$%

C) 75%

D) $130\frac{1}{3}$%

7

54 is 120% of k.

Which of the following proportions could be used to solve the above expression?

A) $\frac{100}{120} = \frac{54}{k}$

B) $\frac{54}{100} = \frac{120}{k}$

C) $\frac{100}{54} = \frac{120}{k}$

D) $\frac{120}{100} = \frac{54}{k}$

8

If Kevin's monthly salary of $4,500 is 72 percent of Paul's monthly salary, what is Paul's monthly salary?

A) $3,240

B) $5,150

C) $5,870

D) $6,250

7-3. Percent Word Problems

Mixture of Two Different Solutions

Example 1 □ How many milliliters of 65% acid solution must be added to 60 milliliters of a 40% acid solution in order to make a 50% acid solution?

Solution □ Let $x =$ the amount of 65% acid solution added.

	Total amount ×	% acid =	Amount of acid
40% solution	60	40%	0.4×60
65% solution	x	65%	$0.65x$
New solution	$60 + x$	50%	$0.5(60 + x)$

Original amount of acid + added acid = new amount of acid

$0.4 \times 60 + 0.65x = 0.5(60 + x)$

$24 + 0.65x = 30 + 0.5x$

$0.15x = 6$

$x = 40$

Therefore, 40 milliliters of 65% acid solution must be added.

Interest and Investments

Example 2 □ Bob invested $7,500 in stocks and bonds. The stocks pay 6.5% interest a year and the bonds pay 8% interest a year. His interest income is $528 this year. How much money was invested in stocks?

Let $x =$ the amount invested in stocks.

Then, $7500 - x =$ the amount invested in bonds.

	Amount invested ×	Rate =	Interest
Stock	x	.065	$0.065x$
Bond	$7500 - x$	.08	$0.08(7500 - x)$

Interest from stocks + interest from bonds = total interest income

$0.065x + .08(7500 - x) = 528$

$0.065x + 600 - .08x = 528$

$-0.015x = -72$

$x = 4800$

Therefore, $4,800 was invested in stocks.

Discounts and Tax

Example 3 □ The sale price of a laptop is $505.44 after 35% discount and 8% additional tax. What was the original price of the laptop before discount and tax?

Let $x =$ the original price of the laptop before discount and tax.

$x - .35x = 0.65x$ The price of laptop after 35% discount.

$0.65x(1 + 0.08) = 0.702x$ The price of laptop after 8% of tax.

$0.702x = 505.44$

$x = 720$

The original price of the laptop was $720.

Exercises - Percent Word Problems

1

There are n candies in a jar. If one candy is removed, what percent of the candies are left in terms of n ?

A) $100(1-n)\%$

B) $100(\frac{1}{n}-1)\%$

C) $100(n-\frac{1}{n})\%$

D) $100(\frac{n-1}{n})\%$

2

The price of a cellphone was discounted by 25% and then discounted an additional 20%, to become $348. What was the original price of the cellphone before it was discounted twice?

A) $580.00

B) $620.00

C) $650.00

D) $680.00

3

A chemist mixes a 40% acid solution and a 30% acid solution. How many liters of the 40% solution must be added to produce 50 liters of a solution that is 36% acid?

A) 24

B) 26

C) 30

D) 32

4

Victor invests part of his $5,000 in a savings account that pays 4.5% annual simple interest. He invests the rest in bonds that pay 8% annual simple interest. Let s be the amount invested in savings and r be the amount invested in bonds. Victor's total income in one year from these investments is $305.50. Which of the following systems of equations represents this relationship?

A) $\begin{cases} 0.045s + 0.08r = 5,000 \\ s + r = 305.50 \end{cases}$

B) $\begin{cases} 0.08s + 0.045r = 5,000 \\ s + r = 305.50 \end{cases}$

C) $\begin{cases} s + r = 5,000 \\ 0.045s + 0.08r = 305.50 \end{cases}$

D) $\begin{cases} s + r = 5,000 \\ 0.08s + 0.045r = 305.50 \end{cases}$

5

A sporting goods store added 50% profit cost and 8% tax to the price of a backpack, which then became $129.60. What was the price of the backpack before adding profit and tax?

6

There are 800 students in a school and 45% of the students are male. If 30% of the male students and 25% of the female students play varsity sports, how many students play varsity sports?

Chapter 7 Practice Test

1

A chemist mixes x mL of a 34% acid solution with a 10% acid solution. If the resulting solution is 40 mL with 25% acidity, what is the value of x?

A) 18.5

B) 20

C) 22.5

D) 25

2

The price of a package of 4 pens is $8.00. The same pens are sold at $2.50 each. If Alex bought three packages of pens rather than buying 12 pens individually, the amount he saved on 12 pens is what percent of the amount he paid?

A) 12%

B) 20%

C) 25%

D) 30%

3

There are 600 bottles of sports drinks in a store. 25% of the bottles are orange flavored drinks. On Monday 30% of the orange flavored drinks in the store were sold and on Tuesday 20% of the remaining orange flavored drinks were sold. How many bottles of orange flavored drinks were sold in the two days?

A) 52

B) 58

C) 66

D) 75

4

A tablet with a list price of x dollars is discounted by 15% and then discounted an additional 12%. What is the final sale price of the tablet, in terms of x?

A) $0.73x$

B) $0.748x$

C) $0.75x$

D) $0.765x$

5

There is a total of n pairs of shoes in a store, all of which are either black or brown. If there are m pairs of brown shoes in the store, then in terms of m and n, what percent of the shoes in the store are black?

A) $\dfrac{m}{n}\%$

B) $\dfrac{n-m}{n}\%$

C) $(1-\dfrac{100m}{n})\%$

D) $100(1-\dfrac{m}{n})\%$

6

The numbers a, b, and c are positive and a equals $3.2bc$. If b is increased by 150% and c is decreased by 60%, then a is

A) increased by 90%

B) increased by 10%

C) unchanged

D) decreased by 10%

7

There are 10 history books in a bookcase. When the number of books increases by x percent, the new number of history books is 24. What is the value of x?

A) 58

B) 70

C) 120

D) 140

8

Number n is 25 less than 120 percent of itself. What is the value of n?

A) 125

B) 120

C) 105

D) 90

9

Of the 500 cars displayed in a certain car dealer, 7 percent are blue and 4 percent are red. The number of blue cars in the car dealer are what percent greater than the number of red cars?

A) 30%

B) 50%

C) 75%

D) 125%

10

If 300% of 0.18 is equivalent to 20% of b, then b is equivalent to what number?

11

Five people contributed $9,000 each toward the purchase of a sailboat. If they ended up paying $38,500 plus 8% sales tax for the boat, how much money should be refunded to each person?

12

A store used to sell an MP3 for $72, which is 50% more than the wholesale cost. At a special holiday sale, the price of the MP3 was 20% less than the wholesale cost. What was the special sale price of the MP3?

Answer Key

Section 7-1

1. C   2. A   3. B   4. B   5. C
6. 5000   7. 16

Section 7-2

1. 25   2. 1.5   3. 0.9   4. 75   5. 4800
6. B   7. D   8. D

Section 7-3

1. D   2. A   3. C   4. C   5. 80
6. 218

Chapter 7 Practice Test

1. D   2. C   3. C   4. B   5. D
6. C   7. D   8. A   9. C   10. 2.7
11. 684   12. 38.4

Answers and Explanations

Section 7-1

1. C

$$0.03 \text{ \% of } 4 = 0.03 \times \frac{1}{100} \times 4 = 0.0012$$

2. A

$$\frac{1}{400} = \frac{1}{400} \times 100\% = \frac{1}{4}\% = 0.25\%$$

3. B

$x - 0.2x$	x is decreased by 20 percent.
$= 0.8x$	Simplify.
$y + 0.2y$	y is increased by 20 percent.
$= 1.2y$	Simplify.

The product of decreased x and increased y is $0.8x \times 1.2y = 0.96xy$. So, the product is decreased by 4 percent.

4. B

Divide 4.5×10^5 by 9×10^4.

$$\frac{4.5 \times 10^5}{9 \times 10^4} = 5$$

So, $4.5 \times 10^5 = (9 \times 10^4) \times 5 = 9 \times 10^4 + 4(9 \times 10^4)$

$$= 9 \times 10^4 + 400\%(9 \times 10^4).$$

Therefore, 4.5×10^5 is 400% greater than 9×10^4.

5. C

$$\text{Percent increase} = \frac{\text{amount of increase}}{\text{original amount}}$$

$$= \frac{72 - 60}{60} = \frac{12}{60} = \frac{1}{5} = 0.2 = 20\%$$

6. 5000

Let x = last year's enrollment in Mesa School District.

$$\underset{\text{this year's enrollment}}{\underline{6000}} = \underset{\text{20\% more than last year's enrollment}}{\underline{x + 0.2x}}$$

$$6000 = 1.2x$$

$$x = \frac{6000}{1.2} = 5000$$

7. 16

$1.25x = 80$	125% of x is 80.
$x = \frac{80}{1.25} = 64$	Solve for x.
$x = n\% \times 400$	x is n % of 400.
$x = n \times \frac{1}{100} \times 400$	Percent means $\frac{1}{100}$.
$x = n \times 4$	Simplify.
$64 = n \times 4$	Substitute 64 for x.
$16 = n$	Divide each side by 4.

Section 7-2

1. 25

$\frac{28}{100} \times n = 7$	28% of a number is 7.
$n = 7 \times \frac{100}{28}$	Multiply each side by $\frac{100}{28}$.
$n = 25$	Simplify.

2. 1.5

$3.6 = 2.4 \times n$	3.6 is 240% of a number.
$\frac{3.6}{2.4} = n$	Divide each side by 2.4.
$1.5 = n$	Simplify.

3. 0.9

$\frac{1}{2} \times \frac{1}{100} \times 180 = n$ $\frac{1}{2}\%$ is $\frac{1}{2} \times \frac{1}{100}$.

$\frac{180}{200} = n$ Simplify.

$0.9 = n$ Simplify.

4. 75

$3\frac{1}{3} \times \frac{1}{100} \times n = 2.5$ $3\frac{1}{3}\%$ is $3\frac{1}{3} \times \frac{1}{100}$.

$\frac{10}{3} \times \frac{1}{100} \times n = 2.5$ Simplify.

$\frac{1}{30} n = 2.5$ Simplify.

$n = 2.5 \times 30 = 75$ Multiply each side by 30.

5. 4800

$26.4 = 0.55 \times \frac{1}{100} \times n$ 0.55% is $0.55 \times \frac{1}{100}$.

$26.4 = 0.0055n$ Simplify.

$\frac{26.4}{0.0055} = \frac{0.0055n}{0.0055}$ Divide each side by 0.0055.

$4800 = n$ Simplify.

6. B

$\underbrace{\frac{n}{100}}_{\text{what percent}} \underset{\text{of}}{\times} 12 = 8$

$n = 8 \cdot \frac{100}{12} \;\Rightarrow\; n = 66\frac{2}{3}$

8 is $66\frac{2}{3}\%$ of 12.

7. D

54 is 120% of k.

The above expression can be written as the equation $54 = 1.2 \times k$. Or it can be written as the proportion $\frac{120}{100} = \frac{54}{k}$.

Choice D is correct.

8. D

Let $x =$ Paul's monthly salary.

$\underset{\text{Kevin's monthly salary}}{4500} = \underset{\text{72 percent}}{0.72} \underset{\text{of}}{\times} \underset{\text{Paul's monthly salary}}{x}$

$4500 = 0.72x$

$x = \frac{4500}{0.72} = 6250$

Section 7-3

1. D

There are n candies in a jar and one candy is removed. So, $n-1$ candies are left in the jar.

The fraction of candies left in the jar is $\frac{n-1}{n}$.

Thus, the percent of candies left in the jar is $(\frac{n-1}{n})100\%$.

2. A

Let $x =$ the original price of the cellphone. The discounted price is 25% off the original price, so $x - 0.25x$, or $0.75x$, is the discounted price. After an additional discount of 20% off the first discounted price, the new price is $0.75x - 0.2(0.75x)$, or $0.6x$, which is the final price of $348. Therefore, $0.6x = 348$. Solving the equation for x yields $x = 580$.

3. C

Let $x =$ the amount of 40% solution to be added. Let $50 - x =$ the amount of 30% solution to be added.

x liters of 40 % acid $+ (50 - x)$ liters of 30 % acid $= 50$ liters of 36 % acid

$0.4x + 0.3(50 - x) = 0.36(50)$
$0.4x + 15 - 0.3x = 18$
$0.1x + 15 = 18$
$0.1x = 3$
$x = 30$

30 liters of 40% acid solution should be added.

4. C

If s is the amount invested in savings and r is the amount invested in bonds, $s + r$ represents the total amount invested, which is equal to $5,000. Therefore, $s + r = 5000$.

If the amount invested in savings pays 4.5% interest and the amount invested in bonds pays 8% interest, $0.045s + 0.08r$ represents the total income from investment, which is equal to $305.50. Therefore, $0.045s + 0.08r = 305.50$.

Choice C is correct.

5. 80

Let x = the price of the backpack before adding profit and tax.
After 50% profit the price of the backpack will be $x + 0.5x$, or $1.5x$.
After 8% tax the price of the backpack will be $1.5x + .08(1.5x)$, or $1.62x$, which is equal to $129.60. Therefore, $1.62x = 129.60$. Solving for x yields $x = 80$.
The price of the backpack before adding profit and tax was $80.

6. 218

The number of male students $= 800 \times 0.45 = 360$.
The number of female students $= 800 - 360 = 440$.
30% of male students $= 360 \times 0.3 = 108$.
25% of female students $= 440 \times 0.25 = 110$.
The number of students who play varsity sports $= 108 + 110 = 218$

Chapter 7 Practice Test

1. D

If x mL of a 34% acid solution is added to a 10% acid solution and the resulting solution is 40 mL of a 25% solution, then the amount of the 10% acid solution should be $40 - x$ mL.

x mL of 34 % acid $+ (40 - x)$ mL of 10% acid
$= 40$ mL of 25 % acid

$0.34x + 0.1(40 - x) = 0.25(40)$
$0.34x + 4 - 0.1x = 10$
$0.24x = 6$
$x = 25$

2. C

The cost of 3 packages of pens is $3 \times \$8.00$, or $24 and the cost of 12 pens bought individually is $12 \times \$2.50$, or $30. The amount saved is $30 - 24$ dollars, or $6. The percent of savings he saved on 12 pens of the amount he paid is
$\dfrac{6}{24} \cdot 100\%$, or 25%.

3. C

The number of orange flavored drinks in the store $= 600 \times 0.25 = 150$.
The number of orange flavored drinks sold on Monday $= 150 \times 0.3 = 45$.
Remaining orange flavored drinks $= 150 - 45 = 105$.

The number of orange flavored drinks sold on Tuesday is 20% of the remaining orange flavored drinks, which is 105×0.2, or 21. Therefore, the number of bottles of orange flavored drinks sold in the two days is $45 + 21$, or 66.

4. B

After 15% discount, the price of the tablet is $x - 0.15x$, or $0.85x$. After an additional 12% discount, the price of the tablet is $0.85x - 0.12(0.85x)$, or $0.748x$.

5. D

n = total number of shoes m = the number of brown shoes. So the number of black shoes is $n - m$. The fraction of black shoes in the store is $\dfrac{n - m}{n}$, so the percent of black shoes in the store is $(\dfrac{n - m}{n}) \times 100\%$. This is equivalent to $(\dfrac{n}{n} - \dfrac{m}{n}) \times 100\%$, or $(1 - \dfrac{m}{n}) \times 100\%$.

6. C

If b is increased by 150%, it becomes $b + 1.5b$, or $2.5b$. If c is decreased by 60%, it becomes $c - 0.6c$, or $0.4c$. Multiplying these new values gives $a = 3.2(2.5b \times 0.4c) = 3.2(bc)$.

Therefore, the value is unchanged.

7. D

If 10 books are increased by x percent, then there will be $10 + 10 \times \dfrac{x}{100}$ books, which is equal to 24.

$10 + 10 \times \dfrac{x}{100} = 24$

$\Rightarrow \ 10 \times \dfrac{x}{100} = 14 \Rightarrow \ \dfrac{x}{10} = 14$

$\Rightarrow \ x = 140$

8. A

Number n is 25 less than 120 percent of itself.
$n = 1.2n - 25$
$-0.2n = -25$
$n = \dfrac{-25}{-0.2} = 125$

9. C

The number of blue cars $= 500 \times 0.07 = 35$
The number of red cars $= 500 \times 0.04 = 20$
Let 35 is n percent greater than 20.

Then $35 = 20 + 20 \cdot \dfrac{n}{100}$.

$35 - 20 = 20 + 20 \cdot \dfrac{n}{100} - 20$

$15 = \dfrac{1}{5}n$

$75 = n$

The number of blue cars is 75% greater than the number of red cars.

10. 2.7

300% of 0.18 is equivalent to 20% of b.

$3 \times 0.18 = 0.2b$	$300\% = 3$, $20\% = 0.2$
$0.54 = 0.2b$	Simplify.
$\dfrac{0.54}{0.2} = \dfrac{0.2}{0.2}b$	Divide each side by 0.2.
$2.7 = b$	Simplify.

11. 684

Total amount contributed by five people
$= \$9,000 \times 5 = \$45,000$.
The price of the sailboat after 8% tax
$= \$38,500 + 0.08 \times \$38,500 = \$41,580$.
The amount that should be refunded
$= \$45,000 - \$41,580 = \$3,420$.
Dividing \$3,420 by 5 yields \$684.

Thus \$684 should be refunded to each person.

12. 38.4

Let $m = $ the wholesale cost of MP3.
The selling price of \$72 is 50% more than the wholesale cost.

$72 = m + 0.5m$
$72 = 1.5m$
$48 = m$

The special holiday sale of the MP3 was 20% less than the wholesale cost. Therefore,
The special price of MP3

$= m - 0.2m$

$= 48 - 0.2 \times 48 \qquad\qquad m = 48$

$= 38.4$

The special sale price of the MP3 was \$38.4.

CHAPTER 8
Statistics

8-1. Mean, Median, Mode, and Range

The **mean** of a data set is the sum of the values in the data set divided by the number of values in the data set. The mean is also called the arithmetic mean.

$$\text{Mean} = \frac{\text{sum of the values}}{\text{number of values}} = \frac{x_1 + x_2 + \cdots + x_n}{n} = \frac{\sum x_i}{n}$$

The sum of the values $= \text{mean} \times \text{number of values}$.

Weighted average of two groups $= \dfrac{\{\text{sum of the values of group 1}\} + \{\text{sum of the values of group 2}\}}{\text{total number of values}}$

The median of a set of data is the middle number when the data are arranged in order. If there are two middle numbers, the median is the mean of the two numbers. In the set of data $\{3, 7, 8, 10, 14\}$, the median is 8 and in the set of data $\{3, 7, 10, 14\}$, the median is $\dfrac{7+10}{2}$, or 8.5.

The **mode** of a set of data is the number that appears most frequently. Some set of data have more than one mode, and others have no mode. In the set of data $\{3, 7, 8, 10, 14\}$, there is no mode since each number appears only once. In the set of data $\{3, 7, 7, 10, 14, 19, 19, 25\}$, the modes are 7 and 19, since both numbers appear twice.

The **range** in a set of data is the difference between the greatest value and the least value of the data.

Example 1 □ Find the mean, median, mode, and range of the data set
$\{132, 149, 152, 164, 164, 175\}$.

Solution □ $\text{Mean} = \dfrac{\text{sum of the values}}{\text{number of values}} = \dfrac{132 + 149 + 152 + 164 + 164 + 175}{6} = \dfrac{936}{6} = 156$

$\text{Median} = \dfrac{152 + 164}{2} = 158$

$\text{Mode} = 164$

$\text{Range} = 175 - 132 = 43$

Example 2 □ In a geometry class of 15 boys and 12 girls, the average (arithmetic mean) test score of the class was 81. If the average score of the 15 boys was 83, what was the average score of the 12 girls?

Solution □ Let $x =$ the average score of 12 girls.

$81 = \dfrac{(83 \times 15) + (x \times 12)}{15 + 12}$ Weighted average formula

$81 = \dfrac{1245 + 12x}{27}$ Simplify.

$81 \times 27 = 1245 + 12x$ Multiply each side by 27.

$2187 - 1245 = 12x$ Subtract 1245 from each side.

$942 = 12x$ Simplify.

$x = 78.5$ Divide each side by 12.

The average score of 12 girls is 78.5.

Exercise - Mean, Median, Mode, and Range

1

Test Scores	67	75	87	91
Number of Students	1	3	2	2

The test scores of 8 students are shown in the table above. Let m be the mean of the scores and M be the median of the score. What is the value of $M - m$?

A) −6

B) 0

C) 3

D) 6

2

The average (arithmetic mean) of five numbers n, $n-3$, $2n+1$, $3n-4$, and $5n+10$ is 8. Which of the following is true?

A) median $= 5$, range $= 18$

B) median $= 5$, range $= 25$

C) median $= 7$, range $= 18$

D) median $= 7$, range $= 25$

3

The average (arithmetic mean) of two numbers is $\frac{1}{2}x+1$. If one of the numbers is x, what is the other number?

A) $x+2$

B) $x-2$

C) -2

D) 2

4

The average (arithmetic mean) of a set of n numbers is 19. If the average of the 6 greatest numbers in the set is 29 and the average of the remaining numbers is 7, what is the value of n?

A) 9

B) 10

C) 11

D) 12

5

The average (arithmetic mean) of m, n, and -1 is 0. What is the value of $m+n$?

6

The average (arithmetic mean) test score for all the students in a class is 84. The average score of m boys in the class was 79, while that of n girls was 87. What is the ratio of m to n?

7

A student has an average (arithmetic mean) score of 86 points for 4 tests. What total score does this student need in the next two tests in order to have an average of 90 for all 6 tests?

8-2. Standard Deviation

The **variance**, denoted d^2, and the **standard deviation** of a data set $\{x_1, x_2, \cdots, x_n\}$ are defined as follows.

Variance $= d^2 = \dfrac{(x_1 - m)^2 + (x_2 - m)^2 + \cdots + (x_n - m)^2}{n}$, in which m is the mean of n numbers.

Standard deviation $= \sqrt{d^2} = \sqrt{\dfrac{(x_1 - m)^2 + (x_2 - m)^2 + \cdots + (x_n - m)^2}{n}}$

In a data set, if the same number k is added to each number, the mean and the median are increased by k, while the range and the standard deviation remain unchanged.

If each number in a data set is multiplied by the same number k, the mean, median, range, and standard deviation are all multiplied by k.

In general, *when the measures are clustered close to the mean the standard deviation is small, and when the measures are widely spread apart the standard deviation is relatively large.*

The graph of the normal distribution, called the **normal curve**, is a symmetrical bell shaped curve which shows the relationship between the standard deviation and the observations.

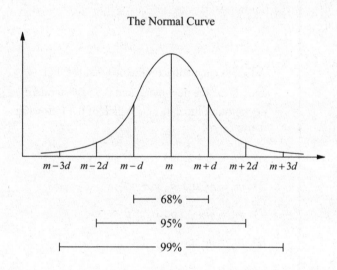

The Normal Curve

Normal distributions have these properties.

1. The mean m is at the center.
2. About 68% of the values are within one standard deviation from the mean.
3. About 95% of the values are within two standard deviations from the mean.
4. About 99% of the values are within three standard deviations from the mean.

Example 1 □ Find the variance and the standard deviation of the data set $\{3, 5, 12, 16, 19\}$.

Solutions □ Mean $= \dfrac{3 + 5 + 12 + 16 + 19}{5} = \dfrac{55}{5} = 11$

Variance $= d^2 = \dfrac{(3-11)^2 + (5-11)^2 + (12-11)^2 + (16-11)^2 + (19-11)^2}{5} = 38$

Standard deviation $= \sqrt{d^2} = \sqrt{38} \approx 6.2$

Example 2 □ On a test, 82 is the arithmetic mean and 6 is the standard deviation. What value is exactly two standard deviations more than the mean?

Solutions □ Two standard deviations more than the mean is $82 + 2(6) = 94$.

Exercise - Standard Deviation

Questions 1-3 refer to the following information.

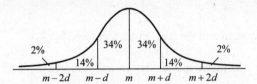

The figure above shows a normal distribution with mean m and standard deviation d, including approximate percentages of the distribution corresponding to the regions shown. Suppose the SAT math scores of 1,200 students entering a certain university are normally distributed with a mean score of 600 and standard deviation of 60.

1

Approximately how many of the students have SAT scores between 660 and 720?

2

Approximately how many of the students have SAT scores less than 540?

3

Approximately how many of the students have SAT scores greater than 720?

Questions 4-6 refer to the following information.

Number of Children	0	1	2	3	4
Frequency	1	2	4	0	1

The table above shows the frequency distribution of the number of children in each of 8 families.

4

Let m be the mean of the data set above. What is the value of m?

5

Let d be the standard deviation of the data set above. What is the value of d?
(Round your answer to the nearest hundredth.)

6

Add 2 to each entry on the original list. Let m_a and d_a be the new mean and the new standard deviation of the data set. Which of the following is true?

A) $m_a = m + 2$ and $d_a = d + 2$

B) $m_a = m$ and $d_a = d + 2$

C) $m_a = m + 2$ and $d_a = d$

D) $m_a = m$ and $d_a = d$

7

Multiply each entry by 2 on the original list. Let m_p and d_p be the new mean and the new standard deviation of the data set. Which of the following is true?

A) $m_p = 2m$ and $d_p = 2d$

B) $m_p = m$ and $d_p = d$

C) $m_p = 2m$ and $d_p = d$

D) $m_p = m$ and $d_p = 2d$

8-3. Graphical Displays

The **frequency** of a particular category is the number of times the category appears in the data.
A **frequency distribution** is a table or graph that presents the categories along with their associated frequencies.
The **relative frequency** of a category is the associated frequency divided by the total number of data.
Relative frequencies may be expressed in terms of percents, fractions, or decimals. The sum of the relative frequencies in a relative frequency distribution is always 1(100%).

Note: In data interpretation questions, you need to *distinguish between the change in absolute numbers and the percent change* in the questions.

A **line graph** shows the change in a certain data over a period of time. The time is always on the horizontal axis, and the variable measured is always on the vertical axis.

In a **bar graph**, rectangular bars represent the categories of data. The height of vertical bars or the length of a horizontal bars show the frequency or relative frequency.

A **histogram** is useful in displaying frequency distributions that are similar to bar graphs, but they have a number line for the horizontal axis. Also, there are no spaces between the bars.

Distributions are **skewed** if the majority of their values fall either to the left or to the right. In right-skewed data the mean is usually greater than the median, while in left-skewed data the mean is usually less than the median.

Outliers are a small group of values that are significantly smaller or larger than the other values in the data. When there are outliers in the data, the mean will be pulled in their direction, while the median remains the same. If outliers are significantly smaller than the other values, the mean will be smaller than the median. If outliers are significantly larger than the other values, the mean will be larger than the median

Patterns of Distribution

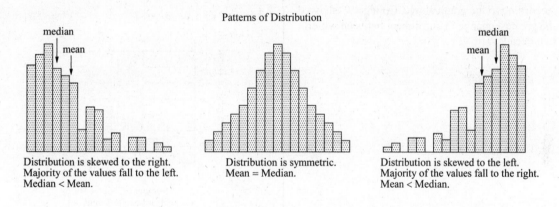

Distribution is skewed to the right.
Majority of the values fall to the left.
Median < Mean.

Distribution is symmetric.
Mean = Median.

Distribution is skewed to the left.
Majority of the values fall to the right.
Mean < Median.

Example 1 □ In the graph below which data set will have a median greater than the mean?

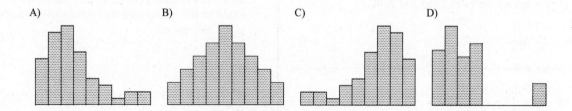

A) B) C) D)

Solutions □ Choice C is correct. When the distribution is skewed to the left, the data set will usually have a greater median than mean. Choice A is incorrect because the distribution is skewed to the right, meaning the mean is greater than the median. Choice B is incorrect because the distribution is symmetric, meaning the median is equal to the mean. Choice D is incorrect because the outlier on the far right pulls the mean to the right but leaves the median alone. So its mean is greater than the median.

Exercise - Graphical Displays

Questions 1-3 refer to the following information.

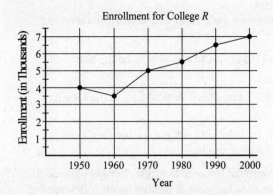

Enrollment for College *R*

The line graph above shows the enrollment for College *R* between 1950 and 2000.

1

According to the graph above, College *R* showed the greatest change in enrollment between which two decades?

A) 1950 to 1960

B) 1960 to 1970

C) 1970 to 1980

D) 1980 to 1990

2

What is the average rate of increase in enrollment per decade between 1950 and 2000?

A) 500

B) 600

C) 750

D) 875

3

If enrollment increases by approximately the same percentage between 2000 and 2010 as it decreased between 1950 and 1960, what is the expected enrollment in 2010?

A) 7,250

B) 7,540

C) 7,650

D) 7,875

4

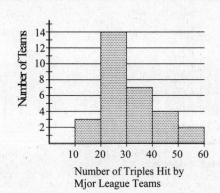

Number of Triples Hit by Mjor League Teams

The histogram above shows the distribution of the number of triples hit by 30 major league baseball teams in a certain year. Which of the following could be the median number of triples represented in the histogram?

A) 19

B) 27

C) 32

D) 34

8-4. Scatter Plots and the Regression Lines

A **scatter plot** is a mathematical diagram represented by a set of dots that display the relationship between two numerical variables.

The x- coordinate of the dot, measured along the horizontal axis, gives the value of one variable and the y- coordinate of the dot, measured along the vertical axis, gives the value of the other variable.

When the set of dots are plotted, usually there is no single line that passes through all the data points, but we can approximate a linear relationship by finding a line that best fits the data. This line is called the **regression line** or the **best fit line**.

If the slope of a regression line is positive, then the two variables have a **positive association**.
If the slope of a regression line is negative, then the two variables have a **negative association**.
If the slope of a regression line cannot be determined, then the two variables have **no association**.

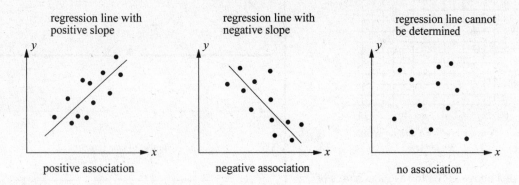

Some scatter plots are not linear. There are quadratic and exponential models too.

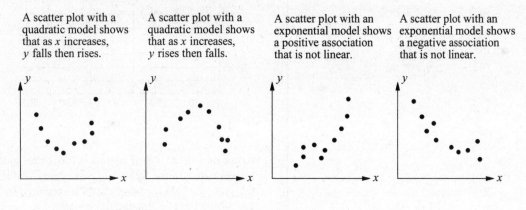

Example 1   □   The scatter plot at the right shows the prices and weights of various boxed products. Of the five labeled products, which has the best unit price?

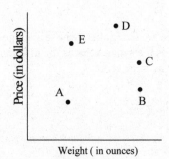

Solutions   □ $\text{unit price} = \dfrac{\text{price}}{\text{number of units}}$
For each of the five points on the graph, product B has the lowest price to weight ratio. Therefore, product B is the one with best unit price.

Exercise - Scatter Plots and the Regression Lines

Questions 1 and 2 refer to the following information.

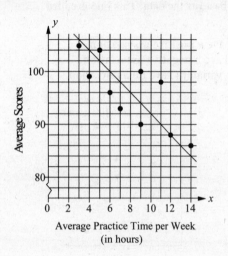

Average Practice Time per Week
(in hours)

The scatter plot above shows the average scores of 10 golfers and their weekly practice times. The line of best fit is also shown.

1

What is the average score of the golfer that is farthest from the line of best fit?

A) 93

B) 96

C) 98

D) 99

2

There are two golfers whose average practice time is the same. What is the difference between their average scores?

A) 4

B) 6

C) 8

D) 10

3

What is the median score of the 10 golfers?

A) 96

B) 97

C) 98

D) 99

4

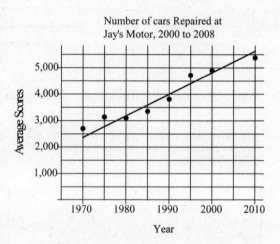

Number of cars Repaired at
Jay's Motor, 2000 to 2008

According to the line of best fit in the scatter plot above, which of the following best approximate the year in which the number of cars repaired by Jay's Motor was estimated to be 4,500?

A) 1996

B) 1998

C) 2000

D) 2002

8-5. Populations, Samples, and Random Selection

In statistics, the word **population** does not necessarily refer to people. It may, for example, refer to the number of smart phones sold or to the number of public high schools in California. The term population refers to the set of all individuals or objects under consideration. In the real world, studying the entire population is usually impractical. Only part of the whole population can be examined, and this part is called the **sample**.

When researchers make generalizations from the part to the whole, we say they make **inferences** from the sample to the population.

A sample that accurately reflects the entire population must satisfy the following two conditions.
1. *Large sample size.*
2. *The sample must be selected at random from the original population of interest.*

Large sample size leads to more reliable conclusions because larger samples experience less sampling variability. A random sample of size 300 from a population of size 100,000 is just as reliable as a random sample of size 300 from a population of size 1,000,000. What is important is the sample size, not the sample-to-population percentage or fraction. But when a selection procedure is biased, taking a large sample does not help.

Bias is the tendency to favor the selection of certain members of a population. When selecting a sample, it is crucial to use randomization. Randomly selecting samples from the original population of interest will most likely result in a decrease in the margin of error.

The **population parameter** is a measured characteristic about the population, calculated from the sample.
Population parameter = fraction of people in the random sample × total population

Example 1 □ An opinion survey about water use was conducted by DWR (Department of Water Resources) in two cities. City A has 120,000 residents and city B has 65,000 residents. Each survey was conducted with a sample of 400 residents from each city. The results of the survey will be used by the state government for future water regulations. Which of the following statements is true?

A) The opinions surveyed at City A are more accurate, since the larger city is more likely to have diversity of opinion.

B) The opinions surveyed at City B are more accurate, since it has a larger percentage of its people surveyed.

C) The opinions surveyed at City A are more accurate, since there is less sampling variability with a larger population.

D) Neither city is more likely to have a more accurately estimate.

Solutions □ Choice D is correct. A random sample of size 400 from a population of size 120,000 is just as reliable as a random sample of size 400 from a population of size 650,000.

Choice A is not correct. It is unclear whether the larger city has more diversity of opinion. Even if it does, how many of those diverse opinions are included in the sample is in question.

Choice B is not correct. In a survey, what is important is the sample size, not the percentage or fraction of the sample to the population.

Choice C is not correct. Larger *samples*, not larger populations, lead to more reliable conclusions because they experience less sampling variability.

Exercise - Populations, Samples, and Random Selection

▼

Questions 1-3 refer to the following information.

	Voted for Candidate A	Voted for Candidate B	Voted for Other Candidates	Total
Ages 18 to 30	84	46	30	160
Ages 31 to 55	72	90	48	210
55 years or older	31	76	23	130
Total	187	212	101	500

A polling organization takes a random sample of 500 voters who voted for the mayoral election of a large western city. The organization gathered data right after the election, as shown in the table above.

1

According to the data above, what percent of people from ages 31 to 55 voted for candidate B ?

A) 38%

B) 43%

C) 45%

D) 48%

3

According to the data above, how many times more likely is it for ages 18 to 30 year olds to vote for candidate A than it is for ages 55 years or older to vote for candidate A ?

A) 2.2

B) 2.4

C) 2.6

D) 2.8

▲

2

The total population of individuals in the city who voted for the election was about 450,000. What is the best estimate of the total number of votes for candidate B ?

A) 144,000

B) 168,000

C) 190,000

D) 210,000

Chapter 8 Practice Test

▼

Questions 1-3 refer to the following information.

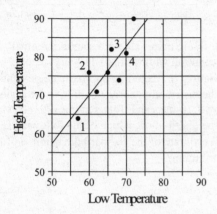

The graph above is a scatter plot with 8 points, each representing the low temperature and high temperature of 8 days in September in a certain city. Both the low temperatures and high temperatures are measured in degrees Fahrenheit. The line of best fit for the data is also shown.

1

Based on the line of best fit for the data shown, how many degrees does the high temperature increase when the low temperature increases by one degree?

A) 0.9

B) 1.3

C) 1.6

D) 1.8

2

What is the predicted high temperature of the day when the low temperature is 58?

A) 65

B) 68

C) 71

D) 74

3

Among the four days marked 1, 2, 3, and 4 in the scatter plot, on which day is the difference between the high temperature and the low temperature minimal?

A) Day 1

B) Day 2

C) Day 3

D) Day 4

▲

4

Number of Hours Worked by the 20 Salespersons in Company G

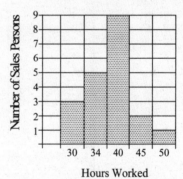

Hours Worked

Based on the histogram above, what is the average number of hours worked by the 20 salespersons in Company G?

A) 36

B) 37

C) 38

D) 39

Questions 5 and 6 refer to the following information.

Frequency Distribution for List *A*

Number	0	4	5	6
Frequency	8	10	12	10

Frequency Distribution for List *B*

Number	7	10	11	15
Frequency	10	8	10	12

The table above shows the frequency distribution of two lists. List *A* and list *B* each contain 40 numbers.

5

What is the difference between the average of the numbers in list *B* and the average of the numbers in list *A*?

A) 6.5

B) 7

C) 7.5

D) 8

6

List *C* contains 80 numbers: the 40 numbers in list *A* and the 40 numbers in list *B*. Let *m* be the average of 80 numbers in list *C* and *M* be the median of 80 numbers in list *C*. What is the value of $m - M$?

A) 1

B) 1.5

C) 2

D) 2.5

7

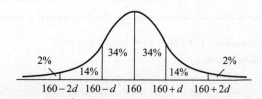

The figure above shows a standard normal distribution with mean of 160 and standard deviation *d*, including approximate percents of the distribution corresponding to the regions shown. If the value 148 is at the 12th percentile of the distribution, which of the following is the best estimate of the standard deviation *d* of the distribution?

A) 5

B) 10

C) 15

D) 20

8

The tables below give the distribution of ratings of two different laptops by 100 people each.

Ratings of Laptop *A* by 100 Reviewers

Ratings	5	4	3	2	1
Frequency	28	45	11	7	9

Ratings of Laptop *B* by 100 Reviewers

Ratings	5	4	3	2	1
Frequency	22	24	18	20	16

Which of the following is true about the data shown for the ratings of the two laptops?

A) The standard deviation of the ratings of laptop *A* is larger.

B) The standard deviation of the ratings of laptop *B* is larger.

C) The standard deviation of the two ratings are the same.

D) The standard deviation of the two ratings cannot be determined with the data provided.

Answer Key

Section 8-1

1. B   2. B   3. D   4. C   5. 1

6. $\dfrac{3}{5}$ 7. 196

Section 8-2

1. 168   2. 192   3. 24   4. 1.75   5. 1.09
6. C   7. A

Section 8-3

1. B   2. B   3. D   4. B

Section 8-4

1. C   2. D   3. B   4. A

Section 8-5

1. B   2. C   3. A

Chapter 8 Practice Test

1. B   2. B   3. A   4. C   5. B
6. A   7. B   8. B

Answers and Explanations

Section 8-1

1. B

$$m = \frac{67 + 75 \times 3 + 87 \times 2 + 91 \times 2}{8} = 81$$

To find the median of the test scores, put all the test scores in order, from least to greatest.

67, 75, 75, 75, 87, 87, 91, 91
There are two middle values, 75 and 87.
The median is the mean of these two values.

$$M = \frac{75 + 87}{2} = 81$$
$$M - m = 81 - 81 = 0$$

2. B

$$\text{Average} = \frac{n + n - 3 + 2n + 1 + 3n - 4 + 5n + 10}{5}$$
$$= \frac{12n + 4}{5}$$

Since the average of five numbers is 8,

$$\frac{12n + 4}{5} = 8.$$

Solving the equation for n yields $n = 3$.
Therefore, the five numbers are 3, 0, 7, 5, and 25.
Arranging the five numbers in order, we get
0, 3, 5, 7, and 25.

The median of this set of numbers is 5, and the range of this set of numbers is $25 - 0$, or 25.

3. D

Let the other number $= y$.

$$\frac{x + y}{2} = \frac{1}{2}x + 1 \qquad \text{Avg. of two numbers is } \tfrac{1}{2}x + 1.$$
$$2(\frac{x + y}{2}) = 2(\frac{1}{2}x + 1) \qquad \text{Multiply each side by 2.}$$
$$x + y = x + 2 \qquad \text{Distributive property}$$
$$y = 2 \qquad \text{Subtract each side by } x.$$

The other number is 2.

4. C

If the average of a set of n numbers is 19, then the sum of n numbers is $19n$.
If the average of the 6 greatest numbers in the set is 29, the sum of those 6 numbers is 6×29, or 174. There are $n - 6$ remaining numbers, with sum $19n - 174$ and average is 7.

Therefore, $\dfrac{19n - 174}{n - 6} = 7$.
$$19n - 174 = 7(n - 6)$$
$$19n - 174 = 7n - 42$$
$$12n = 132$$
$$n = 11$$

5. 1

The average of m, n, and -1 is 0.
$$\frac{m + n + (-1)}{3} = 0$$
$$m + n + (-1) = 0$$
$$m + n = 1$$

6. $\dfrac{3}{5}$

Weighted average of the two groups

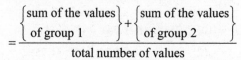

$$84 = \frac{79m + 87n}{m + n} \implies 84(m + n) = 79m + 87n$$

$$\implies 84m + 84n = 79m + 87n \implies 5m = 3n$$

$$\implies m = \frac{3}{5}n \implies \frac{m}{n} = \frac{3}{5}$$

7. 196

The student's total score for his 4 tests is 86×4, or 344. In order to have an average of 90 for all 6 tests, the student needs 90×6, or 540, points total. So the total score needed on the next two tests is $540 - 344$, or 196.

Section 8-2

1. 168

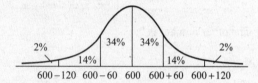

$$600-120 \quad 600-60 \quad 600 \quad 600+60 \quad 600+120$$

Fourteen percent of the students have SAT scores between 660 and 720.
14% of 1,200 is 1200×0.14, or 168.

2. 192

Sixteen percent of the students have SAT scores less than 540.
16% of 1,200 is 1200×0.16, or 192.

3. 24

Two percent of the students have SAT scores greater than 720.
2% of 1,200 is 1200×0.02, or 24.

4. 1.75

First, put all the data in order.
0, 1, 1, 2, 2, 2, 2, 4

$$m = \frac{0+1+1+2+2+2+2+4}{8} = \frac{14}{8} = 1.75$$

5. 1.09

$$d^2 = [(0-1.75)^2 + (1-1.75)^2 + (1-1.75)^2$$
$$+ (2-1.75)^2 + (2-1.75)^2 + (2-1.75)^2$$
$$+ (2-1.75)^2 + (4-1.75)^2] \div 8 = 1.1875$$

$$d = \sqrt{1.1875} \approx 1.09$$

6. C

Add 2 to each entry on the original list. The new list is 2, 3, 3, 4, 4, 4, 4, 6.

$$m_a = \frac{2+3+3+4+4+4+4+6}{8} = \frac{30}{8} = 3.75$$

$$d^2 = [(2-3.75)^2 + (3-3.75)^2 + (3-3.75)^2$$
$$+ (4-3.75)^2 + (4-3.75)^2 + (4-3.75)^2$$
$$+ (4-3.75)^2 + (6-3.75)^2] \div 8 = 1.1875$$

$$d = \sqrt{1.1875} \approx 1.09$$

The mean is increased by 2, but the standard deviation is unchanged.

Choice C is correct.

7. A

Multiply each entry by 2 on the original list. New list is 0, 2, 2, 4, 4, 4, 4, 8.

$$m_p = \frac{0+2+2+4+4+4+4+8}{8} = \frac{28}{8} = 3.5$$

$$d^2 = [(0-3.5)^2 + (2-3.5)^2 + (2-3.5)^2$$
$$+ (4-3.5)^2 + (4-3.5)^2 + (4-3.5)^2$$
$$+ (4-3.5)^2 + (8-3.5)^2] \div 8 = 4.75$$

$$d = \sqrt{4.75} \approx 2.18$$

The mean and standard deviation are multiplied by 2.

Choice A is correct.

Section 8-3

1. B

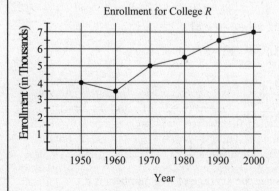

Year	Changes in enrollment	
1950 – 1960	500	decrease
1960 – 1970	1,500	increase
1970 – 1980	500	increase
1980 – 1990	1,000	increase

The greatest change in enrollment occurred between 1960 and 1970.

2. **B**

Average rate of increase in enrollment

$$= \frac{\text{number increased}}{\text{change in decades}} = \frac{7000 - 4000}{5}$$

$$= \frac{3000}{5} = 600$$

3. **D**

Percent of decrease in enrollment between 1950 and 1960 $= \dfrac{\text{number decreased}}{\text{original number}} = \dfrac{500}{4000} = 0.125$

The percent decrease was 12.5%, so the expected increase is 12.5%.

Let x = expected number of increase.
Expected percent increase

$$= \frac{\text{number of increase}}{\text{original number}} = \frac{x}{7000} = 0.125$$

$x = 7000 \times 0.125 = 875$

Therefore, the expected enrollment in 2010 is $7,000 + 875$, or 7,875.

4. **B**

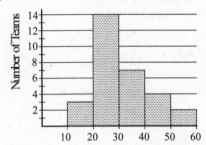

Number of Triples Hit by Mjor League Teams

The median of a data set is the middle value when the data are arranged in order. Since there are 30 teams the middle value is the average of 15th and 16th value. Since there are 3 teams who hit less than 20 triples and 13 teams who hit more than 30 triples, the median number should be between 20 and 30. Therefore, of the choices given, only 27 could be the median number of triples hit by 30 teams.

Choice B is correct.

Section 8-4

1. **C**

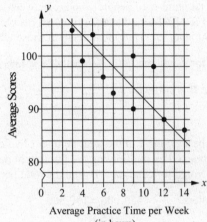

Average Practice Time per Week
(in hours)

The average score of the golfer that is farthest from the line of best fit is located at $(11, 98)$. The golfer's average score is 98.

Choice C is correct.

2. **D**

There are two golfers whose average practice time is 9. The difference between their average scores is $100 - 90$, or 10.

Choice D is correct.

3. **B**

The list of the 10 golfers' average scores listed from highest to lowest is 105, 104, 100, 99, 98, 96, 93, 90, 88, and 86.
There are two middle values, 98 and 96.
The median is the average of these two numbers.

$$\text{Median} = \frac{98 + 96}{2} = 97$$

4. **A**

According to the graph, the horizontal line that represents 4,500 cars repaired by Jay's Motor intersects the line of best fit at a point where the horizontal coordinate is between 1995 and 2000, and closer to 1995 than 2000. Therefore, of the choices given, 1996 best approximates the year in which the number of cars repaired by Jay's Motor was estimated to be 4,500.

Section 8-5

1. B

    The total number of people who are between age 31 and 60 is 210. From that age group, 90 people voted for candidate B. Thus the percent of those who voted for candidate B is $\frac{90}{210} \approx 0.428 \approx 43\%$.
    Choice B is correct.

2. C

    The best estimate of the total number of votes can be obtained by multiplying the fraction of people who voted for candidate B and the total population of voters. $\frac{212}{500} \times 450,000 = 190,800$.
    Therefore, of the choices given, 190,000 is the best estimation.

3. A

    According to the data, 84 out of 160 people whose ages are between 18 and 30 voted for candidate A and 31 out of 130 people who are 55 years or older, voted for candidate A.
    The ratio is $(\frac{84}{160}) \div (\frac{31}{130}) \approx 2.2$.
    2.2 times more likely.

Chapter 8 Practice Test

1. B

    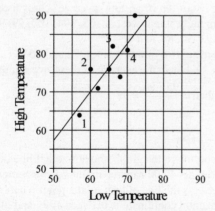

    The slope of the line of best fit is the value of the average increase in high temperature when the low temperature increases by one degree.
    Using approximate values found along the line of best fit $(60, 70)$ and $(76, 90)$, the approximate slope can be calculated as $\frac{90-70}{76-60} = 1.25$.

Of the choices given, 1.3 is the best estimation. Therefore, the high temperature increases 1.3 degrees when the low temperature increases by one degree.

2. B

    When the low temperature is 58, the graph shows that the high temperature is between 65 and 70, but closer to 70. Of the choices given, 68 is the best estimation.

3. A

    In Day 1, the approximate high temperature is 64 and the approximate low temperature is 57. The difference is $64 - 57$, or 7 degrees.

    In Day 2, the approximate high temperature is 76 and the approximate low temperature is 60. The difference is $76 - 60$, or 16 degrees.

    In Day 3, the approximate high temperature is 82 and the approximate low temperature is 67. The difference is $82 - 67$, or 15 degrees.

    In Day 4, the approximate high temperature is 81 and the approximate low temperature is 70. The difference is $81 - 70$, or 11 degrees.

    The difference between the high and the low temperature was minimum on Day 1.

4. C

    3 people worked for 30 hours.
    5 people worked for 34 hours.
    9 people worked for 40 hours.
    2 people worked for 45 hours.
    1 person worked for 50 hours.

    Average number of hours worked
    $= \dfrac{\text{total number of hours}}{\text{total number of people}}$
    $= \dfrac{3 \cdot 30 + 5 \cdot 34 + 9 \cdot 40 + 2 \cdot 45 + 1 \cdot 50}{20}$
    $= \dfrac{760}{20} = 38$

5. B

Frequency Distribution for List A

Number	0	4	5	6
Frequency	8	10	12	10

Frequency Distribution for List B

Number	7	10	11	15
Frequency	10	8	10	12

Average of the numbers in List B

$$= \frac{10 \times 7 + 8 \times 10 + 10 \times 11 + 12 \times 15}{40} = \frac{440}{40} = 11$$

Average of the numbers in List A

$$= \frac{8 \times 0 + 10 \times 4 + 12 \times 5 + 10 \times 6}{40} = \frac{160}{40} = 4$$

Therefore, the difference between the average of the two lists is $11 - 4$, or 7.

6. **A**

Because the lists A and B each contain 40 numbers, the average of the numbers in list C is the average of the individual averages of the numbers in lists A and B. Thus the average of the numbers in list C is $\frac{4+11}{2}$, or 7.5.

If you look at the numbers in the two lists, you will see that the 40 numbers in list A are all less than or equal to 6, and the 40 numbers in list B are all greater than or equal to 7. Thus the two middle numbers in list C are 6 and 7, and the average of these numbers is $\frac{6+7}{2}$, or 6.5.

Therefore, $m = 7.5$ and $M = 6.5$, and $m - M = 7.5 - 6.5 = 1$.

7. **B**

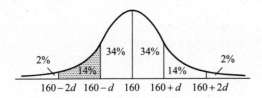

If the value 148 is at the 12th percentile of the distribution, the value must be in the shaded region which is in between $160 - d$ and $160 - 2d$.

If $d = 5$, $160 - d = 160 - 5 = 155$ and $160 - 2d = 160 - 2 \cdot 5 = 150$, which does not include 148.

If $d = 10$, $160 - d = 160 - 10 = 150$ and $160 - 2d = 160 - 2 \cdot 10 = 140$, which includes 148.

If $d = 15$, $160 - d = 160 - 15 = 145$ and $160 - 2d = 160 - 2 \cdot 15 = 130$, which does not include 148.

If $d = 20$, $160 - d = 160 - 20 = 140$ and $160 - 2d = 160 - 2 \cdot 20 = 120$, which does not include 148.

Choice B is correct.

8. **B**

Ratings of Laptop A by 100 Reviewers

Ratings	5	4	3	2	1
Frequency	28	45	11	7	9

Ratings of Laptop B by 100 Reviewers

Ratings	5	4	3	2	1
Frequency	22	24	18	20	16

The standard deviation is a measure of how far the data set values are from the mean. In the data set for laptop A, the large majority of the data are in two of the five possible values, which are the two values closest to the mean. In the data set for laptop B, the data are more spread out, thus by observation, the data for laptop B have a larger standard deviation.

Choice B is correct.

CHAPTER 9
Probability and Categorical Data

9-1. Permutations and Combinations

Fundamental Counting Principles

If an event can occur in m different ways and another event can occur in n different ways, then there are $m \times n$ total ways that both events can occur.

A **factorial** is the product of a whole number n, and all the whole numbers less than n and greater than or equal to 1.

$n! = n(n-1)(n-2) \cdots 3 \cdot 2 \cdot 1$

For example, $6! = 6 \cdot 5 \cdot 4 \cdot 3 \cdot 2 \cdot 1 = 720$

When a group of objects or people is arranged in a certain order, the arrangement is called a **permutation**.

The number of permutations of n distinct objects taken r at a time is defined as $_nP_r = \dfrac{n!}{(n-r)!}$.

When a group of objects or people is selected, and the order is not important, the selection is called a **combination**.

The number of combinations of n distinct objects taken r at a time is defined as $_nC_r = \dfrac{n!}{r!(n-r)!}$.

The basic difference between a permutation and a combination is that **order is considered** in a permutation and **order is not considered** in a combination.

Example 1 □ There are 4 roads from Town A to Town B, and 3 roads from Town B to Town C. If a person travels from Town A to Town C and back, passing through Town B in both directions, how many different routes for the trip are possible?

Solution □ $A \rightarrow B$ 4 different routes
$B \rightarrow C$ 3 different routes
$C \rightarrow B$ 3 different routes
$B \rightarrow A$ 4 different routes

Therefore, there are $4 \times 3 \times 3 \times 4$, or 144, different possible routes for the trip.

Example 2 □ a. There are 2 chairs in a row. If there are 5 students, how many ways can the seats be filled?

b. How many different groups of 2 students can be formed from 5 students?

Solution □ a. In this arrangement, order is considered. AB and BA are not the same.
Use $_nP_r$

$$_5P_2 = \frac{5!}{(5-2)!} = \frac{5 \cdot 4 \cdot 3 \cdot 2 \cdot 1}{3 \cdot 2 \cdot 1} = 20$$

There are 20 possible arrangements.

b. In this arrangement, order is not considered. Therefore, if AB is taken, then BA is excluded.
Use $_nC_r$.

$$_5C_2 = \frac{5!}{2!(5-2)!} = \frac{5!}{2!3!} = 10$$

There are 10 possible combinations.

Exercise - Permutations and Combinations

Questions 1 and 2 refer to the following information.

A hiker is going to hike a mountain where there are four trails to the top of the mountain.

1

In how many different ways can he hike up and down the mountain?

2

If the hiker does not want to take the same trail both ways, in how many different ways can he hike up and down the mountain?

3

In how many ways can the letters of the word SUNDAY be arranged using only 3 of the letters at a time?

Questions 4 and 5 refer to the following information.

Sixteen players participated in a tennis tournament. Three players will be awarded for first, second, and third prize.

4

In how many different ways can the first, second, and third prizes be awarded?

5

How many different groups of 3 people can get prizes?

6

How many different four-letter patterns can be formed from the word MATH if the letters cannot be used more than once?

9-2. Rules of Probability

An **outcome** is one of the possible results that can occur as a result of a trial.

The **probability** of event A, denoted $P(A)$, is:

$$P(A) = \frac{\text{the number of times the desired outcome occurs}}{\text{the total number of outcomes}} .$$

If the outcome of one event does not influence the outcome of the second event, then the events are said to be **independent**. When drawing at random with replacement, the draws are independent. Without replacement, the draws are **dependent**.

If two events A and B are independent, then the probability that both events will occur is
$P(A \text{ and } B) = P(A) \cdot P(B)$.

If two events A and B are dependent, then the probability that both events will occur is
$P(A \text{ and } B) = P(A) \cdot P(B \text{ following } A)$.

If two events A and B cannot occur at the same time, then the probability that either A or B occurs is
$P(A \text{ or } B) = P(A) + P(B)$.

Example 1 □ A bag contains 6 red balls and 4 blue balls. Two balls are selected one at a time.

a. Find the probability of selecting a red ball then a blue ball, if the first ball is *replaced* before the second one is drawn.

b. Find the probability of selecting a red ball then a blue ball, if the first ball is *not replaced* before the second one is drawn.

c. Find the probability that both balls are the same color, if the first ball is *not replaced* before the second one is drawn.

Solution □ a. Since the first ball is replaced, the selection of the first ball does not influence the selection of the second ball. The event is independent.

$$P(r \text{ and } b) = P(r) \cdot P(b) = \frac{6}{10} \cdot \frac{4}{10} = \frac{6}{25}$$

b. Since the first ball is not replaced, the selection of the first ball influence the selection of the second ball. The event is dependent.

$$P(r \text{ and } b) = P(r) \cdot P(b \text{ following } r)$$

$$= \frac{6}{10} \cdot \frac{4}{9} = \frac{4}{15}$$

The conditional probability $P(b \text{ following } r)$ means that the second ball is blue on the condition that the first ball is red.

c. The event is dependent.

$$P(r \text{ and } r) = P(r) \cdot P(r \text{ following } r)$$

$$= \frac{6}{10} \cdot \frac{5}{9} = \frac{30}{90}$$

$P(r \text{ following } r) = \dfrac{5}{9}$ ← 5 red marbles are left
← 9 total marbles are left

$$P(b \text{ and } b) = P(b) \cdot P(b \text{ following } b)$$

$$= \frac{4}{10} \cdot \frac{3}{9} = \frac{12}{90}$$

$P(b \text{ following } b) = \dfrac{3}{9}$ ← 3 blue marbles are left
← 9 total marbles are left

$P(\text{both same color})$

$$= P(r \text{ and } r) + P(b \text{ and } b)$$ $P(A \text{ or } B) = P(A) + P(B)$

$$= \frac{30}{90} + \frac{12}{90} = \frac{42}{90} = \frac{7}{15}$$

Exercise - Rules of Probability

▼

Questions 1 and 2 refer to the following information.

A bag contains 15 balls, numbered 1 through 15.

1

What is the probability of selecting a number that is odd or a multiple of 5?

2

A ball is selected at random then replaced in the bag. A second selection is then made. What is the probability that the first number is a prime number and the second number is a multiple of 3?

▲

3

$$S = \{-5, -2, -1, \ 4\} \qquad T = \{-2, \ 3, \ 7\}$$

Product $p = s \cdot t$ is formed from the two sets above, in which s is a number from set S and t is a number from set T. What is the probability that the product $s \cdot t$ will be a positive number?

▼

Questions 4 and 5 refer to the following information.

Janis is making a flight reservation for her business trip. The travel agent informs that the probability that her flight to Phoenix will arrive on schedule is 90% and the probability that her flight from Phoenix to Atlanta will arrive on schedule is 80%.

4

What is the probability that both flights arrive on schedule?

5

What is the probability that her flight to Phoenix is on schedule but her flight from Phoenix to Atlanta is not?

▲

6

In a box of 12 headlamps 3 are defective. If you choose two headlamps without replacement, what is the probability that both headlamps are defective?

9-3. Categorical Data and Conditional Probabilities

The probability of event A, given that event B occurred, is called the **conditional probability** of A given B and is denoted by $P(A|B)$. [Note: The vertical bar between A and B is read "given."]

$$P(A|B) = \frac{P(A \text{ and } B)}{P(B)} = \frac{\text{population of } A \text{ in } B}{\text{population of } B}$$

Two-way **contingency table** is a type of table in a matrix format that displays relationships between two or more categorical variables.

The table on below left shows 300 randomly selected voters from a large city, categorized by age and voting preferences. The age of voters is the row variable, and the name of parties is the column variable.
The totals are placed in the right and bottom margins of the table and thus are called **marginal frequencies**.
The total of the marginal frequencies is the grand total, which is the size of the sample.
The frequencies in the contingency table are often expressed as percentages or relative frequencies.
The table on below right shows the contingency table expressed as percentages of the grand total.

	Democrat	Republican	Total
Under 40	84	63	147
40 or over	60	93	153
Total	144	156	300

	Democrat	Republican	Total
Under 40	28%	21%	49%
40 or over	20%	31%	51%
Total	48%	52%	100%

Example 1 □ The table below shows the results of a survey regarding Proposition A from two regions of a large city. Four hundred registered voters were surveyed.

	Voted For Proposition A	Voted Against Proposition A	No Opinion for Proposition A	Total
East	90	75	17	182
West	104	96	18	218
Total	194	171	35	400

a. What is the probability that a randomly chosen person has no opinion on Proposition A?

b. What is the probability that a randomly chosen person is from East given that he or she voted for Proposition A?

c. What is the probability that a randomly chosen person voted against Proposition A and is from West?

Solution □ a. Since 35 of the 400 voters have no opinion on Proposition A,

$$P(\text{No opinion for Proposition } A) = \frac{35}{400} \text{ or } \frac{7}{80}.$$

b. This is a conditional probability question. There are 194 voters who voted for Proposition A, and 90 of them are from East. Thus,

$$P(\text{population of East in the population Voted For Proposition } A) = \frac{90}{194} \text{ or } \frac{45}{97}.$$

c. $P(\text{against Proposition } A \text{ and from West}) = \frac{96}{400} = \frac{6}{25}$

Exercise - Categorical Data and Conditional Probabilities

Questions 1- 5 refer to the following information.

The table below shows the number of college faculty members in three departments: biological sciences, education, and social sciences.

	Biological Sciences	Education	Social Sciences	Total
Male	10	26	19	55
Female	15	21	17	53
Total	25	47	36	108

1

What is the probability that a randomly chosen faculty member is a female given that she is from Biological Sciences?

2

What is the probability that a randomly chosen faculty member is a male or from Social Sciences?

3

What is the probability that a randomly chosen faculty member is a female from Education department or a male from Social Sciences?

4

What is the probability that a randomly chosen faculty member is from Biological Sciences given that the faculty member is a male?

5

For Biological Science and Education faculties combined, $\frac{1}{6}$ of the female and $\frac{1}{4}$ of the male faculty members are associate professors. If a person is randomly chosen from these two departments, what is the probability that a faculty member is an associate professor?

Chapter 9 Practice Test

▼

Questions 1-4 refer to the following information.

	Economics	History	Music
Male	24	20	19
Female	18	22	17

The table above shows the distribution of a group of 120 college students by gender and major.

1

If one student is randomly selected from the group, what is the probability that the student is a History major?

A) $\dfrac{36}{120}$

B) $\dfrac{40}{120}$

C) $\dfrac{42}{120}$

D) $\dfrac{46}{120}$

2

If a male student is selected at random, which of the following is closest to the probability that he is a Music major?

A) 0.270

B) 0.302

C) 0.317

D) 0.381

3

If one student is randomly selected from the group what is the probability that the student is a male Economics major?

A) $\dfrac{24}{120}$

B) $\dfrac{42}{120}$

C) $\dfrac{24}{42}$

D) $\dfrac{24}{63}$

4

If a Music major is selected at random, which of the following is closest to the probability that the student is a female?

A) 0.298

B) 0.315

C) 0.386

D) 0.472

▲

Questions 5 and 6 refer to the following information.

	Under 30	30 or older	Total
Male	3		12
Female			20
Total	8	24	32

The incomplete table above shows the distribution of age and gender for 32 people who entered a tennis tournament.

5

If a tennis player is chosen at random, what is the probability that the player will be either a male under age 30 or a female aged 30 or older?

A) $\dfrac{15}{32}$

B) $\dfrac{18}{32}$

C) $\dfrac{20}{32}$

D) $\dfrac{24}{32}$

6

If a person is selected at random from the 30 or older player group, what is the probability that the person is a female?

A) $\dfrac{5}{20}$

B) $\dfrac{15}{20}$

C) $\dfrac{9}{24}$

D) $\dfrac{15}{24}$

Questions 7 and 8 refer to the following information.

Number of Visits to Movie Theaters by Students

	None	1 to 2	3 or more
Juniors	x	$2x$	$\dfrac{1}{2}x$
Seniors	y	$\dfrac{5}{2}y$	$\dfrac{1}{2}y$

The table above summarizes the number of visits to movie theaters by 168 juniors and 152 seniors during summer vacation.

7

If a student is selected at random from those who visited movie theaters at least once, what is the probability that the student is a junior?

A) $\dfrac{16}{39}$

B) $\dfrac{18}{39}$

C) $\dfrac{20}{39}$

D) $\dfrac{22}{39}$

8

If a student is selected at random, which of the following is closest to the probability that the student is a senior and visited movie theaters 1 or 2 times?

A) 0.156

B) 0.205

C) 0.297

D) 0.324

Answer Key

Section 9-1

1. 16　　2. 12　　3. 120　　4. 3360　　5. 560
6. 24

Section 9-2

1. $\dfrac{3}{5}$　　2. $\dfrac{2}{15}$　　3. $\dfrac{5}{12}$　　4. 0.72　　5. 0.18

6. $\dfrac{1}{22}$

Section 9-3

1. $\dfrac{3}{5}$　　2. $\dfrac{2}{3}$　　3. $\dfrac{10}{27}$　　4. $\dfrac{2}{11}$　　5. $\dfrac{5}{24}$

Chapter 9 Practice Test

1. C　　2. B　　3. A　　4. D　　5. B
6. D　　7. C　　8. C

Answers and Explanations

Section 9-1

1. 16

   There are 4 different ways of going up and
   4 different ways of going down, so there are
   4×4, or 16 different ways he can hike up and
   down.

2. 12

   If the hiker does not want to take the same trail both
   ways, then there are 4 different ways of going up
   and 3 different ways of going down, so there are
   4×3, or 12 different ways he can hike up and
   down.

3. 120

   Use $_nP_r$, since order is considered.

   $$_6P_3 = \frac{6!}{(6-3)!} = \frac{6!}{3!} = \frac{6 \cdot 5 \cdot 4 \cdot \cancel{3 \cdot 2 \cdot 1}}{\cancel{3 \cdot 2 \cdot 1}} = 120$$

   Therefore, there are 120 ways the 6 letters in
   SUNDAY can be arranged when the letters are
   taken 3 at a time.

4. 3360

   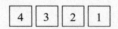

The first choice can be any one of the 16 players,
the second choice can be any one of the 15
remaining players, and the third choice can be
any one of the 14 remaining players. Therefore,
there are $16 \times 15 \times 14$, or 3,360 different ways the
first, second, and third prizes are awarded.

5. 560

   In this case, order does not matter. We must find
   the combination of 16 people taken 3 at a time.

   $$_{16}C_3 = \frac{16!}{3!(16-3)!} = \frac{16!}{3! \times 13!} = \frac{16 \cdot 15 \cdot 14 \cdot 13!}{3 \cdot 2 \cdot 1 \cdot 13!} = 560$$

6. 24

   | 4 | 3 | 2 | 1 |

   The first choice can be any one of the 4 letters,
   the second choice can be any one of the 3
   remaining letters, the third choice can be any one
   of the 2 remaining letters and the fourth choice is
   the 1 remaining letter. Therefore, there are
   $4 \times 3 \times 2 \times 1$, or 24 different ways the 4 letters
   in MATH can be arranged.

Section 9-2

1. $\dfrac{3}{5}$

   There are 8 odd numbers: 1, 3, 5, 7, 9, 11, 13,
   and 15. There are 3 multiples of 5: 5, 10, and 15.
   Therefore, there are 9 numbers which are either
   odd or a multiple of 5.

   $$P(\text{odd or a multiple of 5}) = \frac{9}{15} = \frac{3}{5}$$

2. $\dfrac{2}{15}$

   There are 6 prime numbers: 2, 3, 5, 7, 11, and 13.

   Therefore, $P(\text{prime}) = \dfrac{6}{15}$.

   There are 5 multiples of three: 3, 6, 9, 12, and 15.

   Therefore, $P(\text{multiples of 3}) = \dfrac{5}{15}$.

   The probability that the first number is a prime
   number and the second number is a multiple of 3

   is $\dfrac{6}{15} \times \dfrac{5}{15}$, or $\dfrac{2}{15}$.

3. $\dfrac{5}{12}$

$S = \{-5, -2, -1, 4\} \qquad T = \{-2, 3, 7\}$

Make a table of the possible products of $p = s \cdot t$.

$(-5) \cdot (-2) = 10, \ (-5) \cdot 3 = -15, \ (-5) \cdot 7 = -35$

$(-2) \cdot (-2) = 4, \ (-2) \cdot 3 = -6, \ (-2) \cdot 7 = -14$

$(-1) \cdot (-2) = 2, \ (-1) \cdot 3 = -3, \ (-1) \cdot 7 = -7$

$4 \cdot (-2) = -8, \ 4 \cdot 3 = 12, \ 4 \cdot 7 = 28$

There are 12 products, 5 of which are positive numbers. Therefore,

$P(\text{product is a positive number}) = \dfrac{5}{12}$

4. 0.72

The probability that both flights arrive on schedule is $0.9 \times 0.8 = 0.72$.

5. 0.18

The probability that her flight to Phoenix is on schedule but her flight from Phoenix to Atlanta is not on schedule is $0.9 \times (1 - 0.8) = 0.18$.

6. $\dfrac{1}{22}$

If your first selection is a defective headlamp, 11 headlamps will be left and 2 of them will be defective. The probability that both headlamps are defective is $\dfrac{3}{12} \times \dfrac{2}{11} = \dfrac{1}{22}$.

Section 9-3

1. $\dfrac{3}{5}$

	Biological Sciences	Education	Social Sciences	Total
Male	10	26	19	55
Female	15	21	17	53
Total	25	47	36	108

There are 25 faculty members in Biological Sciences, and 15 of them are female. Therefore, the probability that the person chosen is a female given that she is from Biological Sciences is $\dfrac{15}{25} = \dfrac{3}{5}$.

2. $\dfrac{2}{3}$

There are 55 male faculty members and 36 Social Science faculty members. Since the male faculty in Social Sciences are counted twice you must subtract 19, from the sum of 55 and 36. Therefore, the probability that a randomly chosen faculty member is a male or from Social Sciences is $\dfrac{55}{108} + \dfrac{36}{108} - \dfrac{19}{108}$, or $\dfrac{2}{3}$.

3. $\dfrac{10}{27}$ or 0.37

There are 21 females from Education Department and 19 males from Social Sciences. Therefore, the probability that a randomly chosen faculty member is a female from Education Department or a male from the Social Sciences is $\dfrac{21}{108} + \dfrac{19}{108}$, or $\dfrac{10}{27}$.

4. $\dfrac{2}{11}$

There are 10 male faculty members in Biological Sciences out of 55 males. Therefore, the probability that a randomly chosen faculty member is from the Biological Sciences given that he is a male is $\dfrac{10}{55} = \dfrac{2}{11}$.

5. $\dfrac{5}{24}$

The number of females in both departments combined is $15 + 21$, or 36, and the number of males in both departments combined is $10 + 26$, or 36. The number of female associate professors in both department combined are $36 \times \dfrac{1}{6} = 6$ and the number of male associate professors in both department combined are $36 \times \dfrac{1}{4} = 9$.

There are $25 + 47$, or 72, faculty members in both departments combined and $6 + 9$, or 15, associate professors in both departments combined. Therefore, if a person is randomly chosen from these two departments, the probability that a faculty member is an associate professor is $\dfrac{15}{72} = \dfrac{5}{24}$.

Chapter 9 Practice Test

1. C

	Economics	History	Music
Male	24	20	19
Female	18	22	17

There are 120 student total and 42 students are History majors. Therefore, the probability that the student is a History major is $\dfrac{42}{120}$.

2. B

There are $24 + 20 + 19 = 63$ male students. If a male student is selected at random, the probability that he is a Music major is $\dfrac{19}{63} \approx 0.302$.

3. A

The probability that the student is a male Economics major is $\dfrac{24}{120}$.

4. D

There are $19 + 17$, or 36, Music majors. The probability that a Music major selected at random is a female is $\dfrac{17}{36} \approx 0.472$.

5. B

	Under 30	30 or older	Total
Male	3		12
Female			20
Total	8	24	32

There are 3 males under age of 30. The number of males 30 years or older is $12 - 3 = 9$. Therefore, the number of females 30 years or older is $24 - 9 = 15$. The probability that the player will be either a male under age 30 or a female aged 30 or older is $\dfrac{3+15}{32} = \dfrac{18}{32}$.

6. D

There are 15 females who are aged 30 or older. If a person is selected at random from the 30 or older player group, the probability that the person is a female is $\dfrac{15}{24}$.

7. C

Number of Visits to Movie Theaters by Students

	None	1 to 2	3 or more
Juniors	x	$2x$	$\dfrac{1}{2}x$
Seniors	y	$\dfrac{5}{2}y$	$\dfrac{1}{2}y$

There are 168 juniors and 152 seniors. Therefore, $x + 2x + \dfrac{1}{2}x = 168$, and $y + \dfrac{5}{2}y + \dfrac{1}{2}y = 152$.
Solving the equations give $x = 48$ and $y = 38$.
There are $2x + \dfrac{1}{2}x = \dfrac{5}{2}x = \dfrac{5}{2}(48) = 120$ juniors and $\dfrac{5}{2}y + \dfrac{1}{2}y = 3y = 3(38) = 114$ seniors who visited movie theaters at least once.
If a student is selected at random from those who visited movie theaters at least once, the probability that the student is a junior is $\dfrac{120}{120+114}$, or $\dfrac{20}{39}$.

8. C

Seniors who visited movie theaters 1 or 2 times is $\dfrac{5}{2}y = \dfrac{5}{2}(38) = 95$.
The probability that the student is a senior and visited movie theaters 1 or 2 times is $\dfrac{95}{320} \approx 0.297$

III. Advanced Math

CHAPTER 10
Laws of Exponents and Polynomials

10-1. Laws of Exponents and Scientific Notation

Laws of Exponents

For all integers m and n and any nonzero numbers a and b, the following properties hold.

Symbols	Example

Symbols

$a^m \cdot a^n = a^{m+n}$

$(a^m)^n = a^{m \cdot n}$

$(ab)^m = a^m b^m$

$\dfrac{a^m}{a^n} = a^{m-n}$

$\left(\dfrac{a}{b}\right)^m = \dfrac{a^m}{b^m}$

$a^0 = 1$

$a^{-n} = \dfrac{1}{a^n}$ and $\dfrac{1}{a^{-n}} = a^n$

$\left(\dfrac{a}{b}\right)^{-m} = \left(\dfrac{b}{a}\right)^m = \dfrac{b^m}{a^m}$

Example

$2^3 \cdot 2^5 = 2^{3+5} = 2^8$

$(2^3)^5 = 2^{3 \cdot 5} = 2^{15}$

$(-2x)^5 = (-2)^5 x^5 = -32x^5$

$\dfrac{2^5}{2^3} = 2^{5-3} = 2^2$

$\left(\dfrac{2x}{5}\right)^3 = \dfrac{(2x)^3}{5^3} = \dfrac{8x^3}{125}$

$(-2xy)^0 = 1$

$5^{-2} = \dfrac{1}{5^2}$ and $\dfrac{1}{4^{-3}} = 4^3$

$\left(\dfrac{-2x}{3y^3}\right)^{-2} = \left(\dfrac{3y^3}{-2x}\right)^2 = \dfrac{(3y^3)^2}{(-2x)^2} = \dfrac{9y^6}{4x^2}$

Example 1 □ Simplify.

a. $(-2ab^2)(3a^5b^3) =$

b. $[(a^2)^3]^4 =$

c. $x^{n-2} \cdot x \cdot x^{n+1}$

d. $\dfrac{a^7 b^4 c^2}{a^5 b^2 c} =$

e. $\left(\dfrac{3a^2 bc^3}{2ab^2}\right)^3 =$

f. $\left(\dfrac{7a^{-1}bc^3}{4a^2 b^4}\right)^0 =$

g. $\dfrac{a^{-2} b^3 c^{-3}}{ab^{-2}} =$

h. $\left(\dfrac{2p^2}{3q}\right)^{-3} =$

Solution □ a. $(-2ab^2)(3a^5 b^3) = (-2)(3)(a \cdot a^5)(b^2 \cdot b^3)$ Group the coefficients and variables.

$\qquad = -6a^6 b^5$ $a^m \cdot a^n = a^{m+n}$

b. $[(a^2)^3]^4 = [a^6]^4 = a^{24}$ $(a^m)^n = a^{m \cdot n}$

c. $x^{n-2} \cdot x \cdot x^{n+1} = x^{(n-2)+1+(n+1)}$ $a^m \cdot a^n = a^{m+n}$

$\qquad = x^{2n}$ Simplify.

d. $\dfrac{a^7 b^4 c^2}{a^5 b^2 c} = \left(\dfrac{a^7}{a^5}\right)\left(\dfrac{b^4}{b^2}\right)\left(\dfrac{c^2}{c}\right)$ Group powers that have the same base.

$\qquad = a^2 b^2 c$ $\dfrac{a^m}{a^n} = a^{m-n}$

e. $(\dfrac{3a^2bc^3}{2ab^2})^3 = \dfrac{(3a^2bc^3)^3}{(2ab^2)^3}$ $(\dfrac{a}{b})^m = \dfrac{a^m}{b^m}$

    $= \dfrac{3^3(a^2)^3(b)^3(c^3)^3}{(2)^3(a)^3(b^2)^3}$ $(ab)^m = a^m b^m$

    $= \dfrac{27a^6b^3c^9}{8a^3b^6}$ $(a^m)^n = a^{m \cdot n}$

    $= \dfrac{27a^3c^9}{8b^3}$ $\dfrac{a^m}{a^n} = a^{m-n}$

f. $(\dfrac{7a^{-1}bc^3}{4a^2b^4})^0 = 1$ $a^0 = 1$

g. $\dfrac{a^{-2}b^3c^{-3}}{ab^{-2}} = \dfrac{b^3b^2}{aa^2c^3}$ $a^{-n} = \dfrac{1}{a^n}$ and $\dfrac{1}{a^{-n}} = a^n$

    $= \dfrac{b^5}{a^3c^3}$ Simplify.

h. $(\dfrac{2p^2}{3q})^{-3} = (\dfrac{3q}{2p^2})^3 = \dfrac{(3q)^3}{(2p^2)^3}$ $(\dfrac{a}{b})^{-m} = (\dfrac{b}{a})^m = \dfrac{b^m}{a^m}$

    $= \dfrac{27q^3}{8p^6}$ Simplify.

Scientific Notation

A number is in **scientific notation** when it is in the form $a \times 10^n$, in which $1 \le a < 10$ and n are integers.

Example 2   □   Write each number in scientific notation.

      a. 205,000   b. 0.000107

Simplify and write each number in decimal form.

      c. $(5 \times 10^{-12})(3 \times 10^4)$ d. $\dfrac{6 \times 10^3}{12 \times 10^{-4}}$

Solution   □   a. $205,000 = 2.05 \times 10^5$ Decimal point moved 5 places to the left.

      b. $0.000107 = 1.07 \times 10^{-4}$ Decimal point moved 4 places to the right.

      c. $(5 \times 10^{-12})(3 \times 10^4) = 15 \times 10^{-8}$ $10^{-12} \cdot 10^4 = 10^{-8}$

        $= 1.5 \times 10 \times 10^{-8} = 1.5 \times 10^{-7}$ Simplify.

      d. $\dfrac{6 \times 10^3}{12 \times 10^{-4}} = \dfrac{6}{12} \times \dfrac{10^3}{10^{-4}}$ Group the coefficients and variables.

        $= \dfrac{1}{2} \times 10^7$ $\dfrac{10^3}{10^{-4}} = 10^{3-(-4)} = 10^7$

        $= 0.5 \times 10^7 = 5 \times 10^{-1} \times 10^7 = 5 \times 10^6$ Simplify.

Exercises - Laws of Exponents and Scientific Notation

1

If $(-a^2b^3)(2ab^2)(-3b) = ka^mb^n$, what is the value of $m+n$?

2

If $(\frac{2}{3}a^2b)^2(\frac{4}{3}ab)^{-3} = ka^mb^n$, what is the value of k?

3

If $\dfrac{(x)^3(-y)^2z^{-2}}{(x)^{-2}y^3z} = \dfrac{x^m}{y^nz^p}$, what is the value of $m+n+p$?

4

If $2^x = 5$, what is the value of $2^x + 2^{2x} + 2^{3x}$?

5

$$(3^x + 3^x + 3^x) \cdot 3^x$$

Which of the following is equivalent to the expression shown above?

A) 3^{4x}

B) 3^{3x^2}

C) 3^{1+3x}

D) 3^{1+2x}

6

$$\frac{(6xy^2)(2xy)^2}{8x^2y^2}$$

If the expression above is written in the form ax^my^n, what is the value of $m+n$?

7

If x is not equal to zero, what is the value of $\dfrac{(2x)^3(3x)}{(6x^2)^2}$?

8

If $8,200 \times 300,000$ is equal to 2.46×10^n, what is the value of n?

9

If $\dfrac{240}{80,000} \times \dfrac{6,000}{900,000}$ is equal to $\dfrac{1}{5 \times 10^n}$, what is the value of n?

10-2. Adding, Subtracting, Multiplying, and Dividing Polynomials

An expression with the form ax^n, in which n is a nonnegative integer, is called a **polynomial**.
Polynomials that have only one term are called **monomials**. Polynomials that have two unlike terms
are called **binomials**, and that have three unlike terms are called **trinomials**.

Terms such as $3x^2$ and $-2x^2$ are called **like terms** because they have the same variable to the same power.

The **degree of monomial** is the sum of the exponents of all of the monomial's variables.
The **degree of polynomial** is the greatest degree of any term in the polynomial.

Example 1   □   Find the degree of the polynomial $x - 3xy - 12 + 5x^2y$.

Solution   □   Degree of x, $-3xy$, -12, and $5x^2y$ are 1, $1+1$, 0, and $2+1$ respectively.

Therefore the degree of the polynomial is 3.

Adding and Subtracting Polynomials

To add or subtract two polynomials, add or subtract the coefficient of like terms.

Example 2   □   Find each sum or difference.
a. $(5x^2 - 3x + 14) + (2x^2 + x - 9)$.   b. $(-2p^3 + 7p^2 - 1) - (4p^3 + p - 6)$

Solution   □   a. $(5x^2 - 3x + 14) + (2x^2 + x - 9)$

$= (5x^2 + 2x^2) + (-3x + x) + (14 + (-9))$

$= 7x^2 - 2x + 5$

b. $(-2p^3 + 7p^2 - 1) - (4p^3 + p - 6)$

$= -2p^3 + 7p^2 - 1 - 4p^3 - p + 6$

$= (-2p^3 - 4p^3) + (7p^2) + (-p) + (-1 + 6)$

$= -6p^3 + 7p^2 - p + 5$

Multiplying Polynomials

The Distributive Property and the various laws of exponents can be used to multiply a polynomial by a monomial.

Example 3   □   Simplify each expression.
a. $-3x^2(2x^2 - 3x + 5)$ b. $5(a^2 + 3) - a(a^2 + 7a - 2)$

Solution   □   a. $-3x^2(2x^2 - 3x + 5)$

$= -3x^2(2x^2) - (-3x^2)(3x) - 3x^2(5)$ Distributive Property

$= -6x^4 + 9x^3 - 15x^2$ Simplify.

b. $5(a^2 + 3) - a(a^2 + 7a - 2)$

$= 5(a^2) + 5(3) - a(a^2) - a(7a) - a(-2)$ Distributive Property

$= 5a^2 + 15 - a^3 - 7a^2 + 2a$ Multiply.

$= -a^3 - 2a^2 + 2a + 15$ Combine like terms

Dividing Polynomials

To divide a polynomial by a monomial, divide each term by the monomial, add the results, and simplify.

When dividing a polynomial function $f(x)$ by $ax+b$, **long division,** which is similar to long division in arithmetic, can be used to find quotient $q(x)$ and remainder R.

The division can be written as $\dfrac{f(x)}{ax+b} = q(x) + \dfrac{R}{ax+b}$.

Example 4 ☐ Divide.

a. $(3x^2 - 8x + 4) \div (2x)$
b. $(x^3 + 2x^2 - 5x + 9) \div (x - 2)$

c. $(2x^3 - 15x + 9) \div (x + 3)$

Solution ☐ a. $(3x^2 - 8x + 4) \div (2x)$

$= \dfrac{3x^2 - 8x + 4}{2x}$ Write in fraction form.

$= \dfrac{3x^2}{2x} - \dfrac{8x}{2x} + \dfrac{4}{2x}$ Divide each term in $3x^2 - 8x + 4$ by $2x$.

$= \dfrac{3x}{2} - 4 + \dfrac{2}{x}$ Simplify.

b.

$$
\begin{array}{r}
x^2 + 4x + 3 \\
x - 2 \overline{\smash{\big)}\ x^3 + 2x^2 - 5x + 9} \\
\underline{x^3 - 2x^2} \\
4x^2 - 5x \\
\underline{4x^2 - 8x} \\
3x + 9 \\
\underline{3x - 6} \\
15
\end{array}
$$

Divisor $\longrightarrow x - 2$

Quotient
Dividend
$x^2 \times (x - 2) = x^3 - 2x^2$
Result of subtraction
$4x \times (x - 2) = 4x^2 - 8x$
Result of subtraction
$3 \times (x - 2) = 3x - 6$
The remainder is 15.

$(x^3 + 2x^2 - 5x + 9) \div (x - 2) = x^2 + 4x + 3 + \dfrac{15}{x - 2}$.

c.

$$
\begin{array}{r}
2x^2 - 6x + 3 \\
x + 3 \overline{\smash{\big)}\ 2x^3 + 0x^2 - 15x + 9} \\
\underline{2x^3 + 6x^2} \\
-6x^2 - 15x \\
\underline{-6x^2 - 18x} \\
3x + 9 \\
\underline{3x + 9} \\
0
\end{array}
$$

Divisor $\longrightarrow x + 3$

Quotient
Write $0x^2$.
$2x^2 \times (x + 3) = 2x^3 + 6x^2$
Result of subtraction
$-6x \times (x + 3) = -6x^2 - 18x$
Result of subtraction
$3 \times (x + 3) = 3x + 9$
The remainder is 0.

$(2x^3 - 15x + 9) \div (x + 3) = 2x^2 - 6x + 3$

Exercises – Adding, Subtracting, Multiplying, and Dividing Polynomials

1

$$a(2-a)+(a^2+3)-(2a+1)$$

Which of the following is equivalent to the expression shown above?

A) 2

B) $4a$

C) $2a+2$

D) $2a-2$

2

$$(-m^2n-n^2+3mn^2)-(m^2n-n^2+mn^2)$$

Which of the following is equivalent to the expression shown above?

A) $4mn^2$

B) $4m^2n$

C) $-2m^2n+2mn^2$

D) $2m^2n+2mn^2$

3

$$(2x^2-3x+1)-(-2x^2-3x+2)$$

If the expression above is written in the form ax^2+bx+c, in which a, b, and c are constants, what is the value of $a+b+c$?

A) 2

B) 3

C) 4

D) 5

4

$$(x^3-x^2+3x-3)\div(x-1)$$

Which of the following is the quotient of the expression shown above?

A) x^2-3

B) x^2+3

C) x^2-2x

D) x^2-2x+3

5

$$(14x^2+9x-20)\div(ax-1)=7x+8+\frac{-12}{ax-1}$$

In the equation above, a is a constant and $ax-1\neq 0$. What is the value of a ?

6

If $\dfrac{6x^2-5x+4}{-3x+1}=-2x+1+\dfrac{A}{-3x+1}$, what is the value of A ?

10-3. FOIL Method and Special Products

FOIL Method

The product of two binomials is the sum of the products of the first terms, the outer terms, the inner terms, and the last terms.

$$\begin{array}{cccc} \text{Product of} & \text{Product of} & \text{Product of} & \text{Product of} \\ \text{First Terms} & \text{Outer Terms} & \text{Inner Terms} & \text{Last Terms} \\ \downarrow & \downarrow & \downarrow & \downarrow \end{array}$$

$$(2x+3)(x-5) = (2x)(x) \;+\; (2x)(-5) \;+\; (3)(x) \;+\; (3)(-5)$$

$$= 2x^2 - 10x + 3x - 15$$

$$= 2x^2 - 7x - 15$$

Example 1 □ Simplify.

    a. $(x+3)(2x-9)$ b. $(3n-2)(2n^2-n+5)$

Solution   □   a. $(x+3)(2x-9) = x(2x) + x(-9) + 3(2x) + 3(-9)$

$$= 2x^2 - 9x + 6x - 27 = 2x^2 - 3x - 27$$

       b. $(3n-2)(2n^2-n+5) = 3n(2n^2-n+5) - 2(2n^2-n+5)$

$$= (6n^3 - 3n^2 + 15n) + (-4n^2 + 2n - 10)$$

$$= 6n^3 - 7n^2 + 17n - 10$$

Certain binomial products occur so frequently that their patterns should be memorized.

Special Products

Square of a Sum: $(a+b)^2 = (a+b)(a+b) = a^2 + 2ab + b^2$

Square of a Difference: $(a-b)^2 = (a-b)(a-b) = a^2 - 2ab + b^2$

Product of a Sum and Difference: $(a+b)(a-b) = a^2 - b^2$

Example 2 □ Simplify.

    a. $(2a+3b)^2$ b. $(5n-4)(5n+4)$

    c. $(x-\dfrac{1}{2}y)^2$

Solution   □   a. $(2a+3b)^2 = (2a)^2 + 2(2a)(3b) + (3b)^2$ $(a+b)^2 = (a+b)(a+b) = a^2 + 2ab + b^2$

$$= 2a^2 + 12ab + 9b^2$$

       b. $(5n-4)(5n+4) = (5n)^2 - (4)^2$ $(a+b)(a-b) = a^2 - b^2$

$$= 25n^2 - 16$$

       c. $(x-\dfrac{1}{2}y)^2 = (x)^2 - 2(x)(\dfrac{1}{2}y) + (\dfrac{1}{2}y)^2$ $(a-b)^2 = (a-b)(a-b) = a^2 - 2ab + b^2$

$$= x^2 - xy + \frac{1}{4}y^2$$

Exercises – FOIL Method and Special Products

1

$$(x+3)(x-5)$$

Which of the following is equivalent to the expression shown above?

A) $(x+1)^2 - 14$

B) $(x-1)^2 - 12$

C) $(x-1)^2 - 16$

D) $(x-2)^2 - 12$

2

$$(2-5x)(5x+2)$$

Which of the following is equivalent to the expression shown above?

A) $25x^2 - 4$

B) $-25x^2 + 4$

C) $25x^2 - 10x + 4$

D) $-25x^2 + 10x + 4$

3

$$4x^2 - 12xy + 9y^2$$

Which of the following is equivalent to the expression shown above?

A) $(2x^2 - 3y)^2$

B) $(2x^2 - 3y^2)^2$

C) $(2x - 3y^2)^2$

D) $(2x - 3y)^2$

4

$$(x+y)(x-y)(x^2+y^2)$$

Which of the following is equivalent to the expression shown above?

A) $x^4 - 2x^2y^2 + y^4$

B) $x^4 + 2x^2y^2 + y^4$

C) $x^4 + y^4$

D) $x^4 - y^4$

5

What is the value of $\dfrac{3^{(a-b)} \cdot 3^{(a+b)}}{3^{2a+1}}$?

A) $\dfrac{1}{3}$

B) $\dfrac{1}{9}$

C) 3

D) 9

6

What is the value of $\dfrac{2^{(a-1)(a+1)}}{2^{(a-2)(a+2)}}$?

A) $\dfrac{1}{16}$

B) $\dfrac{1}{8}$

C) 8

D) 16

10-4. Prime Factorization, GCF, and LCM

A **prime number** is an integer greater than 1 that only has the factors 1 and itself.
The first ten prime numbers are 2, 3, 5, 7, 11, 13, 17, 19 23, and 29.

A **composite number** is a positive integer greater than 1 that has factors other than 1 and itself.
The numbers 0 and 1 are neither prime nor composite.

A whole number expressed as the product of prime factors is called the **prime factorization** of the number.

Example 1 □ Find the prime factorization of 420.

Solution   □ Method 1   Find the least prime factors. Continue until all factor are prime.

$$420 = 2 \cdot 210$$
$$= 2 \cdot 2 \cdot 105$$
$$= 2 \cdot 2 \cdot 3 \cdot 35$$
$$= 2 \cdot 2 \cdot 3 \cdot 5 \cdot 7$$

The least prime factor of 420 is 2.
The least prime factor of 210 is 2.
The least prime factor of 105 is 3.
The least prime factor of 35 is 5.

Method 2   Use a factor tree.

$$420 = 10 \cdot 42$$

$$10 = 2 \cdot 5, \quad 42 = 6 \cdot 7$$

$$6 = 2 \cdot 3$$

All of the factors in the last step are prime. Thus the prime factorization
of 420 is $2^2 \cdot 3 \cdot 5 \cdot 7$.

A monomial is in **factored form** when it is expressed as the product of prime numbers and variables,
and no variables has an exponent greater than 1.

Example 2 □ Factor completely.
a. $102a^2b^4$ b. $-28p^2q^3r$

Solution   □ a. $102a^2b^4 = 2 \cdot 51 \cdot a \cdot a \cdot b \cdot b \cdot b \cdot b$ $102 = 2 \cdot 51, \ a^2 = a \cdot a, \ b^4 = b \cdot b \cdot b \cdot b$
$$= 2 \cdot 3 \cdot 17 \cdot a \cdot a \cdot b \cdot b \cdot b \cdot b \qquad 51 = 3 \cdot 17$$

Thus, $102a^2b^4$ in factored form is $2 \cdot 3 \cdot 17 \cdot a \cdot a \cdot b \cdot b \cdot b \cdot b$.

b. $-28p^2q^3r = -1 \cdot 28p^2q^3r$ Express -28 as $-1 \cdot 28$.
$$= -1 \cdot 2 \cdot 14 \cdot p \cdot p \cdot q \cdot q \cdot q \cdot r \qquad 28 = 2 \cdot 14$$
$$= -1 \cdot 2 \cdot 2 \cdot 7 \cdot p \cdot p \cdot q \cdot q \cdot q \cdot r \qquad 14 = 2 \cdot 7$$

Thus, $-28p^2q^3r$ in factored form is $-1 \cdot 2 \cdot 2 \cdot 7 \cdot p \cdot p \cdot q \cdot q \cdot q \cdot r$.

The **greatest common factor** (**GCF**) of two or more integers is the greatest integer that is a factor of each integer. To find the GCF of two or more monomials, take the smallest power of each prime factor and multiply.

The **least common multiple** (**LCM**) of two or more integers is the least positive integer that is a common multiple of two or more integers.
To find the LCM of two or more monomials, take the largest power of each prime factor and multiply.

Example 3 □ Find the GCF and LCM of each set of polynomials.

a. 90, 108

b. $12a^2b^3c$, $36a^5b^2c^2$

c. $28p^3q^4r^5$, $35p^2q^7r^4$, $42p^3q^6r^9$

d. $(x-y)^2(x+y)$, $(x-y)(x+y)^3$

Solution □ a. $90 = 10 \cdot 9 = 2 \cdot 5 \cdot 3 \cdot 3 = 2 \cdot 3^2 \cdot 5$

$108 = 2 \cdot 54 = 2 \cdot 2 \cdot 27 = 2 \cdot 2 \cdot 3 \cdot 3 \cdot 3 = 2^2 \cdot 3^3$

The smallest power of 2 is 2.   The greatest power of 2 is 2^2.

The smallest power of 3 is 3^2.   The greatest power of 3 is 3^3.

5 is not a common factor.   The greatest power of 5 is 5.

The GCF is $2 \cdot 3^2$ or 18.   The LCM is $2^2 \cdot 3^3 \cdot 5$ or 540.

b. $12a^2b^3c = 2^2 \cdot 3a^2b^3c$

$36a^5b^2c^2 = 2^2 \cdot 3^2 a^5b^2c^2$

The smallest power of 2 is 2^2.   The greatest power of 2 is 2^2.

The smallest power of 3 is 3.   The greatest power of 3 is 3^2.

The smallest power of a is a^2.   The greatest power of a is a^5.

The smallest power of b is b^2.   The greatest power of b is b^3.

The smallest power of c is c.   The greatest power of c is c^2.

The GCF is $2^2 \cdot 3a^2b^2c$ or $12a^2b^2c$. The LCM is $2^2 \cdot 3^2 \cdot a^5b^3c^2$ or $36a^5b^3c^2$.

c. $28p^3q^4r^5 = 2^2 \cdot 7p^3q^4r^5$

$35p^2q^7r^4 = 5 \cdot 7p^2q^7r^4$

$42p^3q^6r^9 = 2 \cdot 3 \cdot 7p^3q^6r^9$

2 is not a common factor.   The greatest power of 2 is 2^2.

3 is not a common factor.   The greatest power of 3 is 3.

5 is not a common factor.   The greatest power of 5 is 5.

The smallest power of 7 is 7.   The greatest power of 7 is 7.

The smallest power of p is p^2.   The greatest power of p is p^3.

The smallest power of q is q^4.   The greatest power of q is q^7.

The smallest power of r is r^4.   The greatest power of r is r^9.

The GCF is $7p^2q^4r^4$.   The LCM is $2^2 \cdot 3 \cdot 5 \cdot 7p^3q^7r^9$ or $420p^3q^7r^9$.

d. $(x-y)^2(x+y)$

$(x-y)(x+y)^3$

The smallest power of $(x-y)$ is $(x-y)$ and the greatest power of $(x-y)$ is $(x-y)^2$.

The smallest power of $(x+y)$ is $(x+y)$ and the greatest power of $(x+y)$ is $(x+y)^3$.

The GCF is $(x-y)(x+y)$ and the LCM is $(x-y)^2(x+y)^3$.

Exercises – Prime Factorization, GCF, and LCM

1

$$42x^2y^2 + 63xy^3$$

Which of the following is equivalent to the expression shown above?

A) $21x^2y^2(2x+3y)$

B) $21xy^2(2x+3y)$

C) $21x^2y(2x+3y)$

D) $21xy(2x+3y)$

2

$$12x^2y - 18xy^2z$$

Which of the following is equivalent to the expression shown above?

A) $6xy(2x-3yz)$

B) $6x^2y(2x-3yz)$

C) $6xy^2(2x-3yz)$

D) $6x^2y^2(2x-3yz)$

3

$$5a^2b - 10abc + 5bc^2$$

Which of the following is equivalent to the expression shown above?

A) $5b(a-b)^2$

B) $5c(a-b)^2$

C) $5a(b-c)^2$

D) $5b(a-c)^2$

4

If x and y are positive integers and $12^3 = 2^x \cdot 3^y$, what is the value of $x+y$?

5

If $2 \times 5^9 - k \times 5^8 = 2 \times 5^8$, what is the value of k ?

6

If $12^{99} - 12^{97} = 12^{97} \times n$, what is the value of n ?

10-5. Factoring Using the Distributive Property

You used the Distributive Property to multiply a polynomial by a monomial. You can reverse this process to express a polynomial as the product of a monomial factor and a polynomial factor.

The first step in **factoring** a polynomial is to find the GCF of its terms. Then write each term as the product of the GCF and its remaining factors, and use the Distributive Property to factor out the GCF.

Factoring by Grouping.

To factor polynomials having four or more terms, group pairs of terms with common factors and use Distributive Property.

$$ax + bx + ay + by = x(a+b) + y(a+b)$$
$$= (a+b)(x+y)$$

Example 1 □ Factor each polynomial.

a. $12x^3 - 18x$ b. $6mn - 3n + 2mp - p$

Solution □ a. $12x^3 - 18x$

$= 6x(2x^2) - 6x(3)$ Rewrite each term using the GCF.

$= 6x(2x^2 - 3)$ Use the distributive property.

b. $6mn - 3n + 2mp - p$

$= (6mn - 3n) + (2mp - p)$ Group terms with common factors.

$= 3n(2m - 1) + p(2m - 1)$ Factor the GCF from each grouping.

$= (2m - 1)(3n + p)$ Use the distributive property.

Another helpful tool in factoring polynomials is recognizing factors that are opposites of each other.

Factors	Opposit Factors
$a - b$	$-(a - b) = -a + b = b - a$
$9 - x^2$	$-(9 - x^2) = -9 + x^2 = x^2 - 9$
$p + 2q - r$	$-(p + 2q - r) = -p - 2q + r$

Example 2 □ Factor each polynomial.

a. $3(x - y) - 2x(y - x)$ b. $(a - 2b - 3) - (6c + 4bc - 2ac)$

Solution □ a. $3(x - y) - 2x(y - x)$

$= 3(x - y) - 2x(-(x - y))$ $y - x = -(x - y)$

$= 3(x - y) + 2x(x - y)$ $-(-(x - y)) = x - y$

$= (x - y)(3 + 2x)$ Use the distributive property.

b. $(a - 2b - 3) - (6c + 4bc - 2ac)$

$= (a - 2b - 3) - 2c(3 + 2b - a)$ Factor the GCF.

$= (a - 2b - 3) + 2c(-(3 + 2b - a))$ $-2c(3 + 2b - a) = 2c(-(3 + 2b - a))$

$= (a - 2b - 3) + 2c(a - 2b - 3)$ $-(3 + 2b - a) = a - 2b - 3$

$= (a - 2b - 3)(1 + 2c)$ Use the distributive property.

Exercises – Factoring Using the Distributive Property

1

$$1 + 2x - x(1 + 2x)$$

Which of the following is equivalent to the expression shown above?

A) $(1 - 2x)^2$

B) $(1 + 2x)(1 - x)$

C) $-x(1 + 2x)$

D) $x(1 - 2x)$

2

What is the value of x, if $rx + sx = 3$ and $r + s = \dfrac{1}{3}$?

A) 1

B) 3

C) 9

D) 27

3

$$2ax - 6a - 3x + 9$$

Which of the following is equivalent to the expression shown above?

A) $(2a - 1)(x - 9)$

B) $(2a - 3)(2x - 3)$

C) $(a - 3)(2x - 3)$

D) $(2a - 3)(x - 3)$

4

$$mn - 5n - m + 5$$

Which of the following is equivalent to the expression shown above?

A) $(m - 5)(n - 1)$

B) $(m - 1)(n - 5)$

C) $(m + 5)(n + 1)$

D) $(m - 5)(5n - 1)$

5

$$7y^2 - 21xy - 2y + 6x$$

Which of the following is equivalent to the expression shown above?

A) $(7y - 3)(y - 2x)$

B) $(7y - 2)(2y - 3x)$

C) $(7y - 2)(y - 3x)$

D) $(7y + 2)(2y - 3x)$

6

$$x - 2y + 3z - 2wx + 4wy - 6wz$$

Which of the following is equivalent to the expression shown above?

A) $(1 + 2w)(x + 2y - 3z)$

B) $(1 - 2w)(x - 2y + 3z)$

C) $(1 + 2w)(x - 2y - 3z)$

D) $(1 - 2w)(x - y - 3z)$

Chapter 10 Practice Test

1

$$\frac{2^{(a+b)^2}}{2^{(a-b)^2}}$$

Which of the following is equivalent to the expression shown above?

A) $8^{(a+b)}$

B) 8^{ab}

C) 16^{a+b}

D) 16^{ab}

2

$$2m^2n - mnp - 6m + 3p$$

Which of the following is equivalent to the expression shown above?

A) $(2m-n)(mp-3)$

B) $(2m-p)(mn-3)$

C) $(2m+p)(mn+3)$

D) $(2m-n)(mn-3p)$

3

$$(\frac{a+b}{2})^2 - (\frac{a-b}{2})^2 =$$

A) ab

B) $-ab$

C) $\frac{2ab+b^2}{2}$

D) $ab+b^2$

4

If $(x+\frac{1}{x})^2 = 9$, then $(x-\frac{1}{x})^2 =$

A) 3

B) 5

C) 7

D) 9

5

If $8^{\frac{4}{3}} \cdot 8^{-\frac{8}{3}} = \frac{1}{2^m}$, what is the value of m?

A) $-\frac{4}{3}$

B) -4

C) $\frac{4}{3}$

D) 4

6

If $xy \neq 0$, then $\frac{(-2xy^2)^3}{4x^4y^5} =$

A) $-\frac{xy}{2}$

B) $-\frac{2}{x}$

C) $-\frac{2y}{x^2}$

D) $-\frac{2y}{x}$

7

If $x^{12}=32n^4$ and $x^9=4n$, then $x=$

A) $2n$

B) $2n^{\frac{1}{2}}$

C) $4n^{\frac{1}{2}}$

D) $4n$

8

$$(3x^3-2x^2-7)-(-2x^2+6x+2)$$

Which of the following is equivalent to the expression shown above?

A) $3(x^3+2x-6)$

B) $3(x^3-2x-9)$

C) $3(x^3+2x-3)$

D) $3(x^3-2x-3)$

9

$$9x-(x-3)(x+12)$$

Which of the following is equivalent to the expression shown above?

A) $36-18x-x^2$

B) $36+12x-x^2$

C) $(6-x)(6+x)$

D) $(6-x)^2$

10

If $\dfrac{(2.1\times10^{-3})(2\times10^5)}{7\times10^{-4}}=6\times10^n$, what is the value of n?

11

If $a^{\frac{3}{4}}=8$, what is the value of $a^{-\frac{1}{2}}$?

12

$$\frac{x^2-x-a}{x-2}=x+1-\frac{8}{x-2}$$

In the equation above, what is the value of a?

Answer Key

Section 10-1

1. 9   2. $\dfrac{3}{16}$ 3. 9   4. 155   5. D

6. 3   7. $\dfrac{2}{3}$ 8. 9   9. 4

Section 10-2

1. A   2. C   3. B   4. B   5. 2
6. 3

Section 10-3

1. C   2. B   3. D   4. D   5. A
6. C

Section 10-4

1. B   2. A   3. D   4. 9   5. 8
6. 143

Section 10-5

1. B   2. C   3. D   4. A   5. C
6. B

Chapter 10 Practice Test

1. B   2. B   3. A   4. B   5. D
6. D   7. A   8. D   9. C   10. 5

11. $\dfrac{1}{4}$ 12. 10

Answers and Explanations

Section 10-1

1. 9

$$(-a^2b^3)(2ab^2)(-3b)$$
$$= (-1)(2)(-3)a^2ab^3b^2b$$
$$= 6a^3b^6 = ka^m b^n$$

If the equation is true, $m = 3$ and $n = 6$, thus $m + n = 3 + 6 = 9$.

2. $\dfrac{3}{16}$

$$(\tfrac{2}{3}a^2b)^2(\tfrac{4}{3}ab)^{-3}$$

$$= \frac{(\tfrac{2}{3}a^2b)^2}{(\tfrac{4}{3}ab)^3} \qquad a^{-n} = \frac{1}{a^n}$$

$$= \frac{\tfrac{4}{9}a^4b^2}{\tfrac{64}{27}a^3b^3}$$

$$= \frac{4}{9} \cdot \frac{27}{64}\frac{a}{b} = \frac{3}{16}\frac{a}{b}$$

If $(\tfrac{2}{3}a^2b)^2(\tfrac{4}{3}ab)^{-3} = ka^m b^n$, then $k = \dfrac{3}{16}$.

3. 9

$$\frac{(x)^3(-y)^2 z^{-2}}{(x)^{-2}y^3 z} = \frac{x^3 y^2 (x)^2}{y^3 z z^2} \qquad a^{-n} = \frac{1}{a^n} \text{ and } \frac{1}{a^{-n}} = a^n$$

$$= \frac{x^5 y^2}{y^3 z^3} = \frac{x^5}{y z^3} = \frac{x^m}{y^n z^p}$$

If the equation is true, $m = 5$, $n = 1$, and $p = 3$, thus $m + n + p = 5 + 1 + 3 = 9$.

4. 155

$$2^x + 2^{2x} + 2^{3x}$$
$$= 2^x + (2^x)^2 + (2^x)^3 \qquad (a^m)^n = a^{m \cdot n}$$
$$= (5) + (5)^2 + (5)^3 \qquad 2^x = 5$$
$$= 155$$

5. D

$$(3^x + 3^x + 3^x) \cdot 3^x$$
$$= (3 \cdot 3^x) \cdot 3^x$$
$$= (3^{1+x}) \cdot 3^x \qquad a^m a^n = a^{m+n}$$
$$= 3^{1+2x} \qquad a^m a^n = a^{m+n}$$

6. 3

$$\frac{(6xy^2)(2xy)^2}{8x^2 y^2}$$

$$= \frac{(6xy^2)(4x^2 y^2)}{8x^2 y^2}$$

$$= \frac{24x^3 y^4}{8x^2 y^2} = 3xy^2$$

If the expression above is written in the form $ax^m y^n$, $a = 3$, $m = 1$, and $n = 2$.
Therefore, $m + n = 1 + 2 = 3$.

7. $\dfrac{2}{3}$

$$\frac{(2x)^3(3x)}{(6x^2)^2} = \frac{(8x^3)(3x)}{36x^4} = \frac{24x^4}{36x^4} = \frac{2}{3}$$

8. 9

$$8,200 \times 300,000 = 8.2 \times 10^3 \times 3 \times 10^5$$
$$= 24.6 \times 10^8 = 2.46 \times 10 \times 10^8 = 2.46 \times 10^9$$

9. 4

$$\frac{240}{80,000} \times \frac{6,000}{900,000}$$
$$= \frac{24 \times 6}{8,000 \times 900}$$
$$= \frac{144}{72 \times 10^5} = \frac{2}{10^5}$$
$$= \frac{2}{10 \times 10^4} = \frac{1}{5 \times 10^4}$$

If the above expression is equal to $\dfrac{1}{5 \times 10^n}$,

then the value of n is 4.

Section 10-2

1. A

$$a(2-a) + (a^2+3) - (2a+1)$$
$$= 2a - a^2 + a^2 + 3 - 2a - 1$$
$$= 2$$

2. C

$$(-m^2n - n^2 + 3mn^2) - (m^2n - n^2 + mn^2)$$
$$= -m^2n - n^2 + 3mn^2 - m^2n + n^2 - mn^2$$
$$= -2m^2n + 2mn^2$$

3. B

$$(2x^2 - 3x + 1) - (-2x^2 - 3x + 2)$$
$$= 2x^2 - 3x + 1 + 2x^2 + 3x - 2$$
$$= 4x^2 - 1$$

If the expression above is written in the form
$ax^2 + bx + c$, $a = 4$, $b = 0$, and $c = -1$.
Therefore, $a + b + c = 4 + 0 + (-1) = 3$.

4. B

$$
\begin{array}{r}
x^2 + 3 \\
x-1 \overline{\smash{)}\ x^3 - x^2 + 3x - 3} \\
\underline{x^3 - x^2 } \\
0 \\
3x - 3 \\
\underline{3x - 3} \\
0
\end{array}
$$

Quotient — $x^2 + 3$

Dividend — $x^3 - x^2 + 3x - 3$

$x^2 \times (x-1) = x^3 - x^2$

Result of subtraction

$3 \times (x-1) = 3x - 3$

Result of subtraction

Therefore, $(x^3 - x^2 + 3x - 3) \div (x-1) = x^2 + 3$.

5. 2

$$(14x^2 + 9x - 20) \div (ax - 1) = 7x + 8 + \frac{-12}{ax - 1}$$

Multiply each side of the equation by $ax - 1$.
$$(ax-1)[14x^2 + 9x - 20) \div (ax-1)]$$
$$= (ax-1)[7x + 8 + \frac{-12}{ax-1}]$$
$$\Rightarrow 14x^2 + 9x - 20 = (ax-1)(7x+8) + (-12)$$
$$\Rightarrow 14x^2 + 9x - 20 = 7ax^2 + (8a-7)x - 20$$

The coefficients of x- terms
have to be equal, so $9 = 8a - 7$.

$$14x^2 + 9x - 20 = 7ax^2 + (8a-7)x - 20$$

The coefficients of x^2- terms
have to be equal, so $14 = -7a$.

Since the coefficients of x^2- terms have to be equal
on both sides of the equation, $14 = 7a$, or $a = 2$.

6. 3

$$\frac{6x^2 - 5x + 4}{-3x + 1} = -2x + 1 + \frac{A}{-3x + 1}$$

Multiply each side of the equation by $-3x + 1$.

$$(-3x+1)[\frac{6x^2 - 5x + 4}{-3x + 1}]$$
$$= (-3x+1)[-2x + 1 + \frac{A}{-3x + 1}]$$
$$\Rightarrow 6x^2 - 5x + 4 = 6x^2 - 5x + 1 + A$$

Since the constant terms have to be equal on both
sides of the equation, $4 = 1 + A$, or $A = 3$

Section 10-3

1. C

$$(x+3)(x-5) = x^2 - 5x + 3x - 15$$
$$= x^2 - 2x - 15$$

Choice A gives x-term $+2$ and constant term -13.
Choice B gives x-term -2 and constant term -11.
Choice C gives x-term -2 and constant term -15.
Choice C is correct.

2. B

$$(2-5x)(5x+2)$$
$$= (2)(5x) + (2)(2) - (5x)(5x) - (5x)(2)$$
$$= 10x + 4 - 25x^2 - 10x$$
$$= 4 - 25x^2$$

3. D

$$4x^2 - 12xy + 9y^2$$
$$= (2x)^2 - 2(2x)(3y) + (3y)^2$$
$$= (2x - 3y)^2$$

4. D

$$(x+y)(x-y)(x^2+y^2)$$
$$= (x^2 - y^2)(x^2 + y^2) \qquad (x+y)(x-y) = x^2 - y^2$$
$$= x^2 x^2 + x^2 y^2 - y^2 x^2 - y^2 y^2$$
$$= x^4 - y^4$$

5. A

$$\frac{3^{(a-b)} \cdot 3^{(a+b)}}{3^{2a+1}}$$
$$= 3^{(a-b)+(a+b)-(2a+1)} \qquad a^m a^n = a^{m+n} \text{ and } \frac{a^m}{a^n} = a^{m-n}$$
$$= 3^{-1} = \frac{1}{3}$$

6. C

$$\frac{2^{(a-1)(a+1)}}{2^{(a-2)(a+2)}}$$
$$= \frac{2^{(a^2-1)}}{2^{(a^2-4)}} \qquad \text{FOIL}$$
$$= 2^{(a^2-1)-(a^2-4)} \qquad \frac{a^m}{a^n} = a^{m-n}$$
$$= 2^3 = 8$$

Section 10-4

1. B

$$42x^2 y^2 + 63xy^3$$
$$= 21xy^2(2x + 3y) \qquad \text{GCF is } 21xy^2.$$

2. A

$$12x^2 y - 18xy^2 z$$
$$= 6xy(2x - 3yz) \qquad \text{GCF is } 6xy.$$

3. D

$$5a^2 b - 10abc + 5bc^2$$
$$= 5b(a^2 - 2ac + c^2) \qquad \text{GCF is } 5b.$$
$$= 5b(a - c)^2 \qquad (a-c)^2 = a^2 - 2ac + c^2$$

4. 9

$$12^3 = 2^x \cdot 3^y$$
$$(2^2 \cdot 3)^3 = 2^x \cdot 3^y \qquad 12 = 2^2 \cdot 3$$
$$2^6 \cdot 3^3 = 2^x \cdot 3^y \qquad (2^2)^3 = 2^6$$

So, we can conclude that $x = 6$ and $y = 3$.
Therefore, $x + y = 6 + 3 = 9$.

5. 8

$$2 \times 5^9 - k \times 5^8 = 2 \times 5^8$$
$$2 \times 5 \cdot 5^8 - k \times 5^8 = 2 \times 5^8 \qquad 5^9 = 5 \cdot 5^8$$
$$10 \cdot 5^8 - k \times 5^8 = 2 \times 5^8 \qquad \text{Simplify.}$$
$$(10 - k)5^8 = 2 \times 5^8 \qquad \text{Factor.}$$

Therefore, $10 - k = 2$, or $k = 8$.

6. 143

$$12^{99} - 12^{97} = 12^{97} \times n$$
$$12^2 \times 12^{97} - 12^{97} = 12^{97} \times n \qquad 12^{99} = 12^2 \times 12^{97}$$
$$12^{97}(12^2 - 1) = 12^{97} \times n \qquad \text{Factor.}$$

Therefore, $12^2 - 1 = n$, or $n = 143$.

Section 10-5

1. B

$$1 + 2x - x(1 + 2x)$$
$$= 1(1 + 2x) - x(1 + 2x)$$
$$= (1 + 2x)(1 - x) \qquad \text{GCF is } 1 + 2x.$$

2. C

$$rx + sx = 3$$
$$x(r + s) = 3 \qquad \text{Factor.}$$
$$x(\frac{1}{3}) = 3 \qquad \text{Substitute } \frac{1}{3} \text{ for } r + s.$$
$$x = 9$$

3. D

$$2ax - 6a - 3x + 9$$
$$= (2ax - 6a) - (3x - 9) \qquad \text{Group terms with common}$$
$$\qquad\qquad\qquad\qquad \text{factors. } -3x + 9 = -(3x - 9)$$
$$= 2a(x - 3) - 3(x - 3) \qquad \text{Factor the GCF.}$$
$$= (x - 3)(2a - 3) \qquad \text{Distributive Property}$$

4. A

$$mn - 5n - m + 5$$
$$= (mn - 5n) - (m - 5) \qquad \text{Group terms with common}$$
$$\qquad\qquad\qquad\qquad \text{factors. } -m + 5 = -(m - 5)$$
$$= n(m - 5) - (m - 5) \qquad \text{Factor the GCF.}$$
$$= (m - 5)(n - 1) \qquad \text{Distributive Property}$$

5. C

$$7y^2 - 21xy - 2y + 6x$$
$$= (7y^2 - 21xy) - (2y - 6x)$$
$$= 7y(y - 3x) - 2(y - 3x)$$
$$= (7y - 2)(y - 3x)$$

6. B

$$x - 2y + 3z - 2wx + 4wy - 6wz$$
$$= (x - 2y + 3z) - (2wx - 4wy + 6wz)$$
$$= (x - 2y + 3z) - 2w(x - 2y + 3z)$$
$$= (1 - 2w)(x - 2y + 3z)$$

Chapter 10 Practice Test

1. B

$$\frac{2^{(a+b)^2}}{2^{(a-b)^2}}$$
$$= 2^{(a+b)^2 - (a-b)^2} \qquad \frac{a^m}{a^n} = a^{m-n}$$
$$= 2^{(a^2 + 2ab + b^2) - (a^2 - 2ab + b^2)}$$
$$= 2^{4ab}$$
$$= (2^4)^{ab} \qquad (a^m)^n = a^{m \cdot n}$$
$$= (16)^{ab}$$

2. B

$$2m^2n - mnp - 6m + 3p$$
$$= (2m^2n - mnp) - (6m - 3p)$$
$$= mn(2m - p) - 3(2m - p)$$
$$= (2m - p)(mn - 3)$$

3. A

$$(\frac{a+b}{2})^2 - (\frac{a-b}{2})^2 = \frac{(a+b)^2}{4} - \frac{(a-b)^2}{4}$$
$$= \frac{a^2 + 2ab + b^2}{4} - \frac{a^2 - 2ab + b^2}{4}$$
$$= \frac{4ab}{4} = ab$$

4. B

$$(x + \frac{1}{x})^2 = 9$$
$$x^2 + 2x \cdot \frac{1}{x} + (\frac{1}{x})^2 = 9$$
$$x^2 + 2 + \frac{1}{x^2} = 9$$
$$x^2 + \frac{1}{x^2} = 7$$
$$(x - \frac{1}{x})^2 = x^2 - 2x \cdot \frac{1}{x} + \frac{1}{x^2}$$
$$= x^2 - 2 + \frac{1}{x^2} = x^2 + \frac{1}{x^2} - 2$$
$$= 7 - 2 = 5 \qquad \text{Substitute 7 for } x^2 + \frac{1}{x^2} = 7.$$

5. D

$$8^{\frac{4}{3}} \cdot 8^{-\frac{8}{3}} = 8^{\frac{4}{3} - \frac{8}{3}} = 8^{-\frac{4}{3}} = (2^3)^{-\frac{4}{3}}$$
$$= 2^{-4} = \frac{1}{2^4}$$

If $8^{\frac{4}{3}} \cdot 8^{-\frac{8}{3}} = \frac{1}{2^m}$, then $m = 4$.

6. D

$$\frac{(-2xy^2)^3}{4x^4y^5} = \frac{-8x^3y^6}{4x^4y^5}$$
$$= -\frac{2y}{x}$$

7. **A**

Given $x^{12} = 32n^4$ and $x^9 = 4n$.

$x^{12} = 32n^4$

$\dfrac{x^{12}}{x^9} = \dfrac{32n^4}{x^9}$ Divide each side by x^9.

$x^3 = \dfrac{32n^4}{x^9}$ Simplify.

$x^3 = \dfrac{32n^4}{4n}$ Substitute $4n$ for x^9.

$x^3 = 8n^3$ Simplify.

$(x)^3 = (2n)^3$ $8n^3 = (2n)^3$

Therefore, $x = 2n$.

8. **D**

$(3x^3 - 2x^2 - 7) - (-2x^2 + 6x + 2)$

$= 3x^3 - 2x^2 - 7 + 2x^2 - 6x - 2$

$= 3x^3 - 6x - 9$

$= 3(x^3 - 2x - 3)$

9. **C**

$9x - (x - 3)(x + 12)$

$= 9x - (x^2 + 9x - 36)$

$= 9x - x^2 - 9x + 36$

$= 36 - x^2$

$= (6 - x)(6 + x)$

10. **5**

$\dfrac{(2.1 \times 10^{-3})(2 \times 10^5)}{7 \times 10^{-4}}$

$= \dfrac{4.2 \times 10^2}{7 \times 10^{-4}}$

$= \dfrac{4.2 \times 10^2 \times 10^4}{7}$ $\dfrac{1}{a^{-n}} = a^n$

$= 0.6 \times 10^2 \times 10^4$

$= 0.6 \times 10^6$

$= 6 \times 10^5$

If $\dfrac{(2.1 \times 10^{-3})(2 \times 10^5)}{7 \times 10^{-4}} = 6 \times 10^n$, then $n = 5$.

11. $\dfrac{1}{4}$

$a^{\frac{3}{4}} = 8$

$(a^{\frac{3}{4}})^{\frac{4}{3}} = (8)^{\frac{4}{3}}$

$a = (2^3)^{\frac{4}{3}}$

$a = 2^4$

Therefore, $a^{-\frac{1}{2}} = (2^4)^{-\frac{1}{2}} = 2^{-2} = \dfrac{1}{2^2} = \dfrac{1}{4}$.

12. **10**

$\dfrac{x^2 - x - a}{x - 2} = x + 1 - \dfrac{8}{x - 2}$

Multiply each side of the equation by $x - 2$.

$(x - 2)[\dfrac{x^2 - x - a}{x - 2}] = (x - 2)[x + 1 - \dfrac{8}{x - 2}]$

$\Rightarrow x^2 - x - a = (x - 2)(x + 1) - 8$

$\Rightarrow x^2 - x - a = x^2 - x - 2 - 8$

$\Rightarrow x^2 - x - a = x^2 - x - 10$

Since the constant terms have to be equal on both sides of the equation, $a = 10$.

CHAPTER 11
Quadratic Functions

11-1. Graphs of Quadratic Equations

The **standard form** of a **quadratic function** $y = f(x)$ can be written in the form $f(x) = ax^2 + bx + c$, in which $a \neq 0$. The graph of a quadratic function is called a **parabola**.

If $a > 0$, the graph opens upward and the vertex is the **minimum** point.
If $a < 0$, the graph opens downward and the vertex is the **maximum** point.
The maximum or minimum point of a parabola is called the **vertex**.

The equation of the **axis of symmetry** is $x = -\dfrac{b}{2a}$. The coordinates of the vertex are $(-\dfrac{b}{2a}, f(-\dfrac{b}{2a}))$.

The **vertex form** of a quadratic function can be written in the form $f(x) = a(x-h)^2 + k$, in which (h, k) is the coordinates of vertex of the parabola.

The **solutions** of a quadratic function are the values of x for which $f(x) = 0$. Solutions of functions are also called **roots** or **zeros** of the function. On a graph, the solution of the function is the **x-intercept(s)**.

To find the **y-intercept** of a parabola, let x equal to zero in the equation of the parabola and solve for y.

If the parabola has two x-intercepts, then the *x-intercepts are equidistant from the axis of symmetry*.

The **factored form** of a quadratic function can be written in the form $f(x) = a(x-b)(x-c)$.

The x-intercepts or the solutions of the function are $x = b$ and $x = c$.
A parabola may have no x-intercept, one x-intercept, or two x-intercepts.

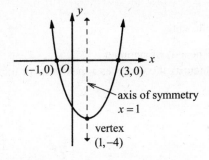

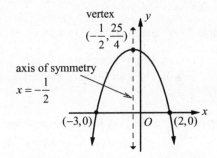

The graph of the quadratic function $y = x^2 - 2x - 3$ opens upward since $a = 1 > 0$, so the vertex is a minimum point. The equation of the axis of symmetry is $x = -\dfrac{-2}{2(1)}$ or $x = 1$.
The vertex form of the function is $y = (x-1)^2 - 4$, from which the coordinates of the vertex can be identified as $(1, -4)$. The factored form of the function is $y = (x+1)(x-3)$. The x-intercepts are -1 and 3, which are equidistant from the axis of symmetry.

The graph of the quadratic function $y = -x^2 - x + 6$ opens downward since $a = -1 < 0$, so the vertex is a maximum point. The equation of the axis of symmetry is $x = -\dfrac{-1}{2(-1)}$ or $x = -\dfrac{1}{2}$.
The vertex form of the function is $y = -(x+\dfrac{1}{2})^2 + \dfrac{25}{4}$, from which the coordinates of the vertex can be identified as $(-\dfrac{1}{2}, \dfrac{25}{4})$. The factored form of the function is $y = -(x+3)(x-2)$. The x-intercepts are -3 and 2, which are equidistant from the axis of symmetry.

Example 1 □ Given $f(x) = x^2 + 2x - 2$, find the following.

      a. The y-intercept.   b. The axis of symmetry.

      c. The coordinate of the vertex.   d. Identify the vertex as a maximum or minimum.

Solution □ a. To find the y-intercept, let $x = 0$.

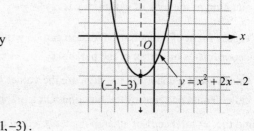

$$f(0) = 0^2 + 2(0) - 2 = -2$$
The y-intercept is -2.

b. The coefficients are $a = 1$, $b = 2$,
and $c = -2$.
The equation of the axis of symmetry

is $x = -\dfrac{b}{2a} = -\dfrac{2}{2(1)}$ or $x = -1$.

c. $f(-1) = (-1)^2 + 2(-1) - 2 = -3$.
The coordinates of the vertex are $(-1, -3)$.

d. Since the coefficient of the x^2 term
is positive, the parabola opens upward
and the vertex is a minimum point.

The graph of the parabola $f(x) = x^2 + 2x - 2$ is shown above.

Example 2 □ Given $f(x) = -(x+2)(x-4)$, find the following.

      a. The x-intercepts.   b. The axis of symmetry.

      c. The coordinate of the vertex.   d. Identify the vertex as a maximum or minimum.

Solution □ a. To find the x-intercept, let $f(x) = 0$.

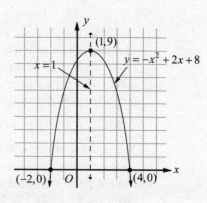

From $f(x) = -(x+2)(x-4) = 0$, we
get x-intercepts, $x = -2$ and $x = 4$.

b. Since the x-intercepts are equidistant
from the axis of symmetry, the axis of
symmetry is the average of the two
x-intercepts.

$$x = \frac{-2+4}{2} \text{ or } x = 1$$

c. $f(1) = -(1+2)(1-4) = 9$.
The coordinates of the vertex are $(1, 9)$.

d. Since the coefficient of the x^2 term
is negative, the parabola opens downward
and the vertex is a maximum point.

The graph of the parabola $f(x) = -(x+2)(x-4)$ is shown above.

Exercises - Graphs of Quadratic Equations

Questions 1 and 2 refer to the following information.

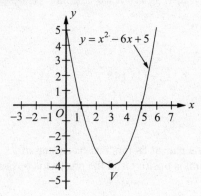

The graph of quadratic function $y = x^2 - 6x + 5$ is shown above.

1

Which of the following is an equivalent form of the equation of the graph shown above, from which the coordinates of vertex V can be identified as constants in the equation?

A) $y = (x-1)(x-5)$

B) $y = (x+1)(x+5)$

C) $y = x(x-6)+5$

D) $y = (x-3)^2 - 4$

2

Which of the following is an equivalent form of the equation of the graph shown above, that displays the x-intercepts of the parabola as constants?

A) $y = (x-1)(x-5)$

B) $y = (x+1)(x+5)$

C) $y = x(x-6)+5$

D) $y = (x-3)^2 - 4$

3

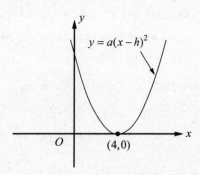

In the xy-plane above, the parabola $y = a(x-h)^2$ has one x-intercept at $(4,0)$. If the y-intercept of the parabola is 9, what is the value of a?

4

In the xy-plane, if the parabola with equation $y = a(x+2)^2 - 15$ passes through $(1,3)$, what is the value of a?

5

The graph of the equation $y = a(x-1)(x+5)$ is a parabola with vertex (h,k). If the minimum value of y is -12, what is the value of a?

11-2. Factoring Trinomials

Factoring Trinomials: $x^2 + bx + c$

To factor trinomials of the form $x^2 + bx + c$, you need to find two integers with sum b and product c.

When two binomials $(x + m)$ and $(x + n)$ are multiplied using FOIL method, $(x + m)(x + n) = x^2 + nx + mx + mn$,

or $x^2 + (m + n)x + mn$. So, you can write $x^2 + bx + c$ as $(x + m)(x + n)$, then as $m + n = b$ and $mn = c$.

Example 1 □ Factor each trinomial.

      a. $x^2 + 9x + 20$ b. $x^2 - 11x + 18$

      c. $x^2 + 5x - 14$

Solution   □   a. Make a list of factors of 20, and look for the pair of factors that has a sum of 9.
           Both integers must be positive since the sum is positive and the product is positive.

Factors of 20	Sum of Factors
1 and 20	$1 + 20 = 21$
2 and 10	$2 + 10 = 12$
4 and 5	$4 + 5 = 9$

The correct factors are 4 and 5.

$$x^2 + 9x + 20 = (x + m)(x + n)$$
$$= (x + 4)(x + 5)$$

Write trinomial as the product of two binomials.

$mn = 20$ and $m + n = 9$

      b. Make a list of factors of 18, and look for the pair of factors that has a sum of -11.
         Both integers must be negative since the sum is negative and the product is positive.

Factors of 18	Sum of Factors
-1 and -18	$-1 + (-18) = -19$
-2 and -9	$-2 + (-9) = -11$
-3 and -6	$-3 + (-6) = -9$

The correct factors are -2 and -9.

$$x^2 - 11x + 18 = (x + m)(x + n)$$
$$= (x - 2)(x - 9)$$

Write trinomial as the product of two binomials.

$mn = 18$ and $m + n = -11$

      c. Make a list of factors of -14, and look for the pair of factors that has a sum of 5.
         One integer is negative and the other is positive since the product is negative.

Factors of -14	Sum of Factors
-1 and 14	$-1 + 14 = 13$
1 and -14	$1 + (-14) = -13$
-2 and 7	$-2 + 7 = 5$
2 and -7	$2 + (-7) = -5$

The correct factors are -2 and 7.

$$x^2 + 5x - 14 = (x + m)(x + n)$$
$$= (x - 2)(x + 7)$$

Write trinomial as the product of two binomials.

$mn = -14$ and $m + n = 5$

Factoring Trinomials: $ax^2 + bx + c$

To factor trinomials of the form $ax^2 + bx + c$, in which $a \neq \pm 1$, you need to find two integers m and n with sum b and product ac. Then write bx as $mx + nx$ and use the method of factoring by grouping.

Example 2 □ Factor each trinomial.

a. $2x^2 - 7x + 6$

b. $5x^2 - 14x - 3$

c. $6x^2 - 5x - 4$

d. $-16x^2 - 40x + 24$

Solution □ a. Find two numbers with a sum of -7 and a product of $2 \cdot 6$, or 12.
The two numbers are -3 and -4.

$$
\begin{aligned}
2x^2 - 7x + 6 &= 2x^2 - 3x - 4x + 6 && \text{Write } -7x \text{ as } -3x - 4x. \\
&= (2x^2 - 3x) - (4x - 6) && \text{Group terms with common factors.} \\
&= x(2x - 3) - 2(2x - 3) && \text{Factor the GCF from each grouping.} \\
&= (2x - 3)(x - 2) && \text{Distributive Property}
\end{aligned}
$$

b. Find two numbers with a sum of -14 and a product of $5 \cdot -3$, or -15.
The two numbers are 1 and -15.

$$
\begin{aligned}
5x^2 - 14x - 3 &= 5x^2 + x - 15x - 3 && \text{Write } -14x \text{ as } +x - 15x. \\
&= (5x^2 + x) - (15x + 3) && \text{Group terms with common factors.} \\
&= x(5x + 1) - 3(5x + 1) && \text{Factor the GCF from each grouping.} \\
&= (5x + 1)(x - 3) && \text{Distributive Property}
\end{aligned}
$$

c. Find two numbers with a sum of -5 and a product of $6 \cdot -4$, or -24.
The two numbers are 3 and -8.

$$
\begin{aligned}
6x^2 - 5x - 4 &= 6x^2 + 3x - 8x - 4 && \text{Write } -5x \text{ as } +3x - 8x. \\
&= (6x^2 + 3x) - (8x + 4) && \text{Group terms with common factors.} \\
&= 3x(2x + 1) - 4(2x + 1) && \text{Factor the GCF from each grouping.} \\
&= (2x + 1)(3x - 4) && \text{Distributive Property}
\end{aligned}
$$

d. The GCF of the terms $-16x^2$, $-40x$, and 24 is -8. Factor it out first.

$$-16x^2 - 40x + 24 = -8(2x^2 + 5x - 3) \qquad \text{Factor out } -8.$$

Now factor $2x^2 + 5x - 3$. Find two numbers with a sum of 5 and a product of $2 \cdot -3$, or -6. The two numbers are 6 and -1.

$$
\begin{aligned}
2x^2 + 5x - 3 &= 2x^2 + 6x - 1x - 3 && \text{Write } 5x \text{ as } 6x - x. \\
&= (2x^2 + 6x) - 1 \cdot (x + 3) && \text{Group terms with common factors.} \\
&= 2x(x + 3) - 1 \cdot (x + 3) && \text{Factor the GCF from each grouping.} \\
&= (x + 3)(2x - 1) && \text{Distributive Property}
\end{aligned}
$$

Thus, the complete factorization of $-16x^2 - 40x + 24$ is $-8(x + 3)(2x - 1)$.

Exercises – Factoring Trinomials

1

$$x^2 - 2x - 24$$

Which of the following is equivalent to the expression above?

A) $(x+3)(x-8)$

B) $(x-3)(x+8)$

C) $(x-6)(x+4)$

D) $(x+6)(x-4)$

2

$$x^2 - 17x + 72$$

Which of the following is equivalent to the expression above?

A) $(x+8)(x-9)$

B) $(x-8)(x-9)$

C) $(x-12)(x-6)$

D) $(x-12)(x+6)$

3

$$-x^2 + 5x + 84$$

Which of the following is equivalent to the expression above?

A) $(12-x)(x+7)$

B) $(12+x)(x-7)$

C) $(21+x)(x-4)$

D) $(21-x)(x+4)$

4

$$3x^2 + 7x - 6$$

Which of the following is equivalent to the expression above?

A) $(3x-2)(x+3)$

B) $(3x+2)(x-3)$

C) $(3x-1)(x+6)$

D) $(3x+1)(x-6)$

5

$$2x^2 + x - 15$$

Which of the following is equivalent to the expression above?

A) $(2x+3)(x-5)$

B) $(2x-3)(x+5)$

C) $(2x-5)(x+3)$

D) $(2x+5)(x-3)$

6

$$-6x^2 + x + 2$$

Which of the following is equivalent to the expression above?

A) $-(6x+1)(x-2)$

B) $-(6x-1)(x+2)$

C) $-(3x+2)(2x-1)$

D) $-(3x-2)(2x+1)$

11-3. Factoring Differences of Squares and Perfect Square Trinomials

The polynomial forms $a^2 + 2ab + b^2$ and $a^2 - 2ab + b^2$ are called **perfect square trinomials**, and they are the result of squaring $(a+b)$ and $(a-b)$. Also, the polynomial $a^2 - b^2$ is called a **difference of squares**, and is the product of $(a+b)$ and $(a-b)$.

Perfect Square Trinomials

$a^2 + 2ab + b^2 = (a+b)^2$

$a^2 - 2ab + b^2 = (a-b)^2$

Difference of Squares

$a^2 - b^2 = (a+b)(a-b)$

Example 1 ☐ Factor each polynomial.

    a. $27x^2 - 3$ b. $4x^2 + 12x + 9$ c. $x^2 - \dfrac{1}{2}x + \dfrac{1}{16}$

Solution ☐ a. $27x^2 - 3 = 3(9x^2 - 1)$ Factor out the GCF.

                    $= 3((3x)^2 - (1)^2)$ Write in the form $a^2 - b^2$.

                    $= 3(3x+1)(3x-1)$ Factor the difference of squares.

          b. Since $4x^2 = (2x)^2$, $9 = 3^2$, and $12x = 2(2x)(3)$, $4x^2 + 12x + 9$ is a perfect square trinomial.

            $4x^2 + 12x + 9 = (2x)^2 + 2(2x)(3) + 3^2$ Write as $a^2 + 2ab + b^2$.

                        $= (2x+3)^2$ Factored as $(a+b)^2$.

          c. Since $x^2 = (x)^2$, $\dfrac{1}{16} = (\dfrac{1}{4})^2$, and $\dfrac{1}{2}x = 2(x)(\dfrac{1}{4})$, $x^2 - \dfrac{1}{2}x + \dfrac{1}{16}$ is a perfect square trinomial.

            $x^2 - \dfrac{1}{2}x + \dfrac{1}{16} = (x)^2 - 2(x)(\dfrac{1}{4}) + (\dfrac{1}{4})^2$ Write as $a^2 - 2ab + b^2$.

                        $= (x - \dfrac{1}{4})^2$ Factored as $(a-b)^2$.

Zero Product Property

If the product $a \cdot b = 0$, then either $a = 0$, $b = 0$, or both a and b equal zero. Factoring and zero product property allow you to solve a quadratic equation by converting it into two linear equations.

Example 2 ☐ Solve each equation.

           a. $(2x-5)(3x-10) = 0$ b. $x^2 - 3x + 28 = 0$

Solution ☐ a. $(2x-5)(3x-10) = 0$

                $2x - 5 = 0$ or $3x - 10 = 0$ Zero Product Property

                $x = \dfrac{5}{2}$ or $x = \dfrac{10}{3}$ Solve each equation.

          b. $x^2 - 3x + 28 = 0$

               $(x+4)(x-7) = 0$ Factor.

               $x + 4 = 0$ or $x - 7 = 0$ Zero Product Property

               $x = -4$ or $x = 7$ Solve each equation.

Exercises – Factoring Differences of Squares and Perfect Square Trinomials

1

$$3x^2 - 48$$

Which of the following is equivalent to the expression above?

A) $3(x-4)(x+4)$

B) $3(x-4)^2$

C) $(3x-4)(x+4)$

D) $(3x+4)(x-4)$

2

$$x - 6\sqrt{x} - 16$$

Which of the following is equivalent to the expression above?

A) $(\sqrt{x}-4)^2$

B) $(\sqrt{x}-4)(\sqrt{x}+4)$

C) $(\sqrt{x}+8)(\sqrt{x}-2)$

D) $(\sqrt{x}-8)(\sqrt{x}+2)$

3

If $x^2 + y^2 = 10$ and $xy = -3$, what is the value of $(x-y)^2$?

A) 12

B) 16

C) 20

D) 25

4

If $x+y=10$ and $x-y=4$, what is the value of $x^2 - y^2$?

A) 20

B) 24

C) 36

D) 40

5

$$6x^2 + 7x - 24 = 0$$

If r and s are two solutions of the equation above and $r > s$, which of the following is the value of $r - s$?

A) $\dfrac{7}{6}$

B) $\dfrac{16}{3}$

C) $\dfrac{25}{6}$

D) $\dfrac{20}{3}$

6

$$x^2 - 3x = 28$$

If r and s are two solutions of the equation above, which of the following is the value of $r + s$?

A) -3

B) 3

C) 6

D) 9

11-4. Solving Quadratic Equations by Completing the Square

Definition of Square Root

For any number $a > 0$, if $x^2 = a$, then x is a square root of a and $x = \pm\sqrt{a}$.

A method called **completing the square** can be used to solve a quadratic equation. To complete the square for a quadratic equation of the form $ax^2 + bx + c = 0$, you can follow the steps below.

1. Subtract c from each side: $ax^2 + bx = -c$

2. If $a \neq 1$, divide both sides by a: $x^2 + \dfrac{b}{a}x = -\dfrac{c}{a}$

3. Add $\dfrac{1}{2}$ of $\dfrac{b}{a}$ square which is $(\dfrac{b}{2a})^2$, to both sides: $x^2 + \dfrac{b}{a}x + (\dfrac{b}{2a})^2 = -\dfrac{c}{a} + (\dfrac{b}{2a})^2$

4. You have completed the square: $(x + \dfrac{b}{2a})^2 = -\dfrac{c}{a} + (\dfrac{b}{2a})^2$

5. Square root each side: $x + \dfrac{b}{2a} = \pm\sqrt{-\dfrac{c}{a} + (\dfrac{b}{2a})^2}$ or $x = -\dfrac{b}{2a} \pm \sqrt{-\dfrac{c}{a} + (\dfrac{b}{2a})^2}$

Definition of Equal Polynomials

If $ax^2 + bx + c = px^2 + qx + r$ for all values of x, then $a = p$, $b = q$, and $c = r$.

Example 1 □ Solve $2x^2 - 6x - 7 = 0$ by completing the square.

Solution □ $2x^2 - 6x = 7$ Add 7 to each side.

$x^2 - 3x = \dfrac{7}{2}$ Divide each side by 2.

$x^2 - 3x + \dfrac{9}{4} = \dfrac{7}{2} + \dfrac{9}{4}$ $\dfrac{1}{2}$ of -3 is $-\dfrac{3}{2}$. Add $(-\dfrac{3}{2})^2 = \dfrac{9}{4}$, to each side.

$(x - \dfrac{3}{2})^2 = \dfrac{23}{4}$ Complete the square and simplify.

$x - \dfrac{3}{2} = \pm\dfrac{\sqrt{23}}{\sqrt{4}}$ Take the square root of each side and simplify.

$x = \dfrac{3}{2} \pm \dfrac{\sqrt{23}}{2}$ Add $\dfrac{3}{2}$ to each side.

Example 2 □ If $s > 0$ and $4x^2 - rx + 9 = (2x - s)^2$ for all values of x, what is the value of $r - s$?

Solution □ $4x^2 - rx + 9 = 4x^2 - 4sx + s^2$ FOIL right side of the equation.

$4x^2 - rx + 9 = 4x^2 - 4sx + s^2$ By the Definition of Equal Polynomials

                 $4 = 4$, $r = 4s$, and $9 = s^2$.

$s = \pm\sqrt{9} = \pm 3$ Definition of square root

Since $s > 0$ is given, $s = 3$.

$r = 4s = 4(3) = 12$

$r - s = 12 - 3 = 9$

Exercises - Solving Quadratic Equations by Completing the Square

1

If $x^2 - 10x = 75$ and $x < 0$, what is the value of $x + 5$?

A) -15

B) -10

C) -5

D) 0

2

If $x^2 - kx = 20$ and $x - \dfrac{k}{2} = 6$, which of the following is a possible value of x?

A) 2

B) 4

C) 6

D) 8

3

$$x^2 - \frac{k}{3}x = 5$$

Which of the following is an equivalent form of the equation shown above, from which the equation could be solved by completing the square?

A) $x^2 - \dfrac{k}{3}x + \dfrac{k}{6} = \dfrac{k}{6} + 5$

B) $x^2 - \dfrac{k}{3}x + \dfrac{k^2}{9} = \dfrac{k^2}{9} + 5$

C) $x^2 - \dfrac{k}{3}x + \dfrac{k^2}{36} = \dfrac{k^2}{36} + 5$

D) $x^2 - \dfrac{k}{3}x + \dfrac{k^2}{6} = \dfrac{k^2}{6} + 5$

4

$$x^2 - rx = \frac{k^2}{4}$$

In the quadratic equation above, k and r are are constants. What are the solutions for x?

A) $x = \dfrac{r}{4} \pm \dfrac{\sqrt{k^2 + 2r^2}}{4}$

B) $x = \dfrac{r}{2} \pm \dfrac{\sqrt{k^2 + 8r^2}}{4}$

C) $x = \dfrac{r}{4} \pm \dfrac{\sqrt{k^2 + r^2}}{2}$

D) $x = \dfrac{r}{2} \pm \dfrac{\sqrt{k^2 + r^2}}{2}$

5

If $(x - 7)(x - s) = x^2 - rx + 14$ for all values of x, what is the value of $r + s$?

6

If $x^2 - \dfrac{3}{2}x + c = (x - k)^2$, what is the value of c?

11-5. Quadratic Formula and the Discriminant

Solving Quadratic Equations by Using the Quadratic Formula

The solutions of the quadratic equation $ax^2 + bx + c$, in which $a \neq 0$, are given by the formula

$$x = \frac{-b \pm \sqrt{b^2 - 4ac}}{2a}.$$

Example 1 □ Use the quadratic formula to solve $2x^2 - 4x - 3 = 0$.

Solution □ For this equation $a = 2$, $b = -4$, and $c = -3$.

$$x = \frac{-b \pm \sqrt{b^2 - 4ac}}{2a} \qquad \text{Quadratic Formula}$$

$$= \frac{-(-4) \pm \sqrt{(-4)^2 - 4(2)(-3)}}{2(2)} \qquad \text{Substitute } a = 2, \ b = -4, \text{ and } c = -3.$$

$$= \frac{4 \pm \sqrt{16 + 24}}{4} = \frac{4 \pm \sqrt{40}}{4} = \frac{2 \pm \sqrt{10}}{2} \qquad \text{Simplify.}$$

$$x = \frac{2 + \sqrt{10}}{2} \text{ or } x = \frac{2 - \sqrt{10}}{2} \qquad \text{Separate the solutions.}$$

The Discriminant

In a Quadratic Formula, the expression under the radical sign $b^2 - 4ac$ is called the **discriminant**.
The value of the discriminant can be used to determine the number of real roots for the quadratic equation.

Example	$-2x^2 + 3x + 5 = 0$	$x^2 + 4x + 4 = 0$	$x^2 + 5x + 8 = 0$
Discriminant	$b^2 - 4ac = 3^2 - 4(-2)(5) = 49$ Positive	$b^2 - 4ac = 4^2 - 4(1)(4) = 0$ Zero	$b^2 - 4ac = 5^2 - 4(1)(8) = -7$ Negative
Number of Real Roots	2	1	0
x - intercepts or Roots of the function	$x = \dfrac{-3 \pm \sqrt{49}}{2(-2)} = \dfrac{-3 \pm 7}{-4}$ $x = 2.5$ or $x = -1$ two real roots	$x = \dfrac{-4 \pm \sqrt{0}}{2(1)} = -2$ one root	$x = \dfrac{-5 \pm \sqrt{-7}}{2(1)}$ no real roots
Graph of Related Function	 $y = -2x^2 + 3x + 5$ The graph crosses the x - axis twice.	 $y = x^2 + 4x + 4$ The graph touches the x - axis once.	 $y = x^2 + 5x + 8$ The graph does not cross the x - axis.

Example 2 □ Find the number of solutions for each system of equations.

$$\text{a. } \begin{cases} y = 5x - 7 \\ y = x^2 + 6x + 1 \end{cases} \qquad\qquad \text{b. } \begin{cases} y = -x + 2 \\ y = x^2 - 3x - 8 \end{cases}$$

Solution □ a. Substitute $5x - 7$ for y in the quadratic equation.

$5x - 7 = x^2 + 6x + 1$ Substitution

$x^2 + x + 8 = 0$ Standard form of a quadratic equation.

For the quadratic equation above $a = 1$, $b = 1$, and $c = 8$.

Discriminant $= b^2 - 4ac = (1)^2 - 4(1)(8) = -31 < 0$

Since the discriminant is negative, the system of equations has no solution.

b. Substitute $-x + 2$ for y in the quadratic equation.

$-x + 2 = x^2 - 3x - 8$ Substitution

$x^2 - 2x - 10 = 0$ Standard form of a quadratic equation.

For the quadratic equation above $a = 1$, $b = -2$, and $c = -10$

Discriminant $= b^2 - 4ac = (-2)^2 - 4(1)(-10) = 44 > 0$

Since the discriminant is positive, the system of equations has two solutions.

Sum of Roots and Product of Roots

If r_1 and r_2 are roots of the quadratic equation $ax^2 + bx + c = 0$, then

$$r_1 + r_2 = \text{sum of roots} = -\frac{b}{a} \text{ and } r_1 \cdot r_2 = \text{product of roots} = \frac{c}{a}.$$

Example 3 □ Find the sum and product of all values x that satisfy $2x^2 - 5x - 1 = 0$.

Solution □ Method 1

Use the quadratic formula to find the roots of the given equation.

$$x = \frac{-b \pm \sqrt{b^2 - 4ac}}{2a} = \frac{-(-5) \pm \sqrt{(-5)^2 - 4(2)(-1)}}{2(2)} = \frac{5 \pm \sqrt{25 + 8}}{4} = \frac{5 \pm \sqrt{33}}{4}$$

The two roots are $x = \dfrac{5 + \sqrt{33}}{4}$ and $x = \dfrac{5 - \sqrt{33}}{4}$

Sum of the roots $= \dfrac{5 + \sqrt{33}}{4} + \dfrac{5 - \sqrt{33}}{4} = \dfrac{10}{4} = \dfrac{5}{2}$

Product of the roots $= (\dfrac{5 + \sqrt{33}}{4})(\dfrac{5 - \sqrt{33}}{4}) = \dfrac{(5 + \sqrt{33})(5 - \sqrt{33})}{16}$

$$= \frac{25 - 5\sqrt{33} + 5\sqrt{33} - 33}{16} = -\frac{8}{16} = -\frac{1}{2}$$

Method 2

Use the sum and products formula.

$$r_1 + r_2 = \text{sum of roots} = -\frac{b}{a} = -\frac{-5}{2} = \frac{5}{2}$$

$$r_1 \cdot r_2 = \text{product of roots} = \frac{c}{a} = \frac{-1}{2}$$

Exercises - Quadratic Formula and the Discriminant

1

$$(p-1)x^2 - 2x - (p+1) = 0$$

In the quadratic equation above, p is a constant. What are the solutions for x?

A) $\dfrac{1+\sqrt{2-p^2}}{p-1}$ and $\dfrac{1-\sqrt{2-p^2}}{p-1}$

B) $\dfrac{1+2p}{p-1}$ and -1

C) $\dfrac{p+1}{p-1}$ and -1

D) $\dfrac{p+1}{p-1}$ and $\dfrac{2p+1}{p-1}$

2

What is the sum of all values of x that satisfy $3x^2 + 12x - 29 = 0$?

A) -4

B) -2

C) 2

D) 4

3

If the quadratic equation $kx^2 + 6x + 4 = 0$ has exactly one solution, what is the value of k?

A) $\dfrac{3}{2}$

B) $\dfrac{5}{2}$

C) $\dfrac{7}{4}$

D) $\dfrac{9}{4}$

4

$$\begin{cases} y = bx - 3 \\ y = ax^2 - 7x \end{cases}$$

In the system of equations above, a and b are constants. For which of the following values of a and b does the system of equations have exactly two real solutions?

A) $a = 3, \ b = -2$

B) $a = 5, \ b = 0$

C) $a = 7, \ b = 2$

D) $a = 9, \ b = 4$

5

What are the solutions to $x^2 + 4 = -6x$?

A) $-3 \pm \sqrt{13}$

B) $-3 \pm \sqrt{5}$

C) $-6 \pm \sqrt{5}$

D) $-6 \pm \sqrt{13}$

6

Which of the following equations has no real solution?

A) $5x^2 - 10x = 6$

B) $4x^2 + 8x + 4 = 0$

C) $3x^2 - 5x = -3$

D) $-\dfrac{1}{3}x^2 + 2x - 2 = 0$

11-6. Solving Systems Consisting Linear and Quadratic Equations

A system containing only quadratic equations or a combination of linear and quadratic equations in the same two variables is called a **quadratic system**. The substitution and elimination methods used to solve linear systems can also be used to solve quadratic systems algebraically. You can use graphs to find the number of real solutions of a quadratic system. If the graphs of a system of equations are a quadratic and a linear, the system will have 0, 1, or 2 solutions. If the graphs of a system of equations are two quadratic equations, the system will have 0, 1, 2, 3, or 4 solutions.

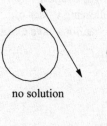
no solution

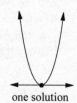
one solution

one solution

two solutions

two solutions

no solution

one solution

two solutions

three solutions

four solutions

Example 1 □ Solve the system of equations.

$$y = x^2 - 5$$
$$x + y = 1$$

Solution □ Rewrite $x + y = 1$ as $y = 1 - x$.

$y = x^2 - 5$	
$1 - x = x^2 - 5$	Substitute $1 - x$ for y.
$x^2 + x - 6 = 0$	Simplify.
$(x + 3)(x - 2) = 0$	Factor.
$x + 3 = 0$ or $x - 2 = 0$	Zero Product Property
$x = -3$ or $x = 2$	Solve for x.
$-3 + y = 1$ or $2 + y = 1$	Substitute -3 and 2 for x in $x + y = 1$.
$y = 4$ or $y = -1$	Solve for y.

The solutions of the system of equations are $(-3, 4)$ and $(2, -1)$.

The equations are graphed in the diagram at the right. As you can see, the graphs have two points of intersection at $(-3, 4)$ and $(2, -1)$.

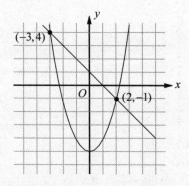

Exercises - Solving Systems Consisting Linear and Quadratic Equations

1

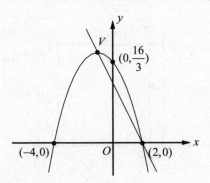

The xy-plane above shows two x-intercepts, a y-intercept and vertex V of a parabola. If the line passes through the points $(2,0)$ and V, which of the following must be the y-intercept of the line?

A) 3

B) $\dfrac{7}{2}$

C) 4

D) $\dfrac{9}{2}$

2

$$\begin{cases} y = x^2 + x \\ y = ax - 1 \end{cases}$$

In the system of equations above, $a > 0$. If the system of equations has exactly one real solution, what is the value of a?

A) $\dfrac{5}{2}$

B) 3

C) $\dfrac{7}{2}$

D) 4

3

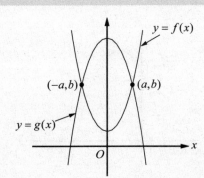

The function f and g, defined by $f(x) = 2x^2 + 2$ and $g(x) = -2x^2 + 18$, are graphed in the xy-plane above. The two graphs intersect at the points (a,b) and $(-a,b)$. What is the value of b?

A) 6

B) 8

C) 10

D) 12

4

$$\begin{cases} x^2 + y^2 = 14 \\ x^2 - y = 2 \end{cases}$$

If (x, y) is a solution to the system of equations above, what is the value of x^2?

A) 2

B) 3

C) 4

D) 5

Chapter 11 Practice Test

1

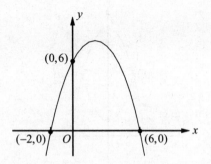

The graph of the quadratic function above shows two x-intercepts and a y-intercept. Which of the following equations represents the graph of the quadratic function above?

A) $y = -\frac{1}{2}(x-1)^2 + 9$

B) $y = -\frac{1}{2}(x-2)^2 + 8$

C) $y = -\frac{1}{2}(x-2)^2 + 9$

D) $y = -\frac{1}{2}(x-3)^2 + 8$

2

If $(x+y)^2 = 324$ and $(x-y)^2 = 16$, what is the value of xy?

A) 33

B) 55

C) 77

D) 99

3

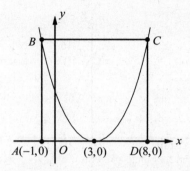

In the figure above, the vertex of the graph of the quadratic function is at $(3,0)$. The points B and C lie on the parabola. If $ABCD$ is a rectangle with perimeter 38, which of the following represents the equation of the parabola?

A) $y = \frac{2}{5}(x-3)^2$

B) $y = \frac{5}{8}(x-3)^2$

C) $y = \frac{3}{4}(x-3)^2$

D) $y = \frac{7}{8}(x-3)^2$

4

If $(ax+b)(2x-5) = 12x^2 + kx - 10$ for all values of x, what is the value of k?

A) −26

B) −10

C) 24

D) 32

Questions 5-8 refer to the following information.

$$h = -\frac{1}{2}gt^2 + v_0 t + h_0$$

The equation above describes the motion of an object thrown upward into the air. In the equation, g is the acceleration due to gravity (9.8m/s^2), t is the time elapsed since the object was thrown upward, v_0 is the initial speed of the object, h_0 is the initial height from which the object was thrown, and h is the height of the object above the ground t seconds after the object was thrown.

5

Which of the following equations represents the motion of the object, if the object was thrown upward from 40 meters above the ground with an initial speed of 35 meters per second (m/s)?

A) $h = -9.8t^2 + 40t + 35$

B) $h = -9.8t^2 + 35t + 40$

C) $h = -4.9t^2 + 40t + 35$

D) $h = -4.9t^2 + 35t + 40$

6

How many seconds will it take the object to reach its maximum height? (hint: The function has a maximum point at $t = -\dfrac{b}{2a}$.)

A) $\dfrac{15}{7}$

B) $\dfrac{20}{7}$

C) $\dfrac{25}{7}$

D) $\dfrac{30}{7}$

7

What is the maximum height from the ground the object will reach, to the nearest meter?

A) 103

B) 112

C) 125

D) 133

8

How long will it take the object to hit the ground, to the nearest second? (hint: Height of the object is zero when the object hits the ground.)

A) 7

B) 8

C) 9

D) 10

9

$$h = -16t^2 + h_0$$

The equation above describes the height of an object t seconds after it dropped from a height of h_0 feet above the ground. If a hiker dropped a water bottle from a cliff 150 feet above the ground, how many seconds will it take to hit the ground? (Round your answer to the nearest second.)

A) 2

B) 3

C) 4

D) 5

Answer Key

Section 11-1

1. D   2. A   3. $\dfrac{9}{16}$ 4. 2   5. $\dfrac{4}{3}$

Section 11-2

1. C   2. B   3. A   4. A   5. C
6. D

Section 11-3

1. A   2. D   3. B   4. D   5. C
6. B

Section 11-4

1. D   2. A   3. C   4. D   5. 11
6. $\dfrac{9}{16}$

Section 11-5

1. C   2. A   3. D   4. D   5. B
6. C

Section 11-6

1. C   2. B   3. C   4. D

Chapter 11 Practice Test

1. B   2. C   3. A   4. A   5. D
6. C   7. A   8. B   9. B

Answers and Explanations

Section 11-1

1. D

Change the given equation into the vertex form
$y = a(x-h)^2 + k$, in which (h,k) is the vertex
of the parabola, by completing the square.
$y = x^2 - 6x + 5$
$\quad = x^2 - 6x + (\dfrac{-6}{2})^2 - (\dfrac{-6}{2})^2 + 5$
$\quad = (x^2 - 6x + 9) - 9 + 5$
$\quad = (x-3)^2 - 4$
The coordinate of the vertex can be read as $(3,-4)$.

2. A

Change the given equation into the factored form
$y = (x-a)(x-b)$, in which $x = a$ and $x = b$ are
the x-intercepts of the parabola. Find two numbers
with a sum of -6 and a product of 5. The two
numbers are -1 and -5.
$y = x^2 - 6x + 5$ can be written in the factored form
$y = (x-1)(x-5)$. The x-intercepts are 1 and 5.

3. $\dfrac{9}{16}$

$y = a(x-h)^2$
$0 = a(4-h)^2$ x-intercept at $(4,0)$
Since $a \neq 0$, $4-h = 0$, or $h = 4$.
The graph of the parabola passes through $(0,9)$,
since the y-intercept of the parabola is 9.
$9 = a(0-h)^2$ y-intercept at $(0,9)$
$9 = ah^2$ Simplify.
$9 = a(4)^2$ Substitute 4 for h.
$\dfrac{9}{16} = a$

4. 2

$y = a(x+2)^2 - 15$
$3 = a(1+2)^2 - 15$ $x = 1$ and $y = 3$
$3 = 9a - 15$
$18 = 9a$
$2 = a$

5. $\dfrac{4}{3}$

The x-intercepts of the graph of the equation
$y = a(x-1)(x+5)$ are -5 and 1. The x-coordinate
of the vertex is the average of the two x-intercepts.
Therefore, $h = \dfrac{-5+1}{2} = -2$. The value of k is -12
because the minimum value of y is -12. So the
coordinate of the vertex is $(-2,-12)$. Substitute
$x = -2$ and $y = -12$ in the given equation.
$-12 = a(-2-1)(-2+5)$
$-12 = -9a$
$\dfrac{12}{9} = a$ or $a = \dfrac{4}{3}$

Section 11-2

1. C

    $x^2 - 2x - 24$

    Find two numbers with a sum of -2 and a product of -24. The two numbers are -6 and 4.

    Therefore, $x^2 - 2x - 24 = (x-6)(x+4)$.

2. B

    $x^2 - 17x + 72$

    Find two numbers with a sum of -17 and a product of 72. The two numbers are -8 and -9.

    Therefore, $x^2 - 17x + 72 = (x-8)(x-9)$.

3. A

    $-x^2 + 5x + 84 = -(x^2 - 5x - 84)$

    Find two numbers with a sum of -5 and a product of -84. The two numbers are -12 and 7.

    $-x^2 + 5x + 84 = -(x^2 - 5x - 84)$
    $= -(x-12)(x+7) = (12-x)(x+7)$

4. A

    $3x^2 + 7x - 6$

    Find two numbers with a sum of 7 and a product of $3 \cdot -6$ or -18. The two numbers are -2 and 9.

    $3x^2 + 7x - 6$
    $= 3x^2 - 2x + 9x - 6$ Write $7x$ as $-2x + 9x$.
    $= (3x^2 - 2x) + (9x - 6)$ Group terms.
    $= x(3x - 2) + 3(3x - 2)$ Factor out the GCF.
    $= (3x - 2)(x + 3)$ Distributive Property

5. C

    $2x^2 + x - 15$

    Find two numbers with a sum of 1 and a product of $2 \cdot -15$ or -30. The two numbers are -5 and 6.

    $2x^2 + x - 15$
    $= 2x^2 - 5x + 6x - 15$ Write x as $-5x + 6x$.
    $= (2x^2 - 5x) + (6x - 15)$ Group terms.
    $= x(2x - 5) + 3(2x - 5)$ Factor out the GCF.
    $= (2x - 5)(x + 3)$ Distributive Property

6. D

    $-6x^2 + x + 2 = -(6x^2 - x - 2)$

    Find two numbers with a sum of -1 and a product of $6 \cdot -2$ or -12. The two numbers are -4 and 3.

    $-6x^2 + x + 2$
    $= -(6x^2 - x - 2)$
    $= -(6x^2 - 4x + 3x - 2)$ Write $-x$ as $-4x + 3x$.
    $= -[(6x^2 - 4x) + (3x - 2)]$ Group terms.
    $= -[2x(3x - 2) + (3x - 2)]$ Factor out the GCF.
    $= -(3x - 2)(2x + 1)$ Distributive Property

Section 11-3

1. A

    $3x^2 - 48$
    $= 3(x^2 - 16)$ Factor out the GCF.
    $= 3((x)^2 - (4)^2)$ Write in the form $a^2 - b^2$.
    $= 3(x - 4)(x + 4)$ Difference of Squares

2. D

    $x - 6\sqrt{x} - 16$
    Let $y = \sqrt{x}$, then $y^2 = x$.

    $x - 6\sqrt{x} - 16$
    $= y^2 - 6y - 16$ $y = \sqrt{x}$ and $y^2 = x$
    $= (y - 8)(y + 2)$
    $= (\sqrt{x} - 8)(\sqrt{x} + 2)$ $y = \sqrt{x}$ and $y^2 = x$

3. B

    $(x - y)^2$
    $= (x - y)(x - y)$
    $= x^2 - 2xy + y^2$
    $= (x^2 + y^2) - 2xy$
    $= 10 - 2(-3) = 16$ $x^2 + y^2 = 10$ and $xy = -3$

4. D

    $x^2 - y^2$
    $= (x + y)(x - y)$
    $= (10)(4)$
    $= 40$ $x + y = 10$ and $x - y = 4$

5. C

$$6x^2 + 7x - 24 = 0$$

$(3x+8)(2x-3) = 0$ Factor.

$3x+8 = 0$ or $2x-3 = 0$ Zero Product Property

$x = -\dfrac{8}{3}$ or $x = \dfrac{3}{2}$ Solve each equation.

Since $\dfrac{3}{2} > -\dfrac{8}{3}$, $r = \dfrac{3}{2}$ and $s = -\dfrac{8}{3}$.

$r - s = \dfrac{3}{2} - \left(-\dfrac{8}{3}\right) = \dfrac{9}{6} + \dfrac{16}{6} = \dfrac{25}{6}$

6. B

$$x^2 - 3x = 28$$

$x^2 - 3x - 28 = 0$ Make one side 0.

$(x-7)(x+4) = 0$ Factor.

$x-7 = 0$ or $x+4 = 0$ Zero Product Property

$x = 7$ or $x = -4$ Solve each equation.

Therefore, $r + s = 7 + (-4) = 3$.

Section 11-4

1. D

$$x^2 - 10x = 75$$

Add $\left(\dfrac{-10}{2}\right)^2$ to each side.

$x^2 - 10x + \left(-\dfrac{10}{2}\right)^2 = 75 + \left(-\dfrac{10}{2}\right)^2$

$x^2 - 10x + 25 = 75 + 25$ Simplify.

$(x-5)^2 = 100$ Factor $x^2 - 10x + 25$.

$x - 5 = \pm 10$ Take the square root.

$x = 5 \pm 10$ Add 5 to each side.

$x = 5 + 10$ or $x = 5 - 10$ Separate the solutions.

$x = 15$ or $x = -5$ Simplify.

If $x < 0$, $x = -5$. Therefore, $x + 5 = -5 + 5 = 0$.

2. A

$$x^2 - kx = 20$$

Add $\left(\dfrac{-k}{2}\right)^2$ to each side.

$x^2 - kx + \left(\dfrac{-k}{2}\right)^2 = 20 + \left(\dfrac{-k}{2}\right)^2$

$x^2 - kx + \dfrac{k^2}{4} = 20 + \dfrac{k^2}{4}$ Simplify.

$\left(x - \dfrac{k}{2}\right)^2 = 20 + \dfrac{k^2}{4}$ Factor $x^2 - kx + \dfrac{k^2}{4}$.

$(6)^2 = 20 + \dfrac{k^2}{4}$ Substitute 6 for $x - \dfrac{k}{2}$.

$16 = \dfrac{k^2}{4}$

Solving for k gives $k = \pm 8$.

Solving the given equation $x - \dfrac{k}{2} = 6$ for x

gives $x = 6 + \dfrac{k}{2}$.

If $k = 8$, $x = 6 + \dfrac{k}{2} = 6 + \dfrac{8}{2} = 10$.

If $k = -8$, $x = 6 + \dfrac{k}{2} = 6 + \dfrac{-8}{2} = 2$.

Of the answer choices, 2 is a possible value of x. Therefore, Choice A is correct.

3. C

$$x^2 - \dfrac{k}{3}x = 5$$

The equation could be solved by completing the

square by adding $\left(\dfrac{1}{2} \cdot \dfrac{k}{3}\right)^2$, or $\dfrac{k^2}{36}$, to each side.

Choice C is correct.

4. D

$$x^2 - rx = \dfrac{k^2}{4}$$

Add $\left(\dfrac{-r}{2}\right)^2$, or $\dfrac{r^2}{4}$, to each side.

$x^2 - rx + \dfrac{r^2}{4} = \dfrac{k^2}{4} + \dfrac{r^2}{4}$

$\left(x - \dfrac{r}{2}\right)^2 = \dfrac{k^2 + r^2}{4}$ Factor $x^2 - rx + \dfrac{r^2}{4}$.

$x - \dfrac{r}{2} = \pm \sqrt{\dfrac{k^2 + r^2}{4}}$ Take the square root.

$x - \dfrac{r}{2} = \pm \dfrac{\sqrt{k^2 + r^2}}{2}$ Simplify.

$x = \dfrac{r}{2} \pm \dfrac{\sqrt{k^2 + r^2}}{2}$ Add $\dfrac{r}{2}$ to each side.

Choice D is correct.

5. 11

$(x-7)(x-s) = x^2 - rx + 14$

$x^2 - (s+7)x + 7s = x^2 - rx + 14$

Since the x-terms and constant terms have
to be equal on both sides of the equation,

$r = s + 7$ and $7s = 14$.

Solving for s gives $s = 2$.

$r = s + 7 = 2 + 7 = 9$

Therefore, $r + s = 9 + 2 = 11$.

6. $\dfrac{9}{16}$

$x^2 - \dfrac{3}{2}x + c = (x - k)^2 \Rightarrow$

$x^2 - \dfrac{3}{2}x + c = x^2 - 2kx + k^2$

Since the x-terms and constant terms have to be equal on both sides of the equation,

$2k = \dfrac{3}{2}$ and $c = k^2$.

Solving for k gives $k = \dfrac{3}{4}$.

Therefore, $c = k^2 = (\dfrac{3}{4})^2 = \dfrac{9}{16}$.

Section 11-5

1. C

$(p-1)x^2 - 2x - (p+1) = 0$

Use the quadratic formula to find the solutions for x.

$x = \dfrac{-b \pm \sqrt{b^2 - 4ac}}{2a}$

$= \dfrac{-(-2) \pm \sqrt{(-2)^2 - 4(p-1)(-(p+1))}}{2(p-1)}$

$= \dfrac{2 \pm \sqrt{4 + 4(p-1)(p+1)}}{2(p-1)}$

$= \dfrac{2 \pm \sqrt{4 + 4p^2 - 4}}{2(p-1)}$

$= \dfrac{2 \pm \sqrt{4p^2}}{2(p-1)} = \dfrac{2 \pm 2p}{2(p-1)}$

$= \dfrac{2(1 \pm p)}{2(p-1)} = \dfrac{1 \pm p}{p-1}$

The solutions are $\dfrac{1+p}{p-1}$ and $\dfrac{1-p}{p-1}$, or -1.

Choice C is correct.

2. A

Let r_1 and r_2 be the solutions of the quadratic

equation $3x^2 + 12x - 29 = 0$.

Use the sum of roots formula.

$r_1 + r_2 = -\dfrac{b}{a} = -\dfrac{12}{3} = -4$.

3. D

$kx^2 + 6x + 4 = 0$

If the quadratic equation has exactly one solution, then $b^2 - 4ac = 0$.

$b^2 - 4ac = 6^2 - 4(k)(4) = 0 \Rightarrow 36 - 16k = 0$

$\Rightarrow k = \dfrac{36}{16} = \dfrac{9}{4}$

4. D

$y = bx - 3$ and $y = ax^2 - 7x$

Substitute $bx - 3$ for y in the quadratic equation.

$bx - 3 = ax^2 - 7x$

$ax^2 + (-7 - b)x + 3 = 0$ Make one side 0.

The system of equations will have exactly two real solutions if the discriminant of the quadratic equation is positive.

$(-7 - b)^2 - 4a(3) > 0$, or $(7 + b)^2 - 12a > 0$.

We need to check each answer choice to find out for which values of a and b the system of equations has exactly two real solutions.

A) If $a = 3$ and $b = -2$, $(7 - 2)^2 - 12(3) < 0$.

B) If $a = 5$ and $b = 0$, $(7 + 0)^2 - 12(5) < 0$.

C) If $a = 7$ and $b = 2$, $(7 + 2)^2 - 12(7) < 0$.

D) If $a = 9$ and $b = 4$, $(7 + 4)^2 - 12(9) > 0$.

Choice D is correct.

5. B

$x^2 + 4 = -6x$

$x^2 + 6x - 4 = 0$

$x = \dfrac{-b \pm \sqrt{b^2 - 4ac}}{2a}$

$= \dfrac{-6 \pm \sqrt{6^2 - 4(1)(4)}}{2(1)}$

$= \dfrac{-6 \pm \sqrt{20}}{2} = \dfrac{-6 \pm 2\sqrt{5}}{2}$

$= -3 \pm \sqrt{5}$

6. C

If the quadratic equation has no real solution, the discriminant, $b^2 - 4ac,$ must be negative. Check each answer choice.

A) $5x^2 - 10x = 6 \implies 5x^2 - 10x - 6 = 0$
    $b^2 - 4ac = (-10)^2 - 4(5)(-6) > 0$

B) $4x^2 + 8x + 4 = 0$
    $b^2 - 4ac = (8)^2 - 4(4)(4) = 0$

C) $3x^2 - 5x = -3 \implies 3x^2 - 5x + 3 = 0$
    $b^2 - 4ac = (-5)^2 - 4(3)(3) < 0$

Choice C is correct.

Section 11-6

1. C

Since the two x-intercepts are -4 and 2, the equation of the parabola can be written as $y = a(x+4)(x-2)$. Substitute $x = 0$ and $y = \dfrac{16}{3}$ in the equation, since the graph of the parabola passes through $(0, \dfrac{16}{3})$.

$$\frac{16}{3} = a(0+4)(0-2)$$

Solving the equation for a gives $a = -\dfrac{2}{3}$.

Thus the equation of the parabola is

$$y = -\frac{2}{3}(x+4)(x-2).$$

The x-coordinate of the vertex is the average of the two x-intercepts: $\dfrac{-4+2}{2}$, or -1.

The y-coordinate of the vertex can be found by substituting -1 for x in the equation of the parabola: $y = -\dfrac{2}{3}(-1+4)(-1-2) = 6$.

The line passes through $(2,0)$ and $(-1,6)$.

The slope of the line is $\dfrac{6-0}{-1-2} = -2$. The equation of the line in point-slope form is $y - 0 = -2(x-2)$. To find the y-intercept of the line, substitute 0 for x. $y = -2(0-2) = 4$

Choice C is correct.

2. B

$y = x^2 + x$ and $y = ax - 1$
Substitute $ax - 1$ for y in the quadratic equation.

$ax - 1 = x^2 + x$
$x^2 + (-a+1)x + 1 = 0$ Make one side 0.

If the system of equations has exactly one real solution, the discriminant $b^2 - 4ac$ must be equal to 0.

$(-a+1)^2 - 4(1)(1) = 0$	$b^2 - 4ac = 0$
$a^2 - 2a + 1 - 4 = 0$	Simplify.
$a^2 - 2a - 3 = 0$	Simplify.
$(a-3)(a+1) = 0$	Factor.
$a = 3$ or $a = -1$	Solutions

Since $a > 0$, $a = 3$.

3. C

One can find the intersection points of the two graphs by setting the two functions $f(x)$ and $g(x)$ equal to one another and then solving for x. This yields $2x^2 + 2 = -2x^2 + 18$. Adding $2x^2 - 2$ to each side of the equation gives $4x^2 = 16$. Solving for x gives $x = \pm 2$.
$f(2) = 2(2)^2 + 2 = 10$ and also $f(-2) = 10$. The two point of intersections are $(2,10)$ and $(-2,10)$. Therefore, the value of b is 10.

4. D

$x^2 + y^2 = 14$	First equation
$x^2 - y = 2$	Second equation
$x^2 = y + 2$	Second equation solved for x^2.
$y + 2 + y^2 = 14$	Substitute $y+2$ for x^2 in first equation.
$y^2 + y - 12 = 0$	Make one side 0.
$(y+4)(y-3) = 0$	Factor.
$y = -4$ or $y = 3$	Solve for y.

Substitute -4 and 3 for y and solve for x^2.

$x^2 = y + 2 = -4 + 2 = -2$.

Since x^2 cannot be negative, $y = -4$ is not a solution.

$x^2 = y + 2 = 3 + 2 = 5$

The value of x^2 is 5.

Chapter 11 Practice Test

1. **B**

    The x-coordinate of the vertex is the average of the x-intercepts. Thus the x-coordinate of the vertex is $x = \dfrac{-2+6}{2} = 2$. The vertex form of the parabola can be written as $y = a(x-2)^2 + k$. Choices A and D are incorrect because the x-coordinate of the vertex is not 2. Also, the parabola passes through $(0, 6)$. Check choices B and C.

    B) $y = -\dfrac{1}{2}(x-2)^2 + 8$

    $6 = -\dfrac{1}{2}(0-2)^2 + 8$ Correct.

    C) $y = -\dfrac{1}{2}(x-2)^2 + 9$

    $6 = -\dfrac{1}{2}(0-2)^2 + 9$ Not correct.

    Choice B is correct.

2. **C**

    $(x+y)^2 = 324 \implies x^2 + 2xy + y^2 = 324$
    $x^2 + y^2 = 324 - 2xy$
    $(x-y)^2 = 16 \implies x^2 - 2xy + y^2 = 16$
    $\implies x^2 + y^2 = 16 + 2xy$
    Substituting $16 + 2xy$ for $x^2 + y^2$ in the equation $x^2 + y^2 = 324 - 2xy$ yields
    $16 + 2xy = 324 - 2xy$.
    Solving this equation for xy yields $xy = 77$.

3. **A**

    From the graph we read the length of AD, which is 9. Let the length of $CD = w$.
    Perimeter of rectangle $ABCD$ is 38.
    $2 \cdot 9 + 2w = 38 \implies 2w = 20 \implies w = 10$
    Therefore, the coordinates of B are $(-1, 10)$ and the coordinates of C are $(8, 10)$.
    The equation of the parabola can be written in vertex form as $y = a(x-3)^2$.
    Now substitute 8 for x and 10 for y in the equation. $10 = a(8-3)^2$. Solving for a gives $a = \dfrac{10}{25} = \dfrac{2}{5}$. Choice A is correct.

4. **A**

    $(ax + b)(2x - 5) = 12x^2 + kx - 10$

    FOIL the left side of the equation.
    $2ax^2 + (-5a + 2b)x - 5b = 12x^2 + kx - 10$

    By the definition of equal polynomials, $2a = 12$, $-5a + 2b = k$, and $5b = 10$. Thus, $a = 6$ and $b = 2$, and $k = -5a + 2b = -5(6) + 2(2) = -26$.

5. **D**

    $h = -\dfrac{1}{2}gt^2 + v_0 t + h_0$

    In the equation, $g = 9.8$, initial height $h_0 = 40$, and initial speed $v_0 = 35$. Therefore, the equation of the motion is $h = -\dfrac{1}{2}(9.8)t^2 + 35t + 40$.
    Choice D is correct.

6. **C**

    In the quadratic equation, $y = ax^2 + bx + c$, the x-coordinate of the maximum or minimum point is at $x = -\dfrac{b}{2a}$.
    Therefore, the object reaches its maximum height when $t = -\dfrac{35}{2(-4.9)} = \dfrac{25}{7}$.

7. **A**

    The object reaches to its maximum height when $t = \dfrac{25}{7}$. So substitute $t = \dfrac{25}{7}$ in the equation.

    $h = -4.9(\dfrac{25}{7})^2 + 35(\dfrac{25}{7}) + 40 = 102.5$

    To the nearest meter, the object reaches a maximum height of 103 meters.

8. **B**

    Height of the object is zero when the object hits the ground.

    $0 = -4.9t^2 + 35t + 40$

    Use quadratic formula to solve for t.

    $t = \dfrac{-35 \pm \sqrt{35^2 - 4(-4.9)(40)}}{2(-4.9)}$

    $= \dfrac{-35 \pm \sqrt{2009}}{-9.8} \approx \dfrac{-35 \pm 44.82}{-9.8}$

Solving for t gives $t \approx -1$ or $t \approx 8.1$.
Since time cannot be negative, the object hits the
ground about 8 seconds after it was thrown.

9. B

When an object hits the ground, $h = 0$.
$h_0 = 150$ is given.

$0 = -16t^2 + 150$ Substitution

$16t^2 = 150$ Add $16t^2$ to each side.

$t^2 = \dfrac{150}{16}$ Divide each side by 16.

$t = \sqrt{\dfrac{150}{16}} \approx 3.06$

CHAPTER 12
Composition, Recursion, and Exponential Functions

12-1 Composition of Functions

Given the two functions f and g, the **composite function**, denoted by $f \circ g$, is defined as $(f \circ g)(x) = f \circ g(x) = f(g(x))$, read "$f$ of g of x."

In order for a value of x to be in the domain of $f \circ g$, two conditions must be satisfied:

1) x must be in the domain of g.

2) $g(x)$ must be in the domain of f.

Example 1 ☐ If $f(x) = x^2 + 1$ and $g(x) = x - 2$, find the following.

a. $(f \circ g)(x)$ b. $(g \circ f)(x)$ c. $(f \circ g)(3)$

Solution ☐ a. $(f \circ g)(x) = f(g(x))$

$\qquad = f(x-2)$ Substitute $x - 2$ for $g(x)$.

$\qquad = (x-2)^2 + 1$ Evaluate f when x is $x - 2$.

$\qquad = x^2 - 4x + 5$ Simplify.

b. $(g \circ f)(x) = g(f(x))$

$\qquad = g(x^2 + 1)$ Substitute $x^2 + 1$ for $g(x)$.

$\qquad = (x^2 + 1) - 2$ Evaluate g when x is $x^2 + 1$.

$\qquad = x^2 - 1$ Simplify.

c. $(f \circ g)(3) = f(g(3))$

$\qquad = f(3-2)$ $g(3) = 3 - 2$.

$\qquad = f(1)$ Simplify.

$\qquad = 1^2 + 1$ $f(1) = 1^2 + 1$

$\qquad = 2$ Simplify.

Example 2 ☐ If $f = \{(-1,-3), (2,5), (4,1)\}$ and $g = \{(-2,2), (1,3), (6,-1)\}$, find the following.

a. $(f \circ g)(-2)$ b. $(g \circ f)(4)$ c. $(f \circ g)(6)$

Solution ☐ a. $(f \circ g)(-2) = f(g(-2))$

$\qquad = f(2)$ $g(-2) = 2$

$\qquad = 5$ Simplify.

b. $(g \circ f)(4) = g(f(4))$

$\qquad = g(1)$ $f(4) = 1$

$\qquad = 3$ Simplify.

c. $(f \circ g)(6) = f(g(6))$

$\qquad = f(-1)$ $g(6) = -1$

$\qquad = -3$ Simplify.

Exercises - Operations on Functions and Composition of Functions

1

If $f(x) = x^2 - 3x - 1$ and $g(x) = 1 - x$, what is the value of $f \circ g(-2)$?

A) -3

B) -1

C) 1

D) 3

2

If $f = \{(-4,12), (-2,4), (2,0), (3,\frac{3}{2})\}$ and $g = \{(-2,5), (0,1), (4,-7), (5,-9)\}$, what is the value of $g \circ f(2)$?

A) -9

B) -7

C) 1

D) 5

3

A function f satisfies $f(-1) = 8$ and $f(1) = -2$. A function g satisfies $g(2) = 5$ and $g(-1) = 1$. What is the value of $f(g(-1))$?

A) -2

B) 1

C) 5

D) 8

4

If $f(x) = \dfrac{1-5x}{2}$ and $g(x) = 2 - x$, what is the value of $f(g(3))$?

A) -7

B) -2

C) 2

D) 3

Questions 5 and 6 refer to the following information.

x	$f(x)$	$g(x)$
-2	-5	0
0	6	4
3	0	-5

The table above gives values of f and g at selected values of x.

5

What is the value of $f(g(-2))$?

6

What is the value of $g(f(3))$?

12-2 Recursive Formula

A **recursive formula** for a sequence describes how to find the n th term from the term(s) before it.

A recursive formula consists of two parts:
1. An initial condition that shows where the sequence starts.
2. A recursion equation that shows how to find each term from the term(s) before it.

The process of composing a function from itself repeatedly is a special type of recursion.
For example, the composition of function $f \circ f(x)$ is a recursion.
The compound interest formula also involves recursion.

Example 1 □ A sequence is recursively defined by $a_n = a_{n-1} + \dfrac{2}{n}$. If $a_0 = 3$, what is the value of a_3?

Solution □ $a_1 = a_0 + \dfrac{2}{1} = 3 + 2 = 5$ Substitute 1 for n and 3 for a_0.

$a_2 = a_1 + \dfrac{2}{2} = 5 + 1 = 6$ Substitute 2 for n and 5 for a_1.

$a_3 = a_2 + \dfrac{2}{3} = 6 + \dfrac{2}{3} = \dfrac{20}{3}$ Substitute 3 for n and 6 for a_2.

Example 2 □ Let $f(x) = \sqrt{x^2 + 5}$, find $f \circ f \circ f(1)$.

Solution □ $f(1) = \sqrt{(1)^2 + 5} = \sqrt{6}$

$f \circ f(1) = f(\sqrt{6}) = \sqrt{(\sqrt{6})^2 + 5} = \sqrt{11}$

$f \circ f \circ f(1) = f(\sqrt{11}) = \sqrt{(\sqrt{11})^2 + 5} = \sqrt{16} = 4$

Example 3 □ For next year's vacation, Cabrera deposited \$2,000 into a savings account that pays 0.5% compounded monthly. In addition to this initial deposit, on the first day of each month, he deposits \$200 into the account. The amount of money n months after he opened the account can be calculated by the equation, $A_n = (1 + 0.005) \cdot A_{n-1} + 200$.

According to the formula, what will be the amount in Cabrera's savings account three months after he started it?

Solution □ One month after, the amount will be:
$A_1 = (1 + 0.005) \cdot A_0 + 200 = (1.005) \cdot 2000 + 200 = 2210$
Two months after, the amount will be:
$A_2 = (1 + 0.005) \cdot A_1 + 200 = (1.005) \cdot 2210 + 200 = 2421.05$
Three months after, the amount will be:
$A_3 = (1 + 0.005) \cdot A_2 + 200 = (1.005) \cdot 2421.05 + 200 = 2633.16$

Exercises - Recursive Formula

1

A sequence is recursively defined by
$a_n = \sqrt{(a_{n-1})^2 + 2}$. If $a_0 = \sqrt{2}$, what
is the value of a_2?

A) $\sqrt{5}$

B) $\sqrt{6}$

C) $\sqrt{8}$

D) 3

2

A sequence is recursively defined by
$a_{n+1} = a_n - \dfrac{f(a_n)}{g(a_n)}$. If $a_0 = 1$, $f(x) = x^2 - 3x$,
and $g(x) = 2x - 3$, what is the value of a_2?

A) -3

B) $-\dfrac{1}{5}$

C) 2

D) $\dfrac{3}{2}$

3

If $f(x) = \sqrt{2x^2 - 1}$, what is the value
of $f \circ f \circ f(2)$?

A) $\sqrt{10}$

B) $\sqrt{15}$

C) $\sqrt{21}$

D) 5

4

If A_0 is the initial amount deposited into a savings
account that earns at a fixed rate of r percent per
year, and a constant amount of $12b$ is added to
the account each year, then amount A_n of the
savings n years after the initial deposit is made
is given by the equation $A_n = (1 + \dfrac{r}{100}) \cdot A_{n-1} + 12b$.
What is A_3, the amount you have in the savings
three years after you made the initial deposit, if
$r = 5$, $A_0 = 12,000$, and $b = 400$?

A) $\$23,070.00$

B) $\$26,048.00$

C) $\$29,023.50$

D) $\$35,274.68$

5

The number of gallons, P_n, of a pollutant in
a lake at the end of each month is given by the
recursively defined formula $P_n = 0.85P_{n-1} + 20$.
If the initial amount P_0 of a pollutant in the lake
is 400 gallons, what is P_3, the amount of pollutant
in the lake at the end of the third month, to the
nearest gallon?

A) 297

B) 285

C) 273

D) 262

12-3. Exponential Functions and Graphs

An **exponential function** is a function of the form $f(x) = ab^x$, in which $a \neq 0$, $b > 0$, and $b \neq 1$.

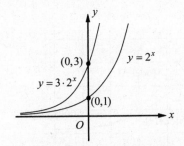

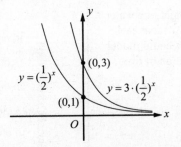

Any function of the form $f(x) = ab^x$, in which $a > 0$, $b > 0$, and $b \neq 1$, the domain is the set of all real numbers and the range is the set of positive real numbers.

If $b > 1$, the graph rises as x increases. The graph shows exponential growth.

If $0 < b < 1$, the graph falls as x increases. The graph shows exponential decay.

Example 1 □ In the diagram below, each exponential curve represents the population of bacteria in a petri dish as a function of time, in hours. At time $t = 0$, the population of Dish 1 is 2,000 and the population of Dish 2 is 3,000.

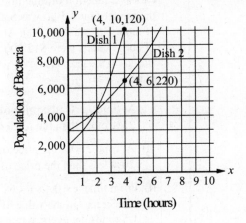

a. At time $t = 0$, the number of bacteria in Dish 2 is what percent more than the number of bacteria in Dish 1?

b. Find the average growth rate of bacteria in Dish 1 and in Dish 2 from time $t = 0$ to time $t = 4$.

Solution □ a. $\dfrac{\text{number of bacteria in Dish 2} - \text{number of bacteria in Dish 1 at time } t = 0}{\text{number of bacteria in Dish 2 at time } t = 0}$

$= \dfrac{3,000 - 2,000}{3,000} = \dfrac{1}{3} = 33\dfrac{1}{3}\%$

At time $t = 0$, the number of bacteria in Dish 2 is $33\dfrac{1}{3}\%$ more than the number of bacteria in Dish 1.

b. Average groth rate of Dish 1 $= \dfrac{10,120 - 2,000}{4 - 0} = 2,030$ bacteria per hour

Average groth rate of Dish 2 $= \dfrac{6,220 - 3,000}{4 - 0} = 805$ bacteria per hour

Exercises - Exponential Functions and Graphs

1

During a decade of continuous drought, the water level of a lake has decreased by 10 percent each year. Which of the following graphs could model the water level of the lake as a function of time?

A)
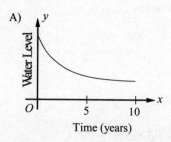

B)
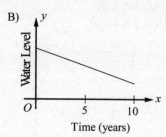

C)
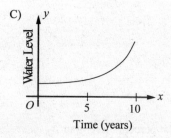

D)
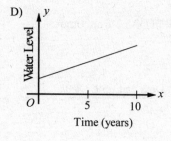

2

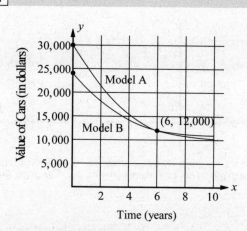

In the graph above, each exponential curve represents the values, in dollars, of two different cars as a function of time in years. At time $t = 0$, the price of model A was \$30,000 and the price of model B was \$24,000. At time $t = 6$, the price of both models were \$12,000.
Based on the graphs above, which of the following must be true?

I. At time $t = 0$, the price of model A was 25% more than the price of model B.

II. At time $t = 0$, the price of model B was 20% less than the price of model A.

III. From time $t = 0$ to $t = 6$, the average rate of decrease in the value of model A was 1.5 times the average rate of decrease in the value of model B.

A) I and II only

B) I and III only

C) II and III only

D) I, II, and III

3

If $f(x) = 12,000(0.9)^x$ and $g(x) = 14,000(0.85)^x$, what is the value of $g(2) - f(2)$?

12-4. Exponential Growth and Decay

Compound Interest Formulas

If initial amount P is invested at annual interest rate r, the investment will grow to final amount A in t years. $A = P(1+r)^t$

We can use the same formula for the population or value of goods that is increasing or decreasing.

Exponential Growth and **Doubling-Time Growth Formula**

If a population is increasing at a constant rate r each year, the population at the end of t years would be $A = P(1+r)^t$.

If an initial population of size P doubles every d years (or any other unit of time), the final number A in t years is given by $A = P(2)^{t/d}$.

Exponential Decay and **Half-Life Decay Formula**

If a population is decreasing at a constant rate r each year, the population at the end of t years would be $A = P(1-r)^t$.

The **half-life** of a substance is the amount of time it takes for half of the substance to decay. If an initial population of size P has a half-life of d years (or any other unit of time), the final

number A in t years is given by $A = P(\frac{1}{2})^{t/d}$.

Example 1 □   a. Mark invests \$1,500 at a rate of 6% interest compounded annually. How much is the investment worth after 5 years?

b. The price of a new automobile is \$28,000. If the value of the automobile decreases 12% per year, what will be the price of the automobile after 5 years?

c. The population of a western town doubles in size every 12 years. If the population of town is 8,000, what will the population be 18 years from now?

d. The half-life of carbon-14 is approximately 6000 years. How much of 800 g of this substance will remain after 30,000 years?

Solution □   a. $A = P(1+r)^t$ Compound Interest Formula

$= 1,500(1+0.06)^5$ Substitute $P = 1500$, $r = 0.06$, and $t = 5$.

$= 2,007.34$ Use a calculator.

b. $A = P(1-r)^t$ Exponential Decay Formula

$= 28,000(1-0.12)^5$ Substitute $P = 28,000$, $r = 0.12$, and $t = 5$.

$\approx 14,776.49$ Use a calculator.

c. $A = P(2)^{t/d}$ Doubling-Time Growth Formula

$= 8,000 \cdot 2^{18/12}$ Substitute $P = 8,000$, $t = 18$, and $d = 12$.

$\approx 22,627$ Use a calculator.

d. $A = P(\frac{1}{2})^{t/d}$ Half-Life Decay Formula

$A = 800(\frac{1}{2})^{30,000/6,000}$ $P = 800$, $t = 30,000$, and $d = 6,000$.

$= 25$ Use a calculator.

Exercises - Exponential Growth and Decay

1

The number of rabbits in a certain population doubles every 40 days. If the population starts with 12 rabbits, which of the following gives the total number of rabbits in the population after t days?

A) $12(2)(\dfrac{t}{40})$

B) $12(2)(\dfrac{40}{t})$

C) $12(2)^{\frac{40}{t}}$

D) $12(2)^{\frac{t}{40}}$

2

Population P of a town is 80,000 this year. If the population of the town decreases at a rate of 4 percent each year, which of the following expressions gives population P after t years?

A) $80,000(0.6)^t$

B) $80,000(0.96)^t$

C) $80,000(0.96t)$

D) $80,000(1-0.04t)$

3

A house bought ten years ago for $150,000 was sold for $240,000 this year. Which of the following equations can be used to solve the annual growth rate r of the value of the house?

A) $240,000 = 150,000(1+\dfrac{r}{10})$

B) $240,000 = 150,000(1+10r)$

C) $240,000 = 150,000(1+r)^{10}$

D) $240,000 = 150,000(r)^{10}$

4

A certain radioactive substance has a half-life of 12 days. This means that every 12 days, half of the original amount of the substance decays. If there are 128 milligrams of the radioactive substance today, how many milligrams will be left after 48 days?

A) 4

B) 8

C) 16

D) 32

▼

Questions 5 and 6 refer to the following information.

Evelyn deposited $3,000 into her bank account, which earns 4 percent interest compounded annually. She uses the expression $\$3,000(x)^t$ to find the value of the account after t years.

5

What is the value of x in the expression?

6

Evelyn deposited the same amount into an account that earns 5 percent interest rate compounded annually. How much more money than her original deposit in the account with 4 percent interest rate compounded annually will she have earned in 10 years?
(Round your answer to the nearest dollar.)

▲

Chapter 12 Practice Test

1

If $f(x) = \sqrt{2x}$ and $g(x) = 2x^2$, what is the value of $f(g(1)) - g(f(1))$?

A) -4

B) -2

C) 2

D) 4

2

If $f(x) = \sqrt{625 - x^2}$ and $g(x) = \sqrt{225 - x^2}$, what is the value of $f(f(5)) - g((g5))$?

A) 0

B) 5

C) 10

D) 20

3

The population of a certain town doubles every 25 years. If the population of the town was 51,200 in 1980, in what year was the population 6,400?

A) 1855

B) 1880

C) 1905

D) 1930

4

The half-life of a radioactive substance is the amount of time it takes for half of the substance to decay. The table below shows the time (in years) and the amount of substance left for a certain radioactive substance.

Time (years)	Amount (grams)
0	1,200
14	850
28	600
42	425
56	300

How much of the original amount of the substance, to the nearest whole gram, will remain after 140 years?

A) 85

B) 75

C) 53

D) 38

5

A radioactive substance decays at a rate of 18% per year. If the initial amount of the substance is 100 grams, which of the following functions models the remaining amount of the substance, in grams, after t years?

A) $f(t) = 100(0.18)^t$

B) $f(t) = 100(0.82)^t$

C) $f(t) = 100 - 100(0.18)^t$

D) $f(t) = 100 - 100(0.82)^t$

6

$$5,000(1+\frac{r}{100})^t$$

The expression above gives the value of an investment, in dollars, that pays an annual interest rate of $r\%$ compounded yearly. 5,000 is the initial amount and t is the number of years after the initial amount was deposited. Which of the following expressions shows the difference between the value of a 15 year investment at 6% annual compound interest and a 12 year investment at 6% annual compound interest?

A) $5,000\left[(1.06)^{\frac{15}{12}}\right]$

B) $5,000\left[\dfrac{(1.06)^{15}}{(1.06)^{12}}\right]$

C) $5,000\left[(1.06)^{15}-(1.06)^{12}\right]$

D) $5,000\left[(1.06)^{15-12}\right]$

7

The price P, in dollars, of a truck t years after it was purchased is given by the function $P(t)=24,000(\frac{1}{2})^{\frac{t}{6}}$. To the nearest dollar, what is the price of the truck 9 years after it was purchased?

Questions 8 and 9 refer to the following information.

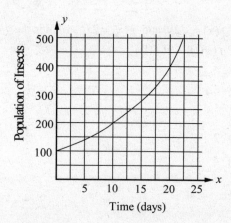

Time (days)

The graph above shows the size of a certain insect population over 25 days. The population at time $t=0$ was 100. A biologist used the equation $f(t)=100(2)^{\frac{t}{d}}$ to model the population.

8

What is the value of d in the equation?

9

What was the population of the insect after 15 days, to the nearest whole number?

Answer Key

Section 12-1

1. B   2. C   3. A   4. D   5. 6
6. 4

Section 12-2

1. B   2. B   3. D   4. C   5. A

Section 12-3

1. A   2. D   3. 395

Section 12-4

1. D   2. B   3. C   4. B   5. 1.04
6. 446

Chapter 12 Practice Test

1. B   2. A   3. C   4. D   5. B
6. C   7. 8485   8. 10   9. 283

Answers and Explanations

Section 12-1

1. B

$g(x) = 1 - x$

$g(-2) = 1 - (-2)$ Substitute -2 for x.

$= 3$

$f(x) = x^2 - 3x - 1$

$f \circ g(-2) = f(g(-2))$

$= f(3)$ $g(-2) = 3$

$= (3)^2 - 3(3) - 1$ Substitute 3 for x.

$= -1$

2. C

$f = \{(-4, 12), (-2, 4), (2, 0), (3, \frac{3}{2})\} \Rightarrow$

$f(-4) = 12$, $f(-2) = 4$, $f(2) = 0$ and $f(3) = \frac{3}{2}$

$g = \{(-2, 5), (0, 1), (4, -7), (5, -9)\} \Rightarrow$

$g(-2) = 5$, $g(0) = 1$, $g(4) = -7$, $g(5) = -9$

$g \circ f(2) = g(f(2))$

$= g(0)$ $f(2) = 0$

$= 1$ $g(0) = 1$

3. A

$f(g(-1))$

$= f(1)$ $g(-1) = 1$

$= -2$ $f(1) = -2$

4. D

$g(x) = 2 - x$

$g(3) = 2 - 3$ Substitute 3 for x.

$= -1$

$f(g(3))$

$= f(-1)$ $g(3) = -1$

$= \dfrac{1 - 5(-1)}{2}$ Substitute -1 for x.

$= 3$

5. 6

x	$f(x)$	$g(x)$
-2	-5	0
0	6	4
3	0	-5

Based on the table, $g(-2) = 0$.

$f(g(-2))$

$= f(0)$ $g(-2) = 0$

$= 6$

6. 4

Based on the table, $f(3) = 0$.

$g(f(3))$

$= g(0)$ $f(3) = 0$

$= 4$

Section 12-2

1. B

$a_n = \sqrt{(a_{n-1})^2 + 2}$

$a_1 = \sqrt{(a_0)^2 + 2}$ $n = 1$

$= \sqrt{(\sqrt{2})^2 + 2}$ $a_0 = \sqrt{2}$

$= \sqrt{4} = 2$

$$a_2 = \sqrt{(a_1)^2 + 2} \qquad\qquad n = 2$$

$$= \sqrt{(2)^2 + 2} \qquad\qquad a_1 = 2$$

$$= \sqrt{6}$$

2. B

$$a_{n+1} = a_n - \frac{f(a_n)}{g(a_n)}$$

$$a_1 = a_0 - \frac{f(a_0)}{g(a_0)} \qquad\qquad n = 0$$

$$= 1 - \frac{f(1)}{g(1)} \qquad\qquad a_0 = 1$$

Since $f(x) = x^2 - 3x$ and $g(x) = 2x - 3$,

$f(1) = (1)^2 - 3(1) = -2$ and $g(1) = 2(1) - 3 = -1$.

Thus, $a_1 = 1 - \dfrac{f(1)}{g(1)} = 1 - \dfrac{-2}{-1} = -1$.

$$a_2 = a_1 - \frac{f(a_1)}{g(a_1)} \qquad\qquad n = 1$$

$$= -1 - \frac{f(-1)}{g(-1)} \qquad\qquad a_1 = -1$$

$f(-1) = (-1)^2 - 3(-1) = 4$ and

$g(-1) = 2(-1) - 3 = -5$.

Thus, $a_2 = -1 - \dfrac{f(-1)}{g(-1)} = -1 - \dfrac{4}{-5} = -\dfrac{1}{5}$

3. D

$$f(x) = \sqrt{2x^2 - 1}$$

$$f \circ f \circ f(2)$$

$$= f(f(f(2))) = f(f(\sqrt{2(2)^2 - 1}))$$

$$= f(f(\sqrt{7})) = f(\sqrt{2(\sqrt{7})^2 - 1})$$

$$= f(\sqrt{13}) = \sqrt{2(\sqrt{13})^2 - 1}$$

$$= \sqrt{25} = 5$$

4. C

$$A_n = (1 + \frac{r}{100}) \cdot A_{n-1} + 12b$$

$$A_1 = (1 + \frac{r}{100}) \cdot A_0 + 12b \qquad\qquad n = 1$$

$$= (1 + \frac{5}{100}) \cdot 12,000 + 12(400)$$

$$= 17,400$$

$$A_2 = (1 + \frac{r}{100}) \cdot A_1 + 12b \qquad\qquad n = 2$$

$$= (1 + \frac{5}{100}) \cdot 17,400 + 12(400) \quad A_1 = 17,400$$

$$= 23,070$$

$$A_3 = (1 + \frac{r}{100}) \cdot A_2 + 12b \qquad\qquad n = 3$$

$$= (1 + \frac{5}{100}) \cdot 23,070 + 12(400) \quad A_2 = 23,070$$

$$= 29,023.50$$

5. A

$$P_n = 0.85P_{n-1} + 20$$

$$P_1 = 0.85P_0 + 20 \qquad\qquad n = 1$$

$$= 0.85(400) + 20 \qquad\qquad P_0 = 400$$

$$= 360$$

$$P_2 = 0.85P_1 + 20 \qquad\qquad n = 2$$

$$= 0.85(360) + 20 \qquad\qquad P_1 = 360$$

$$= 326$$

$$P_3 = 0.85P_2 + 20 \qquad\qquad n = 2$$

$$= 0.85(326) + 20 \qquad\qquad P_2 = 326$$

$$= 297.1$$

Section 12-3

1. A

Suppose the initial water level was 100 units. If the water level decreases by 10 percent each year, the water level will be $100(1 - 0.1)^n$, or $100(0.9)^n$, n years later. The water level decreases exponentially, not linearly.
Of the graphs shown, only choice A would appropriately model exponential decrease.

2. D

I. At time $t = 0$, the price of model A was $30,000 and the price of model B was $24,000. To find out what percent the price of model A was higher than the price of model B, use the following equation.

$$30,000 = 24,000(1 \underbrace{+ \frac{x}{100}}_{x\% \text{ more than}})$$

$$\frac{30,000}{24,000} = 1 + \frac{x}{100}$$

$$\Rightarrow 1.25 = 1 + \frac{x}{100} \Rightarrow 0.25 = \frac{x}{100}$$

$$\Rightarrow 25 = x$$

Therefore the price of model A was 25% higher than and the price of model B.

Roman numeral I is true.

To find out what percent the price of model B was less than the price of model A, use the following equation.

$$24,000 = 30,000(1 \underset{\underset{x\% \text{ less than}}{\underline{\dfrac{x}{100}}}}{})$$

$$\frac{24,000}{30,000} = 1 - \frac{x}{100}$$

$$0.8 = 1 - \frac{x}{100} \Rightarrow 0.2 = \frac{x}{100}$$

$$\Rightarrow 20 = x$$

Therefore the price of model B was 20% less than the price of model A.

Roman numeral II is true.

From time $t = 0$ to $t = 6$, the average rate of decrease in the value of model A

$$= \frac{\text{amount of decrease}}{\text{change in years}} = \frac{30,000 - 12,000}{6}$$

$$= 3,000$$

From time $t = 0$ to $t = 6$, the average rate of decrease in the value of model B

$$= \frac{\text{amount of decrease}}{\text{change in years}} = \frac{24,000 - 12,000}{6}$$

$$= 2,000$$

Therefore, from time $t = 0$ to $t = 6$, the average rate of decrease in the value of model A was 1.5 times the average rate of decrease in the value of model B.

Roman numeral III is also true.

Choice D is correct.

3. 395

$f(x) = 12,000(0.9)^x$ and $g(x) = 14,000(0.85)^x$

$g(2) - f(2) = 14,000(0.85)^2 - 12,000(0.9)^2$

$= 10,115 - 9720 = 395$

Section 12-4

1. D

The present population must be multiplied by a factor of 2 to double. If a certain population doubles every 40 days, the population grows by a multiple of $(2)^{\frac{1}{40}}$ each day. After t days, the population will be multiplied by $(2)^{\frac{t}{40}}$. If the population starts with 12 rabbits, after t days, the population will be $12 \times (2)^{\frac{t}{40}}$.

2. B

For the present population to decrease by 4%, the initial population must be multiplied by a factor of 0.96. If population P is 80,000 this year, it will be

80,000(0.96) one year later,

80,000(0.96)(0.96) two years later,

80,000(0.96)(0.96)(0.96) three years later,

and so on. After t years, the population will be

$80,000(0.96)^t$.

3. C

For the price of a house to increase at an annual growth rate of r, it must be multiplied by a factor of $(1 + r)$ each year. If the price of the house is $150,000 this year, it will be

$150,000(1 + r)$ one year later,

$150,000(1 + r)(1 + r)$ two years later,

$150,000(1 + r)(1 + r)(1 + r)$ three years later,

and so on. Thus, 10 years later, the price of the house will be $150,000(1 + r)^{10}$.

4. B

If the half-life of a substance is 12 days, half of the substance decays every 12 days.
Make a chart.

Amount	Days
128	0
$128 \times \dfrac{1}{2}$	12 days after
$128 \times \dfrac{1}{2} \times \dfrac{1}{2}$	24 days after
$128 \times \dfrac{1}{2} \times \dfrac{1}{2} \times \dfrac{1}{2}$	36 days after
$128 \times \dfrac{1}{2} \times \dfrac{1}{2} \times \dfrac{1}{2} \times \dfrac{1}{2}$	48 days after

Therefore, after 48 days, there will be

$128 \times \dfrac{1}{2} \times \dfrac{1}{2} \times \dfrac{1}{2} \times \dfrac{1}{2}$, or 8 milligrams, of the radioactive substance left.

5. 1.04

The initial deposit earns 4 percent interest compounded annually. Thus at the end of one year, the new value of the account is the initial deposit of $3,000 plus 4 percent of the initial deposit: $\$3,000 + 0.04(\$3,000) = \$3,000(1 + 0.04)$.

Since the interest is compounded annually, the value at the end of each succeeding year is the previous year's value plus 4 percent of the previous year's value. Thus after 2 years, the value will be $\$3,000(1.04)(1.04)$. After 3 years, the value will be $\$3,000(1.04)(1.04)(1.04)$.

After t years, the value will be $\$3,000(1.04)^t$. Therefore, the value of x in the expression $\$3,000(x)^t$ is 1.04.

6. 446

The difference in the amount after 10 years will be $\$3,000(1.05)^{10} - \$3,000(1.04)^{10}$ $\approx \$445.95$.
To the nearest dollar the difference in the amount will be $446.

Chapter 12 Practice Test

1. B

$f(x) = \sqrt{2x}$ and $g(x) = 2x^2$

$g(1) = 2(1)^2 = 2$ and $f(1) = \sqrt{2(1)} = \sqrt{2}$

$f(g(1)) - g(f(1))$

$= f(2) - g(\sqrt{2})$

$= \sqrt{2(2)} - 2(\sqrt{2})^2$

$= \sqrt{4} - 2(2) = 2 - 4 = -2$

2. A

$f(x) = \sqrt{625 - x^2}$ and $g(x) = \sqrt{225 - x^2}$

$f(5) = \sqrt{625 - 5^2} = \sqrt{600}$

$g(5) = \sqrt{225 - 5^2} = \sqrt{200}$

$f(f(5)) - g((g5))$

$= f(\sqrt{600}) - g(\sqrt{200})$

$= (\sqrt{625 - (\sqrt{600})^2}) - (\sqrt{225 - (\sqrt{200})^2})$

$= \sqrt{625 - 600} - \sqrt{225 - 200}$

$= \sqrt{25} - \sqrt{25} = 0$

3. C

Method I:

You can keep dividing by 2 until you get to a population of 6,400.

Year	Population
1980	51,200
1955	25,600
1930	12,800
1905	6,400

Method II:

Use the half-life formula, $A = P(\frac{1}{2})^{t/d}$.

$6,400 = 51,200(\frac{1}{2})^{t/25}$

$\dfrac{6,400}{51,200} = (\frac{1}{2})^{t/25}$ Divide each side by 51,200.

$\dfrac{1}{8} = (\frac{1}{2})^{t/25}$ Simplify.

$(\frac{1}{2})^3 = (\frac{1}{2})^{t/25}$ $\dfrac{1}{8} = (\frac{1}{2})^3$

$3 = \dfrac{t}{25}$ If $b^x = b^y$, then $x = y$.

$75 = t$

Therefore, in year $1980 - 75$, or 1905, the population of the town was 6,400.

4. D

The table shows that one-half of the substance decays every 28 years. Therefore, the half-life of the radioactive substance is 28 years. Use the half-life formula, $A = P(\frac{1}{2})^{t/d}$, to find out how much of the original amount of the substance will remain after 140 years. P is the initial amount, t is the number of years and d is the half-life.

$A = 1,200(\frac{1}{2})^{140/28}$

$= 37.5$ Use a calculator.

To the nearest gram, 38 grams of the substance will remain after 140 years.

5. B

If the substance decays at a rate of 18% per year the amount of substance remaining each year will be multiplied by $(1 - 0.18)$, or 0.82.
The initial amount of 100 grams will become

$100(1-0.18)$ one year later,

$100(1-0.18)(1-0.18)$ two years later,

$100(1-0.18)(1-0.18)(1-0.18)$ three years later, and so on. Thus, t years later, the remaining amount of the substance, in grams, is

$f(t)=100(0.82)^t$.

6. **C**

$5,000(1+\dfrac{r}{100})^t$

The value of the 15 year investment at 6% annual compound interest

$=5,000(1+\dfrac{6}{100})^{15}=5,000(1.06)^{15}$.

The value of the 12 year investment at 6% annual compound interest

$=5,000(1+\dfrac{6}{100})^{12}=5,000(1.06)^{12}$.

The difference is

$=5,000(1.06)^{15}-5,000(1.06)^{12}$

$=5,000\left[(1.06)^{15}-(1.06)^{12}\right]$

7. **8485**

$P(t)=24,000(\dfrac{1}{2})^{\frac{t}{6}}$

$P(9)=24,000(\dfrac{1}{2})^{\frac{9}{6}}$ Substitute 9 for t.

$=24,000(\dfrac{1}{2})^{\frac{3}{2}}$

$\approx 8,485.28$ Use a calculator.

To the nearest dollar, the price of the truck 9 years after it was purchased is $8,485.

8. **10**

Time (days)

$f(t)=100(2)^{\frac{t}{d}}$

In the equation, d represents the amount of time it takes to double the population. The graph shows that the population was 100 at $t=0$, 200 at $t=10$, and 400 at $t=20$. Therefore, the value of doubling time d is 10 days.

9. **283**

$f(t)=100(2)^{\frac{t}{d}}$

$f(15)=100(2)^{\frac{15}{10}}=100(2)^{1.5}$

≈ 282.84 Use a calculator.

The population of the insect after 15 days was 283, to the nearest whole number.

CHAPTER 13
Polynomial and Radical Functions

13-1. Polynomial Functions and Their Graphs

A **polynomial function** is a function of the form $f(x) = a_n x^n + a_{n-1} x^{n-1} + \cdots + a_2 x^2 + a_1 x + a_0$,
in which the coefficients $a_n, a_{n-1}, \cdots, a_2, a_1, a_0$ are real numbers and n is a nonnegative integer.
The degree of a polynomial function is its greatest exponent of x. The graphs of several polynomial
functions are shown below. The maximum number of zeros, which are the x-intercepts, is equal to
the degree of the function.

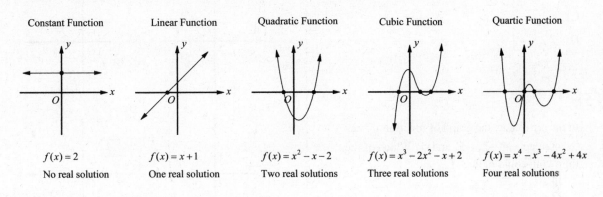

Constant Function	Linear Function	Quadratic Function	Cubic Function	Quartic Function
$f(x) = 2$	$f(x) = x + 1$	$f(x) = x^2 - x - 2$	$f(x) = x^3 - 2x^2 - x + 2$	$f(x) = x^4 - x^3 - 4x^2 + 4x$
No real solution	One real solution	Two real solutions	Three real solutions	Four real solutions

A function f is **increasing** on an interval if the value
of f increases as x increases in the interval.
A function f is **decreasing** on an interval if the value
of f decreases as x increases in the interval.
In the graph shown at the right, function f increases
on the intervals $(-\infty, a)$ and (b, ∞), and decreases on the
interval (a, b). At a point where the graph changes from
increasing to decreasing, f has a local **maximum value**,
and at a point where the graph changes from decreasing
to increasing, f has a local **minimum value**.

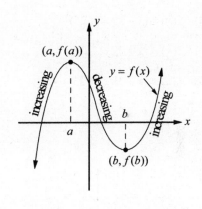

Example 1 □ The complete graph of function f is shown
at the right.

a. Find the x-intercepts of $f(x)$.

b. For what value of x is the value of $f(x)$
at its maximum?

c. Find the interval where $f(x)$ is strictly decreasing.

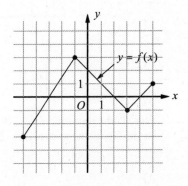

Solution □ a. The x-intercepts are -3, 2, and 4.

b. The value of $f(x)$ is maximum at $x = -1$.

c. $f(x)$ is strictly decreasing between -1 and 3.

Exercises - Polynomial Functions and Their Graphs

1

The graph of $f(x) = ax^3 + x^2 - 18x - 9$ intersects the x-axis at $(3,0)$. What is the value of a?

A) -1

B) 0

C) 1

D) 2

2

In the xy-plane, the graph of function f has x-intercepts at -7, -5, and 5. Which of the following could define f?

A) $f(x) = (x-7)(x^2 - 25)$

B) $f(x) = (x-7)(x^2 + 25)$

C) $f(x) = (x+7)(x^2 - 25)$

D) $f(x) = (x+7)(x^2 + 25)$

3

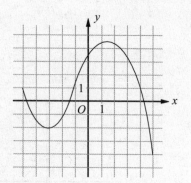

What is the minimum value of the function graphed on the xy-plane above, for $-5 \le x \le 5$?

A) -4

B) -3

C) -2

D) $-\infty$

4

If function f has four distinct zeros, which of the following could represent the complete graph of f in the xy-plane?

A) 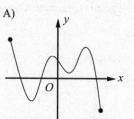   B)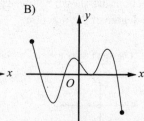

C) 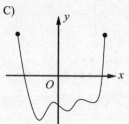   D)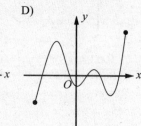

5

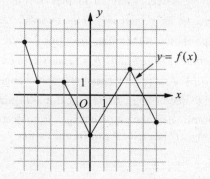

The complete graph of function f is shown on the xy-plane above, for $-5 \le x \le 5$. Which of the following is/are true?

I. f is strictly decreasing for $-5 < x < 0$.

II. $f(-3) = 1$

III. f is minimum at $x = 5$.

A) I only

B) II only

C) III only

D) I and II only

13-2. Remainder Theorem and Factor Theorem

Remainder Theorem

If a polynomial $f(x)$ is divided by $x-c$, the remainder is $f(c)$.

Since Dividend = Divisor × Quotient + Remainder ,

$f(x) = (x-c)q(x) + f(c)$, in which $q(x)$ is the quotient.

Factor Theorem

The polynomial $f(x)$ has $x-c$ as a factor if and only if $f(c) = 0$.

The following statements are equivalent for a polynomial $f(x)$ and a real number c:

- c is a **solution** to the equation $f(x) = 0$.
- c is a **zero** of $f(x)$.
- c is a **root** of $f(x)$.
- $x-c$ is a **factor** of $f(x)$.
- $f(x)$ is **divisible** by $x-c$.
- c is an **x-intercept** of the graph of $f(x)$.

Example 1 □ Find the remainder of $f(x) = x^3 + x^2 - 6x - 7$ divided by $x+2$.

Solution □ To find the remainder of $f(x)$ divided by $x+2 = x-(-2)$,

evaluate $f(-2)$. $f(-2) = (-2)^3 + (-2)^2 - 6(-2) - 7 = 1$

By the remainder theorem the remainder is 1.

Example 2 □ Find the value of a if $x-3$ is a factor of $f(x) = x^3 - 11x + a$.

Solution □ If $x-3$ is a factor of $f(x)$, then $f(3) = 0$

$f(3) = (3)^3 - 11(3) + a = 0 \implies -6 + a = 0 \implies a = 6$

Example 3 □ Find the value of k if $f(x) = 3(x^2 + 3x - 4) - 8(x - k)$ is divisible by x.

Solution □ If $f(x)$ is divisible by x, since $x = x - 0$, $f(0) = 0$ by the factor theorem.

$f(0) = 3(0^2 + 3(0) - 4) - 8(0 - k) = -12 + 8k = 0$

$8k = 12 \implies k = \dfrac{12}{8} = \dfrac{3}{2}$

Example 4 □ Find the x-intercepts of f if $f(x) = 2x^2 + x - 10$.

Solution □ $f(x) = 2x^2 + x - 10 = (2x+5)(x-2)$ Factor.

$(2x+5)(x-2) = 0$ Let $f(x) = 0$.

$2x + 5 = 0$ or $x - 2 = 0$ Zero Product Property

$x = -\dfrac{5}{2}$ or $x = 2$ Solve.

The x-intercepts of f are $-\dfrac{5}{2}$ and 2.

Exercises - Polynomial Functions and Their Graphs

1

If -1 and 1 are two real roots of the polynomial function $f(x) = ax^3 + bx^2 + cx + d$ and $(0,3)$ is the y-intercept of graph of f, what is the value of b?

A) -3

B) -1

C) 2

D) 4

2

What is the remainder of polynomial $p(x) = 81x^5 - 121x^3 - 36$ divided by $x + 1$?

A) -76

B) -36

C) 4

D) 6

3

If $x - 2$ is a factor of polynomial $p(x) = a(x^3 - 2x) + b(x^2 - 5)$, which of the following must be true?

A) $a + b = 0$

B) $2a - b = 0$

C) $2a + b = 0$

D) $4a - b = 0$

4

x	$f(x)$
-4	-10
-3	0
-1	-4
2	20

The function f is defined by a polynomial. Some values of x and $f(x)$ are shown in the table above. Which of the following must be a factor of $f(x)$?

A) $x + 4$

B) $x + 3$

C) $x + 1$

D) $x - 2$

5

$$x^3 - 8x^2 + 3x - 24 = 0$$

For what real value of x is the equation above true?

6

If $x > 0$, what is the solution to the equation $x^4 - 8x^2 = 9$?

13-3. Radical Expressions

The symbol $\sqrt[n]{a}$ is called a **radical**. Each part of a radical is given a name as indicated below.

index $\longrightarrow$ $\sqrt[n]{a}$ $\longleftarrow$ radicand

with labels: radical sign, radicand

Definition of nth root

For any real numbers x or a, and any positive integer n, if $x^n = a$, then x is an nth root of a.
If n is even, $x = \pm\sqrt[n]{a}$. If n is odd, $x = \sqrt[n]{a}$.

Definition of $a^{\frac{1}{2}}$ and $a^{\frac{1}{3}}$

For any nonnegative number a, $a^{\frac{1}{2}} = \sqrt{a}$. For any real number a, $a^{\frac{1}{3}} = \sqrt[3]{a}$.

Product and Quotient Property of Radicals

For any nonnegative number a or b, $\sqrt{ab} = \sqrt{a}\sqrt{b}$ and $\sqrt{\dfrac{a}{b}} = \dfrac{\sqrt{a}}{\sqrt{b}}$.

For any real number a or b, $\sqrt[3]{ab} = \sqrt[3]{a}\sqrt[3]{b}$ and $\sqrt[3]{\dfrac{a}{b}} = \dfrac{\sqrt[3]{a}}{\sqrt[3]{b}}$ if $b \neq 0$.

Example 1 □ Solve.

    a. $(x-5)^4 = 16$ b. $x^3 + 1 = -26$

Solution □ a. $(x-5)^4 = 16$

    $x - 5 = \pm\sqrt[4]{16}$ Definition of nth root, for when n is even.

    $x - 5 = \pm 2$ $\sqrt[4]{16} = \sqrt[4]{2^4} = 2$

    $x = 5 \pm 2$ Add 5 to each side.

    $x = 7$ or $x = 3$ Answer

b. $x^3 + 1 = -26$

    $x^3 = -27$ Subtract 1 from each side.

    $x = \sqrt[3]{-27} = (-27)^{\frac{1}{3}} = ((-3)^3)^{\frac{1}{3}}$ Definition of nth root, for when n is odd.

    $= -3$ Answer

Example 2 □ Simplify.

    a. $\sqrt{50}\sqrt{6}$ b. $\sqrt{18a^2b^3}$

Solution □ a. $\sqrt{50}\sqrt{6} = \sqrt{25}\sqrt{2}\sqrt{2}\sqrt{3}$ $\sqrt{50} = \sqrt{25}\sqrt{2}$, $\sqrt{6} = \sqrt{2}\sqrt{3}$

    $= 5 \cdot 2 \cdot \sqrt{3} = 10\sqrt{3}$

b. $\sqrt{18a^2b^3} = \sqrt{3^2 \cdot 2 \cdot a^2 \cdot b^2 \cdot b}$

    $= \sqrt{3^2} \cdot \sqrt{2} \cdot \sqrt{a^2} \cdot \sqrt{b^2} \cdot \sqrt{b}$ $\sqrt{ab} = \sqrt{a}\sqrt{b}$

    $= 3 \cdot \sqrt{2} \cdot a \cdot b \cdot \sqrt{b} = 3ab\sqrt{2b}$ $\sqrt{3^2} = 3$, $\sqrt{a^2} = a$, $\sqrt{b^2} = b$

A method used to eliminate radicals from a denominator is called **rationalizing the denominator**. Binomials of the form $\sqrt{a}+\sqrt{b}$ and $\sqrt{a}-\sqrt{b}$ are called **conjugates**. The product of conjugates is always an integer if a and b are integers. You can use conjugates to rationalize denominators.

Adding and Subtracting Radical Expressions

Radical expressions in which the radicands are alike can be added or subtracted in the same way that like monomials are added or subtracted.

Multiplying Radical Expressions

Multiplying two radical expressions with different radicands is similar to multiplying binomials.

Example 3 □ Simplify.

a. $\dfrac{1}{2-\sqrt{3}}$

b. $(\sqrt{6}-\sqrt{2})(\sqrt{3}+1)$

c. $\sqrt{50}-\sqrt{18}+\sqrt{8}$

d. $\sqrt{6}-\dfrac{\sqrt{2}}{\sqrt{3}}+\dfrac{\sqrt{3}}{\sqrt{2}}$

Solution □ a. $\dfrac{1}{2-\sqrt{3}}=\dfrac{1}{2-\sqrt{3}}\cdot\dfrac{2+\sqrt{3}}{2+\sqrt{3}}$ The conjugate of $2-\sqrt{3}$ is $2+\sqrt{3}$.

$\qquad=\dfrac{2+\sqrt{3}}{2^2-(\sqrt{3})^2}$ $(a-b)(a+b)=a^2-b^2$

$\qquad=\dfrac{2+\sqrt{3}}{4-3}=2+\sqrt{3}$

b. $(\sqrt{6}-\sqrt{2})(\sqrt{3}+1)$

$\quad=\sqrt{6}\cdot\sqrt{3}+\sqrt{6}\cdot1-\sqrt{2}\cdot\sqrt{3}-\sqrt{2}\cdot1$ FOIL

$\quad=\sqrt{2}\cdot\sqrt{3}\cdot\sqrt{3}+\sqrt{6}-\sqrt{6}-\sqrt{2}$ $\sqrt{6}=\sqrt{2}\cdot\sqrt{3}$

$\quad=3\sqrt{2}-\sqrt{2}=2\sqrt{2}$

c. $\sqrt{50}-\sqrt{18}+\sqrt{8}$

$\quad=\sqrt{25\cdot2}-\sqrt{9\cdot2}+\sqrt{4\cdot2}$

$\quad=\sqrt{25}\sqrt{2}-\sqrt{9}\sqrt{2}+\sqrt{4}\sqrt{2}$ $\sqrt{ab}=\sqrt{a}\sqrt{b}$

$\quad=5\sqrt{2}-3\sqrt{2}+2\sqrt{2}$

$\quad=4\sqrt{2}$ Combine like radicals.

d. $\sqrt{6}-\dfrac{\sqrt{2}}{\sqrt{3}}+\dfrac{\sqrt{3}}{\sqrt{2}}$

$\quad=\sqrt{6}-\dfrac{\sqrt{2}}{\sqrt{3}}\cdot\dfrac{\sqrt{3}}{\sqrt{3}}+\dfrac{\sqrt{3}}{\sqrt{2}}\cdot\dfrac{\sqrt{2}}{\sqrt{2}}$ Rationalize the denominator.

$\quad=\sqrt{6}-\dfrac{\sqrt{6}}{3}+\dfrac{\sqrt{6}}{2}$ Simplify.

$\quad=\sqrt{6}(1-\dfrac{1}{3}+\dfrac{1}{2})$ Factor.

$\quad=\dfrac{7\sqrt{6}}{6}$

Exercises - Radical Expressions

1

Which of the following is equal to $a^{-\frac{1}{2}}$?

A) $-\sqrt{a}$

B) $\dfrac{1}{\sqrt{a}}$

C) $-\dfrac{1}{\sqrt{a}}$

D) $\dfrac{1}{a^2}$

2

Which of the following is equal to $\dfrac{1}{3-2\sqrt{2}}$?

A) $3-\sqrt{2}$

B) $3+\sqrt{2}$

C) $3+2\sqrt{2}$

D) $3+4\sqrt{2}$

3

If $(x+1)^3 = -64$, what is the value of x ?

A) -6

B) -5

C) -4

D) -3

4

Which of the following is equal to
$\sqrt{8}+\sqrt{18}-\sqrt{32}$?

A) $\sqrt{2}$

B) $2\sqrt{2}$

C) $3\sqrt{2}$

D) $\sqrt{3}$

5

Which of the following is equal to
$(1+\sqrt{3})(2-\sqrt{3})$?

A) $1-\sqrt{3}$

B) $1+\sqrt{3}$

C) $-1-\sqrt{3}$

D) $-1+\sqrt{3}$

6

Which of the following is equal to $b^{\frac{5}{3}}$?

A) $b \cdot \sqrt{b}$

B) $b \cdot \sqrt{b^{\frac{1}{3}}}$

C) $b \cdot \sqrt[3]{b}$

D) $b \cdot \sqrt[3]{b^2}$

13-4. Solving Radical Equations

An equation which contains a radical with a variable in the radicand is called a **radical equation**.
To solve such an equation, first isolate the radical on one side of the equation. Then square each side of the
equation to eliminate the radical.

Example 1   □   Solve each equation.

       a. $\sqrt{5-2x} = 3$ b. $4 + \sqrt{\dfrac{1}{2}x} = 7$

Solution   □   a. $(\sqrt{5-2x})^2 = (3)^2$ Square each side.

                 $5 - 2x = 9$

                 $-2x = 4$ Subtract 5 from each side.

                 $x = -2$ ◄ Divide each side by -2.

         b. $4 + \sqrt{\dfrac{1}{2}x} = 7$ Original Equation

            $\sqrt{\dfrac{1}{2}x} = 3$ Subtract 3 from each side.

           $(\sqrt{\dfrac{1}{2}x})^2 = (3)^2$ Square each side.

            $\dfrac{1}{2}x = 9$ Simplify.

            $x = 18$ Multiply each side by 2.

When you square both sides of a radical equation, the resulting equation may have a solution that is not
a solution of the original equation. Such a solution is called an **extraneous solution**. Therefore, you must
check all the possible solutions in the original equation and disregard the extraneous solutions.

Example 2   □   Solve $\sqrt{x+2} = x$.

Solution   □   a. $\sqrt{x+2} = x$ Original equation

            $(\sqrt{x+2})^2 = (x)^2$ Square each side.

            $x + 2 = x^2$ Simplify.

            $0 = x^2 - x - 2$ Subtract x and 2 from each side.

            $0 = (x-2)(x+1)$ Factor.

            $x - 2 = 0$ or $x + 1 = 0$ Zero Product Property

            $x = 2$ or $x = -1$ Solve.

         Check the results by substituting 2 and -1 for x in the original equation.

         Check: $\sqrt{x+2} = x$ $\sqrt{x+2} = x$

                   $\sqrt{2+2} = 2$ $\sqrt{-1+2} = -1$

                     $\sqrt{4} = 2$ $\sqrt{1} = -1$

                     $2 = 2$ ✔ True $\sqrt{1} \neq -1$ ✗ False

         Since -1 does not satisfy the original equation, 2 is the only solution.

Exercises - Solving Radical Equations

1

$$11 - \sqrt{2x+3} = 8$$

What is the solution set of the equation above?

A) 0

B) 3

C) 6

D) 9

2

$$\sqrt{-3x+4} = 7$$

What is the solution set of the equation above?

A) −15

B) −12

C) −8

D) −6

3

$$\sqrt{x+18} = x-2$$

What is the solution set of the equation above?

A) $\{-2\}$

B) $\{7\}$

C) $\{-2, 7\}$

D) $\{2, -7\}$

4

$$\sqrt{5x-12} = 3\sqrt{2}$$

What is the solution set of the equation above?

A) 2

B) 4

C) 6

D) 8

5

If $a = \sqrt{3}$ and $\sqrt{2-3x} = \dfrac{1}{3}a$, what is the value of x?

6

If $k = 8 - \sqrt{2}$ and $\sqrt[3]{x-k} = -2$, what is the value of x^2?

13-5. Complex Numbers

Definition of i

$$i = \sqrt{-1} \quad \text{and} \quad i^2 = -1$$

For real numbers a and b, the expression $a + bi$ is called a **complex number**.
Number a is called the **real part** and number b is called the **imaginary part** of the complex number $a + bi$.

To add or subtract complex numbers, combine the real parts and combine the imaginary parts.
$$(a + bi) + (c + di) = (a + c) + (b + d)i$$
$$(a + bi) - (c + di) = (a - c) + (b - d)i$$

Example 1   □   Simplify.

    a. i^{35} b. $\sqrt{-5} \cdot \sqrt{-10}$

    c. $(4 - 3i) + (5 + 4i)$ d. $2(-3 + i) - 5(1 - i)$

Solution   □   a. $i^{35} = i \cdot i^{34}$ $a^m \cdot a^n = a^{m+n}$

                  $= i \cdot (i^2)^{17}$ $(a^m)^n = a^{mn}$

                  $= i \cdot (-1)^{17}$ $i^2 = -1$

                  $= -i$ $(-1)^{17} = -1$

          b. $\sqrt{-5} \cdot \sqrt{-10}$

              $= (i \cdot \sqrt{5})(i\sqrt{10})$ $\sqrt{-5} = \sqrt{5} \cdot \sqrt{-1} = i\sqrt{5}$, $\sqrt{-10} = i\sqrt{10}$

              $= i^2 \sqrt{50}$ Multiply.

              $= (-1)(\sqrt{25} \cdot \sqrt{2})$ $i^2 = -1$, $\sqrt{50} = \sqrt{25} \cdot \sqrt{2}$

              $= -5\sqrt{2}$ Simplify.

          c. $(4 - 3i) + (5 + 4i)$

              $= (4 + 5) + (-3i + 4i)$ Combine the real parts and the imaginary parts.

              $= 9 + i$ Simplify.

          d. $2(-3 + i) - 5(1 - i)$

              $= -6 + 2i - 5 + 5i$ Multiply.

              $= -11 + 7i$ Simplify.

Example 2   □   Solve $3x^2 + 75 = 0$.

Solution   □ $3x^2 + 75 = 0$

          $3x^2 = -75$ Subtract 75 from each side.

          $x^2 = -25$ Divide each side by 3.

          $x = \pm\sqrt{-25}$ Take the square root of each side.

          $x = \pm\sqrt{25}\sqrt{-1}$ Product Property of Radicals

          $x = \pm 5i$ $\sqrt{-1} = i$

To multiply two complex numbers, use the FOIL method and use the fact that $i^2 = -1$.

$$(a + bi)(c + di) = ac + adi + bci + bdi^2 = (ac - bd) + (ad + bc)i$$

Imaginary numbers of the form $a + bi$ and $a - bi$ are called **complex conjugates**, and their product is the real number $a^2 + b^2$. This fact can be used to simplify the quotient of two imaginary numbers.

Definition of Equal Complex Numbers

Two complex numbers are equal if and only if their real parts are equal and their imaginary parts are equal. $a + bi = c + di$ if and only if $a = c$ and $b = d$.

Example 3 □ Simplify.

    a. $(6 - i)(2 + 3i)$ b. $(\sqrt{3} + \sqrt{-2})(\sqrt{3} - \sqrt{-2})$

    c. $\dfrac{10}{(1 + 3i)}$ d. $\dfrac{2 + 3i}{4 - 3i}$

Solution □ a. $(6 - i)(2 + 3i)$

    $= 12 + 18i - 2i - 3i^2$ FOIL

    $= 12 + 16i - 3(-1)$ $i^2 = -1$

    $= 15 + 16i$ Simplify.

b. $(\sqrt{3} - \sqrt{-2})(\sqrt{3} + \sqrt{-2})$

    $= (\sqrt{3} + i\sqrt{2})(\sqrt{3} - i\sqrt{2})$ $\sqrt{-2} = i\sqrt{2}$

    $= (\sqrt{3})^2 - (i\sqrt{2})^2$ $(a + b)(a - b) = a^2 - b^2$

    $= 3 - 2i^2$

    $= 5$ $i^2 = -1$

c. $\dfrac{10}{(1 + 3i)}$

    $= \dfrac{10}{(1 + 3i)} \cdot \dfrac{(1 - 3i)}{(1 - 3i)}$ Rationalize the denominator.

    $= \dfrac{10(1 - 3i)}{1 - 9i^2}$ $(a + b)(a - b) = a^2 - b^2$

    $= \dfrac{\cancel{10}(1 - 3i)}{\cancel{10}}$ $i^2 = -1$

    $= 1 - 3i$ Simplify.

d. $\dfrac{2 + 3i}{4 - 3i}$

    $= \dfrac{2 + 3i}{4 - 3i} \cdot \dfrac{4 + 3i}{4 + 3i}$ Rationalize the denominator.

    $= \dfrac{8 + 6i + 12i + 9i^2}{16 - 9i^2}$ FOIL

    $= \dfrac{-1 + 18i}{25}$ $i^2 = -1$

Exercises - Complex Numbers

1

Which of the following is equal
to $\sqrt{-1} - \sqrt{-4} + \sqrt{-9}$?

A) i

B) $2i$

C) $3i$

D) $4i$

2

Which of the following is equal
to $\sqrt{-2} \cdot \sqrt{-8}$?

A) $-4i$

B) $4i$

C) -4

D) 4

3

Which of the following complex numbers is equal
to $\dfrac{3-i}{3+i}$?

A) $\dfrac{9}{10} - \dfrac{3i}{5}$

B) $\dfrac{9}{10} + \dfrac{3i}{5}$

C) $\dfrac{3}{5} - \dfrac{3i}{5}$

D) $\dfrac{4}{5} - \dfrac{3i}{5}$

4

Which of the following is equal
to $\dfrac{1}{2}(5i - 3) - \dfrac{1}{3}(4i + 5)$?

A) $\dfrac{3}{2}i - \dfrac{5}{2}$

B) $\dfrac{7}{6}i - \dfrac{7}{3}$

C) $\dfrac{7}{6}i - \dfrac{19}{6}$

D) $\dfrac{5}{6}i - \dfrac{17}{6}$

5

If $(4+i)^2 = a + bi$, what is the value of $a+b$?

6

If the expression $\dfrac{3-i}{1-2i}$ is rewritten in the form
$a + bi$, in which a and b are real numbers, what
is the value of $a+b$?

Chapter 13 Practice Test

1

If the graph of $f(x) = 2x^3 + bx^2 + 4x - 4$ intersects the x-axis at $(\frac{1}{2}, 0)$, and $(-2, k)$ lies on the graph of f, what is the value of k?

A) −4

B) −2

C)   0

D)   2

2

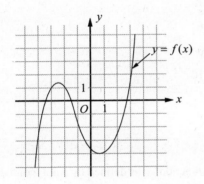

The function $y = f(x)$ is graphed on the xy-plane above. If k is a constant such that the equation $f(x) = k$ has one real solution, which of the following could be the value of k?

A) −3

B) −1

C)   1

D)   3

3

What is the value of a if $x + 2$ is a factor of $f(x) = -(x^3 + 3x^2) - 4(x - a)$?

A) −2

B) −1

C)   0

D)   1

4

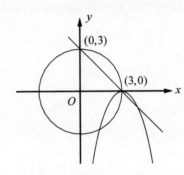

$$x^2 + y^2 = 9$$
$$y = -(x - 3)^2$$
$$x + y = 3$$

A system of three equations and their graphs on the xy-plane are shown above. How many solutions does the system have?

A) 1

B) 2

C) 3

D) 4

5

Which of the following complex numbers is equivalent to $\dfrac{(1-i)^2}{1+i}$?

A) $-\dfrac{i}{2}-\dfrac{1}{2}$

B) $-\dfrac{i}{2}+\dfrac{1}{2}$

C) $-i-1$

D) $-i+1$

6

Which of the following is equal to $a\sqrt[3]{a}$?

A) $a^{\frac{2}{3}}$

B) $a^{\frac{4}{3}}$

C) $a^{\frac{5}{3}}$

D) $a^{\frac{7}{3}}$

7

$$p(x) = -2x^3 + 4x^2 - 10x$$

$$q(x) = x^2 - 2x + 5$$

The polynomials $p(x)$ and $q(x)$ are defined above. Which of the following polynomials is divisible by $x-1$?

A) $f(x) = p(x) - \dfrac{1}{2}q(x)$

B) $g(x) = -\dfrac{1}{2}p(x) - q(x)$

C) $h(x) = -p(x) + \dfrac{1}{2}q(x)$

D) $k(x) = \dfrac{1}{2}p(x) + q(x)$

8

$$\sqrt{2x+6} = x+3$$

What is the solution set of the equation above?

A) $\{-3\}$

B) $\{-1\}$

C) $\{-3, 2\}$

D) $\{-3, -1\}$

9

What is the remainder when polynomial $p(x) = 24x^3 - 36x^2 + 14$ is divided by $x - \dfrac{1}{2}$?

A) 4

B) 6

C) 8

D) 10

10

The function f is defined by a polynomial. If $x+2$, $x+1$, and $x-1$ are factors of f, which of the following table could define f ?

A)

x	$f(x)$
-2	4
-1	0
1	0
2	0

B)

x	$f(x)$
-2	0
-1	4
1	0
2	0

C)

x	$f(x)$
-2	0
-1	0
1	4
2	0

D)

x	$f(x)$
-2	0
-1	0
1	0
2	4

Answer Key

Section 13-1

1. D   2. C   3. A   4. B   5. B

Section 13-2

1. A   2. C   3. D   4. B   5. 8

6. 3

Section 13-3

1. B   2. C   3. B   4. A   5. D

6. D

Section 13-4

1. B   2. A   3. B   4. C   5. $\dfrac{5}{9}$

6. 2

Section 13-5

1. B   2. C   3. D   4. C   5. 23

6. 2

Chapter 13 Practice Test

1. C   2. D   3. B   4. A   5. C

6. B   7. B   8. D   9. C   10. D

Answers and Explanations

Section 13-1

1. D

$f(x) = ax^3 + x^2 - 18x - 9$

If point $(3,0)$ lies on the graph of f, substitute
0 for f and 3 for x.

$0 = a(3)^3 + (3)^2 - 18(3) - 9$.

$0 = 27a - 54$

$2 = a$

2. C

If the graph of a polynomial function f has an
x-intercept at a, then $(x - a)$ is a factor of $f(x)$.
Since the graph of function f has x-intercepts
at -7, -5, and 5, $(x+7)$, $(x+5)$, and $(x-5)$
must each be a factor of $f(x)$. Therefore,

$f(x) = (x+7)(x+5)(x-5) = (x+7)(x^2 - 5)$.

3. A

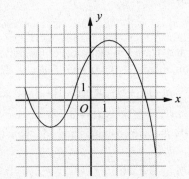

The minimum value of a graphed function is the
minimum y-value of all the points on the graph.
For the graph shown, when $x = -3$, $y = -2$ and
when $x = 5$, $y = -4$, so the minimum is at $(5, -4)$
and the minimum value is -4.

4. B

A zero of a function corresponds to an x-intercept
of the graph of the function on the xy-plane.
Only the graph in choice B has four x-intercepts.
Therefore, it has the four distinct zeros of function
f.

5. B

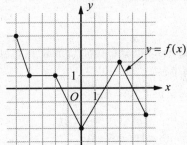

I. f is not strictly decreasing for $-5 < x < 0$,
     because on the interval $-4 < x < -2$, f is
     not decreasing.

     Roman numeral I is not true.

II. The coordinates $(-3, 1)$ is on the graph of f,
     therefore, $f(-3) = 1$

     Roman numeral II is true.

III. For the graph shown, when $x = 0$, $y = -3$ and
     when $x = 5$, $y = -2$, so f is minimum at
     $x = 0$.

     Roman numeral III is not true.

Section 13-2

1. **A**

    If -1 and 1 are two real roots of the polynomial function, then $f(-1) = 0$ and $f(1) = 0$. Thus
    $f(-1) = a(-1)^3 + b(-1)^2 + c(-1) + d = 0$ and
    $f(1) = a(1)^3 + b(1)^2 + c(1) + d = 0$.
    Simplify the two equations and add them to each other.

    $$-a + b - c + d = 0$$
    $$+\underline{a + b + c + d = 0}$$
    $$2b + 2d = 0 \text{ or } b + d = 0.$$

    Also $f(0) = 3$, since the graph of the polynomial passes through $(0, 3)$.

    $f(0) = a(0)^3 + b(0)^2 + c(0) + d = 3$ implies $d = 3$.

    Substituting $d = 3$ in the equation $b + d = 0$ gives $b + 3 = 0$, or $b = -3$.

2. **C**

    If polynomial $p(x) = 81x^5 - 121x^3 - 36$ is divided by $x + 1$, the remainder is $p(-1)$.

    $p(-1) = 81(-1)^5 - 121(-1)^3 - 36 = 4$
    The remainder is 4.

3. **D**

    If $x - 2$ is a factor for polynomial $p(x)$, then $p(2) = 0$.

    $p(x) = a(x^3 - 2x) + b(x^2 - 5)$
    $p(2) = a(2^3 - 2(2)) + b(2^2 - 5)$
    $ = a(8 - 4) + b(4 - 5)$
    $ = 4a - b = 0$

4. **B**

    If $(x - a)$ is a factor of $f(x)$, then $f(a)$ must be equal to 0. Based on the table, $f(-3) = 0$.

    Therefore, $x + 3$ must be a factor of $f(x)$.

5. **8**

    $x^3 - 8x^2 + 3x - 24 = 0$
    $(x^3 - 8x^2) + (3x - 24) = 0$ $\qquad$ Group terms.
    $x^2(x - 8) + 3(x - 8) = 0$ $\qquad$ Factor out the GCF.
    $(x^2 + 3)(x - 8) = 0$ $\qquad$ Distributive Property
    $x^2 + 3 = 0$ or $x - 8 = 0$ $\qquad$ Solutions

Since $x^2 + 3 = 0$ does not have a real solution, $x - 8 = 0$, or $x = 8$, is the only solution that makes the equation true.

6. **3**

    $x^4 - 8x^2 = 9$
    $x^4 - 8x^2 - 9 = 0$ $\qquad$ Make one side 0.
    $(x^2 - 9)(x^2 + 1) = 0$ $\qquad$ Factor.
    $(x + 3)(x - 3)(x^2 + 1) = 0$ $\qquad$ Factor.

    Since $x^2 + 1 = 0$ does not have a real solution, the solutions for x are $x = -3$ and $x = 3$. Since it is given that $x > 0$, $x = 3$ is the only solution to the equation.

Section 13-3

1. **B**

    $$a^{-\frac{1}{2}} = \frac{1}{a^{\frac{1}{2}}} = \frac{1}{\sqrt{a}}$$

2. **C**

    $\dfrac{1}{3 - 2\sqrt{2}}$

    $= \dfrac{1}{3 - 2\sqrt{2}} \cdot \dfrac{3 + 2\sqrt{2}}{3 + 2\sqrt{2}}$ $\qquad$ Multiply the conjugate of of the denominator.

    $= \dfrac{3 + 2\sqrt{2}}{(3)^2 - (2\sqrt{2})^2}$ $\qquad$ $(a - b)(a + b) = a^2 - b^2$

    $= \dfrac{3 + 2\sqrt{2}}{9 - 8}$ $\qquad$ Simplify.

    $= 3 + 2\sqrt{2}$

3. **B**

    $(x + 1)^3 = -64$
    $x + 1 = \sqrt[3]{-64}$ $\qquad$ Definition of cube root.
    $x + 1 = -4$ $\qquad$ $\sqrt[3]{-64} = (-64)^{\frac{1}{3}} = -4$
    $x = -5$ $\qquad$ Subtract 1 from each side.

4. **A**

    $\sqrt{8} + \sqrt{18} - \sqrt{32}$
    $= \sqrt{4}\sqrt{2} + \sqrt{9}\sqrt{2} - \sqrt{16}\sqrt{2}$
    $= 2\sqrt{2} + 3\sqrt{2} - 4\sqrt{2}$
    $= \sqrt{2}$

5. D

$$(1+\sqrt{3})(2-\sqrt{3})$$

$= 2 - \sqrt{3} + 2\sqrt{3} - \sqrt{3}\sqrt{3}$ FOIL

$= 2 + \sqrt{3} - 3$ Combine like radicals.

$= -1 + \sqrt{3}$ Simplify.

6. D

$$b^{\frac{5}{3}} = b^1 \cdot b^{\frac{2}{3}} = b \cdot (b^2)^{\frac{1}{3}} = b \cdot \sqrt[3]{b^2}$$

Section 13-4

1. B

$$11 - \sqrt{2x+3} = 8$$

$11 - \sqrt{2x+3} - 11 = 8 - 11$ Subtract 11 from each side.

$-\sqrt{2x+3} = -3$ Simplify.

$(-\sqrt{2x+3})^2 = (-3)^2$ Square each side.

$2x+3 = 9$ Simplify.

$2x = 6$ Subtract 3 from each side.

$x = 3$ Divide each side by 2.

2. A

$$\sqrt{-3x+4} = 7$$

$(\sqrt{-3x+4})^2 = (7)^2$ Square each side.

$-3x+4 = 49$ Simplify.

$-3x = 45$ Subtract 4 from each side.

$x = -15$ Divide each side by -3.

3. B

$$\sqrt{x+18} = x-2$$

$(\sqrt{x+18})^2 = (x-2)^2$ Square each side.

$x+18 = x^2 - 4x + 4$ Simplify.

$0 = x^2 - 5x - 14$ Make one side 0.

$0 = (x-7)(x+2)$ Factor.

$0 = x-7$ or $0 = x+2$ Zero Product Property

$7 = x$ or $-2 = x$

Check each x-value in the original equation.

$\sqrt{7+18} = 7-2$ $x = 7$

$\sqrt{25} = 5$ Simplify.

$5 = 5$ True

$\sqrt{-2+18} = -2-2$ $x = -2$

$\sqrt{16} = -4$ Simplify.

$4 = -4$ False

Thus, 7 is the only solution.

4. C

$$\sqrt{5x-12} = 3\sqrt{2}$$

$(\sqrt{5x-12})^2 = (3\sqrt{2})^2$ Square each side.

$5x-12 = 18$ Simplify.

$5x = 30$ Add 12 to each side.

$x = 6$ Divide by 5 on each side.

5. $\dfrac{5}{9}$

$$\sqrt{2-3x} = \frac{1}{3}a$$

$\sqrt{2-3x} = \frac{1}{3}\sqrt{3}$ $a = \sqrt{3}$

$(\sqrt{2-3x})^2 = (\frac{1}{3}\sqrt{3})^2$ Square each side.

$2-3x = \frac{1}{3}$ Simplify.

$-3x = -\frac{5}{3}$ Subtract 2 from each side.

$-\frac{1}{3}(-3x) = -\frac{1}{3}(-\frac{5}{3})$ Multiply each side by $-\frac{1}{3}$.

$x = \frac{5}{9}$ Simplify.

6. 2

$$\sqrt[3]{x-k} = -2$$

$(\sqrt[3]{x-k})^3 = (-2)^3$ Cube each side.

$x-k = -8$ Simplify.

$x-(8-\sqrt{2}) = -8$ $k = 8-\sqrt{2}$

$x-8+\sqrt{2} = -8$ Simplify.

$x+\sqrt{2} = 0$ Add 8 to each side.

$x = -\sqrt{2}$ Subtract $\sqrt{2}$.

$(x)^2 = (-\sqrt{2})^2$ Square each side.

$x^2 = 2$ Simplify.

Section 13-5

1. B

$$\sqrt{-1} - \sqrt{-4} + \sqrt{-9}$$

$= i - i\sqrt{4} + i\sqrt{9}$ $i = \sqrt{-1}$

$= i - 2i + 3i$

$= 2i$

2. C

$$\sqrt{-2} \cdot \sqrt{-8}$$
$$= i\sqrt{2} \cdot i\sqrt{8} \qquad \sqrt{-2} = i\sqrt{2}, \ \sqrt{-8} = i\sqrt{8}$$
$$= i^2\sqrt{16}$$
$$= -4 \qquad\qquad\quad i^2 = -1$$

3. D

$$\frac{3-i}{3+i}$$
$$= \frac{3-i}{3+i} \cdot \frac{3-i}{3-i} \qquad \text{Rationalize the denominator.}$$
$$= \frac{9-6i+i^2}{9-i^2} \qquad \text{FOIL}$$
$$= \frac{9-6i-1}{9+1} \qquad i^2 = -1$$
$$= \frac{8-6i}{10} \qquad \text{Simplify.}$$
$$= \frac{4-3i}{5} \ \text{ or } \ \frac{4}{5} - \frac{3i}{5}$$

4. C

$$\frac{1}{2}(5i-3) - \frac{1}{3}(4i+5)$$
$$= \frac{5}{2}i - \frac{3}{2} - \frac{4i}{3} - \frac{5}{3} \qquad \text{Distributive Property}$$
$$= \frac{15}{6}i - \frac{9}{6} - \frac{8i}{6} - \frac{10}{6} \qquad \text{6 is the GCD.}$$
$$= \frac{7}{6}i - \frac{19}{6} \qquad\qquad \text{Simplify.}$$

5. 23

$$(4+i)^2 = a+bi$$
$$16+8i+i^2 = a+bi \qquad \text{FOIL}$$
$$16+8i-1 = a+bi \qquad i^2 = -1$$
$$15+8i = a+bi \qquad \text{Simplify.}$$
$$15 = a \text{ and } 8 = b \qquad \text{Definition of Equal Complex Numbers}$$

Therefore, $a+b = 15+8 = 23$.

6. 2

$$\frac{3-i}{1-2i} = \frac{3-i}{1-2i} \cdot \frac{1+2i}{1+2i} = \frac{3+6i-i-2i^2}{1-4i^2}$$
$$= \frac{3+6i-i+2}{1+4} = \frac{5+5i}{5} = 1+i = a+bi$$

Therefore, $a=1$ and $b=1$, and $a+b = 1+1 = 2$.

Chapter 13 Practice Test

1. C

$$f(x) = 2x^3 + bx^2 + 4x - 4$$

$f(\frac{1}{2}) = 0$ because the graph of f intersects the

x- axis at $(\frac{1}{2}, 0)$.

$$f(\frac{1}{2}) = 2(\frac{1}{2})^3 + b(\frac{1}{2})^2 + 4(\frac{1}{2}) - 4 = 0$$

Solving the equation for b gives $b = 7$.

Thus $f(x) = 2x^3 + 7x^2 + 4x - 4$.

Also $k = f(-2)$, because $(-2, k)$ lies on the graph

of f.

$$k = f(-2) = 2(-2)^3 + 7(-2)^2 + 4(-2) - 4$$

Solving the equation for k gives $k = 0$.

2. D

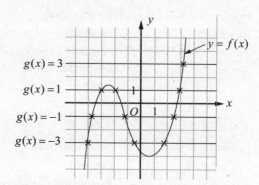

$g(x) = -3$ has 3 points of intersection with

$y = f(x)$, so there are 3 real solutions.

$g(x) = -1$ has 3 points of intersection with

$y = f(x)$, so there are 3 real solutions.

$g(x) = 1$ has 3 points of intersection with

$y = f(x)$, so there are 3 real solutions.

$g(x) = 3$ has 1 point of intersection with

$y = f(x)$, so there is 1 real solution.

Choice D is correct

3. B

If $x+2$ is a factor of

$f(x) = -(x^3 + 3x^2) - 4(x-a)$, then $f(-2) = 0$.

$$f(-2) = -((-2)^3 + 3(-2)^2) - 4(-2-a) = 0$$
$$-(-8+12) + 8 + 4a = 0$$
$$4 + 4a = 0$$
$$a = -1$$

4. A

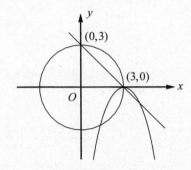

The solutions to the system of equations are the points where the circle, parabola, and line all intersect. That point is $(3,0)$ and is therefore the only solution to the system.

5. C

$$\frac{(1-i)^2}{1+i}$$

$$=\frac{1-2i+i^2}{1+i}$$ FOIL the numerator.

$$=\frac{1-2i-1}{1+i}$$ $i^2=-1$

$$=\frac{-2i}{1+i}$$ Simplify.

$$=\frac{-2i}{1+i}\cdot\frac{1-i}{1-i}$$ Rationalize the denominator.

$$=\frac{-2i+2i^2}{1-i^2}$$ FOIL

$$=\frac{-2i-2}{2}$$ $i^2=-1$

$$=-i-1$$

6. B

$$a\sqrt[3]{a}=a\cdot a^{\frac{1}{3}}=a^{1+\frac{1}{3}}=a^{\frac{4}{3}}$$

7. B

$$p(x)=-2x^3+4x^2-10x$$

$$q(x)=x^2-2x+5$$

In $p(x)$, factoring out the GCF, $-2x$, yields

$$p(x)=-2x(x^2-2x+5)=-2x\cdot q(x).$$

Let's check each answer choice.

A) $f(x)=p(x)-\frac{1}{2}q(x)$

$$=-2x\cdot q(x)-\frac{1}{2}q(x)=(-2x-\frac{1}{2})q(x)$$

$q(x)$ is not a factor of $x-1$ and $(-2x-\frac{1}{2})$ is not a factor of $x-1$. $f(x)$ is not divisible by $x-1$.

B) $g(x)=-\frac{1}{2}p(x)-q(x)$

$$=-\frac{1}{2}[-2x\cdot q(x)]-q(x)=(x-1)q(x)$$

Since $g(x)$ is $x-1$ times $q(x)$, $g(x)$ is divisible by $x-1$.

Choices C and D are incorrect because $x-1$ is not a factor of the polynomials $h(x)$ and $k(x)$.

8. D

$$\sqrt{2x+6}=x+3$$

$$(\sqrt{2x+6})^2=(x+3)^2$$ Square each side.

$$2x+6=x^2+6x+9$$ Simplify.

$$x^2+4x+3=0$$ Make one side 0.

$$(x+1)(x+3)=0$$ Factor.

$$x+1=0 \text{ or } x+3=0$$ Zero Product Property

$$x=-1 \text{ or } x=-3$$

Check each x-value in the original equation.

$$\sqrt{2(-1)+6}=-1+3$$ $x=-1$

$$\sqrt{4}=2$$ Simplify.

$$2=2$$ True

$$\sqrt{2(-3)+6}=-3+3$$ $x=-3$

$$0=0$$ True

Thus, -1 and -3 are both solutions to the equation.

9. C

Use the remainder theorem.

$$p(\frac{1}{2})=24(\frac{1}{2})^3-36(\frac{1}{2})^2+14=8$$

Therefore, the remainder of polynomial

$p(x)=24x^3-36x^2+14$ divided by $x-\frac{1}{2}$

is 8.

10. D

If $(x-a)$ is a factor of $f(x)$, then $f(a)$ must equal to 0. Thus, if $x+2$, $x+1$ and $x-1$ are factors of f, we have $f(-2)=f(-1)=f(1)=0$.

Choice D is correct.

CHAPTER 14
Rational Expressions

14-1. Rational Expressions

A **rational expression** is an algebraic fraction whose numerator and denominator are polynomials. Any value of a variable that makes the denominator of a rational expression zero must be excluded from the domain of that variable.

Rule for Multiplying and Dividing Rational Expressions

$$\frac{a}{b} \cdot \frac{c}{d} = \frac{ac}{bd} \quad \text{and} \quad \frac{a}{b} \div \frac{c}{d} = \frac{ad}{bc}, \text{ if the denominators are not zero.}$$

Rule for Adding and Subtracting Rational Expressions

$$\frac{a}{c} + \frac{b}{c} = \frac{a+b}{c} \quad \text{and} \quad \frac{a}{c} - \frac{b}{c} = \frac{a-b}{c}$$

The **least common denominator** (**LCD**) is the LCM of the denominators.

Use the following steps to add or subtract fractions with unlike denominators.

1. Find the LCD of the fractions.
2. Express each fraction as an equivalent fraction with the LCD as denominator.
3. Add or subtract the numerator, then simplify if necessary.

Example 1 □ Simplify.

a. $\dfrac{x^2 - 2x - 8}{3x - 6} \cdot \dfrac{4x - 8}{x - 4}$ b. $\dfrac{2x^2 - 8}{4x + 12} \div \dfrac{x + 2}{x + 3}$ c. $\dfrac{2}{x^2} + \dfrac{3}{2x}$

Solution □ a. $\dfrac{x^2 - 2x - 8}{3x - 6} \cdot \dfrac{4x - 8}{x - 4}$

$= \dfrac{(x-4)(x+2)}{3(x-2)} \cdot \dfrac{4(x-2)}{(x-4)}$ Factor and cancel.

$= \dfrac{4(x+2)}{3}$ Simplify.

b. $\dfrac{2x^2 - 8}{4x + 12} \div \dfrac{x + 2}{x + 3} = \dfrac{2x^2 - 8}{4x + 12} \cdot \dfrac{x + 3}{x + 2}$ Multiply by $\dfrac{x+3}{x+2}$, the reciprocal of $\dfrac{x+2}{x+3}$.

$= \dfrac{2(x^2 - 4)}{4(x + 3)} \cdot \dfrac{x + 3}{x + 2}$ Factor $2x^2 - 8$ and $4x + 12$.

$= \dfrac{\overset{1}{2}(x+2)(x-2)}{\underset{2}{4}(x+3)} \cdot \dfrac{x+3}{x+2}$ Factor $x^2 - 4$ and cancel.

$= \dfrac{x - 2}{2}$ Simplify.

c. $\dfrac{2}{x^2} + \dfrac{3}{2x} = \dfrac{2}{x^2} \cdot \dfrac{2}{2} + \dfrac{3}{2x} \cdot \dfrac{x}{x}$ The LCD is $2x^2$.

$= \dfrac{4}{2x^2} + \dfrac{3x}{2x^2}$ Simplify.

$= \dfrac{3x + 4}{2x^2}$ Add the numerators.

The sum or difference of a polynomial and a fraction is called a **mixed expression**. An expression like $2 - \dfrac{1}{x+9}$

is called a mixed expression because it contains the sum of monomial 2 and the rational expression $\dfrac{1}{x+9}$.

If a fraction has one or more fractions in the numerator or denominator, it is called a **complex fraction**.
To simplify a complex fraction, express the fraction as a quotient using the $\div$ sign.

$$\dfrac{\dfrac{a}{b}}{\dfrac{c}{d}} = \dfrac{a}{b} \div \dfrac{c}{d} = \dfrac{a}{b} \times \dfrac{d}{c} = \dfrac{ad}{bc}, \text{ in which } bcd \neq 0.$$

Example 2 □ Simplify.

a. $\dfrac{3\frac{3}{4}\text{ ft}}{6\frac{2}{3}\text{ in}}$

b. $x - \dfrac{x+1}{x-3}$

c. $\dfrac{\dfrac{5x}{x-3}}{\dfrac{15}{x^2-9}}$

Solution □ a. $\dfrac{3\frac{3}{4}\text{ ft}}{6\frac{2}{3}\text{ in}} = \dfrac{3\frac{3}{4}\text{ ft}}{6\frac{2}{3}\text{ in}} \cdot \dfrac{12\text{ in}}{1\text{ ft}}$

Convert feet to inches.
Divide by common units.

$= \dfrac{\dfrac{15}{1} \cdot \dfrac{\cancel{12}^{3}}{1}}{\dfrac{20}{3}} = \dfrac{\dfrac{45}{1}}{\dfrac{20}{3}}$

Express each term as an improper fraction.

$= \dfrac{\cancel{45}^{9}}{1} \cdot \dfrac{3}{\cancel{20}_{4}}$

$\dfrac{\dfrac{a}{b}}{\dfrac{c}{d}} = \dfrac{ad}{bc}$

$= \dfrac{27}{4}$ or $6\dfrac{3}{4}$

Simplify.

b. $x - \dfrac{x+1}{x-3} = \dfrac{x(x-3)}{x-3} - \dfrac{x+1}{x-3}$

The LCD is $x-3$. Multiply x by $\dfrac{x-3}{x-3}$.

$= \dfrac{x(x-3)-(x+1)}{x-3}$

Add the numerators.

$= \dfrac{x^2-4x-1}{x-3}$

Simplify the numerator.

c. $\dfrac{\dfrac{5x}{x-3}}{\dfrac{15}{x^2-9}} = \dfrac{5x}{x-3} \div \dfrac{15}{x^2-9}$

Rewrite as a division sentence.

$= \dfrac{5x}{x-3} \times \dfrac{x^2-9}{15}$

Multiply by the reciprocal, $\dfrac{x^2-9}{15}$.

$= \dfrac{\cancel{5}^{1}x}{\cancel{x-3}} \times \dfrac{(x+3)\cancel{(x-3)}}{\cancel{15}^{3}} = \dfrac{x(x+3)}{3}$

Factor and simplify.

Exercises - Rational Expressions

1

If $n \neq 4$, which of the following is equivalent

to $\dfrac{n^2}{n-4} + \dfrac{4n}{4-n}$?

A) n

B) $\dfrac{n(n+4)}{n-4}$

C) $\dfrac{n}{n-4}$

D) $\dfrac{n+4}{n-4}$

2

If $a \neq \pm 1$, which of the following is equivalent

to $\dfrac{a}{a^2-1} - \dfrac{1}{a+1}$?

A) $\dfrac{1}{a-1}$

B) $\dfrac{1}{a+1}$

C) $\dfrac{2a-1}{a^2-1}$

D) $\dfrac{1}{a^2-1}$

3

If $y \neq -1$ and $y \neq 0$, which of the following is

equivalent to $\dfrac{y^2-1}{1+\dfrac{1}{y}}$?

A) $\dfrac{y-1}{y}$

B) $y(y-1)$

C) $\dfrac{y}{y+1}$

D) $y-1$

4

If $x \neq \pm 1$, which of the following is equivalent

to $\dfrac{1-\dfrac{1}{x+1}}{1+\dfrac{1}{x^2-1}}$?

A) $\dfrac{x-1}{x}$

B) $\dfrac{x+1}{x}$

C) $\dfrac{x-1}{x^2}$

D) $\dfrac{x+1}{x^2}$

5

If $x > 3$, which of the following is equivalent

to $\dfrac{x-3}{\dfrac{1}{x+2} - \dfrac{1}{2x-1}}$?

A) $\dfrac{x-3}{(x+2)(2x-1)}$

B) $\dfrac{(x+2)(2x-1)}{x-3}$

C) $(x+2)(2x-1)$

D) $2x-1$

6

If $\dfrac{x^2-xy}{2x} \div \dfrac{x-y}{3x^2} = ax^2$, what is the value of a ?

14-2. Solving Rational Equations

Rational equations are equations that contain rational expressions.

To solve rational equations, multiply the LCD of all the fractions on both sides of the equation. This will eliminate all of the fractions. Then solve the resulting equation.

You can also use cross products to solve rational equations, if both sides of the equation are single fractions.

Example 1 □ Solve each equation.

a. $\dfrac{x}{2x+5} - \dfrac{x+1}{4x+10} = \dfrac{1}{8}$.

b. $\dfrac{x-1}{2x} = \dfrac{x}{x+6}$

Solution □ a. $\dfrac{x}{2x+5} - \dfrac{x+1}{2(2x+5)} = \dfrac{1}{8}$ Factor.

$8(2x+5)(\dfrac{x}{2x+5} - \dfrac{x+1}{2(2x+5)})$ The LCD is $8(2x+5)$. Multiply each side by $8(2x+5)$.

$= 8(2x+5) \cdot \dfrac{1}{8}$

$8x - 4(x+1) = 2x+5$ Distributive Property

$4x - 4 = 2x + 5$ Simplify.

$2x = 9$ Simplify.

$x = \dfrac{9}{2}$ Solve for x.

b. $\dfrac{x-1}{2x} = \dfrac{x}{x+6}$ Both sides of the equation are single fractions.

$(x-1)(x+6) = 2x \cdot x$ Cross multiply.

$x^2 + 5x - 6 = 2x^2$ FOIL

$x^2 - 5x + 6 = 0$ Make one side 0.

$(x-2)(x-3) = 0$ Factor.

$x - 2 = 0$ or $x - 3 = 0$ Zero Product Property

$x = 2$ or $x = 3$ Solve for x.

A rational equation is **undefined** when the denominator is equal to zero. Multiplying both sides of a rational equation by the LCD can yield solutions with a denominator of zero. Such solutions are called **extraneous solutions**, which must be excluded from solutions to the original equation.

Example 2 □ Solve $\dfrac{9x}{x-2} - \dfrac{5x+8}{x-2} = 6$.

Solution □ $(x-2)(\dfrac{9x}{x-2} - \dfrac{5x+8}{x-2}) = 6(x-2)$ Multiply each side by $x-2$.

$9x - (5x+8) = 6x - 12$ Distributive Property

$4x - 8 = 6x - 12$ Simplify.

$4 = 2x$ Simplify.

$2 = x$ Solve for x.

If we substitute 2 for x in the original equation, we get undefined expressions.
So, this equation has no solution.

Exercises - Solving Rational Equations

1

$$\frac{x}{x-1} = \frac{x-2}{x+1}$$

What is the solution set of the equation above?

A) -2

B) $-\dfrac{1}{2}$

C) $\dfrac{1}{2}$

D) 2

2

$$\frac{x}{x-3} - 2 = \frac{4}{x-2}$$

What is the solution set of the equation above?

A) $\{0\}$

B) $\{2\}$

C) $\{0, 2\}$

D) $\{0, 4\}$

3

$$\frac{1}{x} - \frac{2}{x-2} = \frac{-4}{x^2 - 2x}$$

What is the solution set of the equation above?

A) -2

B) 0

C) 2

D) There is no solution to the equation.

4

$$\frac{3}{x^2 - 3x} + \frac{1}{3-x} = 2$$

What is the solution set of the equation above?

A) $\{-\dfrac{1}{2}\}$

B) $\{3\}$

C) $\{-\dfrac{1}{2}, 3\}$

D) $\{-\dfrac{1}{2}, -3\}$

5

If $f(x) = \dfrac{1}{(x-a)^2 - 4(x-a) + 4}$ is undefined
when $x = 6$, what is the value of a ?

6

$$g(x) = \frac{1}{(x+3)^2 - 24(x+3) + 144}$$

For what value of x is function g above
undefined?

14-3. Direct, Inverse, and Joint Variations

A **direct variation** is an equation of the form $y = kx$, in which $k \neq 0$.

It is expressed as, *y varies directly as x*.

The graph of a direct variation is a straight line with slope k, and passes through the origin.

An **inverse variation** is an equation of the form $xy = k$ or $y = \dfrac{k}{x}$, in which $x \neq 0$.

It is expressed as, *y varies inversely as x*.

A **joint variation** is an equation of the form $z = kxy$, in which $k \neq 0$.

It is expressed as, *z varies jointly as x and y*.

Example 1   □   a. If y varies directly as x, and $y = 4$ when $x = 6$, find y when $x = 18$.

b. If w varies inversely as x, and $w = \dfrac{1}{3}$ when $x = 15$, find w when $x = 25$.

c. If z varies jointly as x and y, and $z = 18$ when $x = 2$ and $y = 3$, find z

when $x = \dfrac{2}{3}$ and $y = \dfrac{5}{8}$.

Solution   □   a. $y = kx$ Direct variation formula

$4 = k(6)$ Replace y with 4 and x with 2.

$k = \dfrac{2}{3}$ Solve for k.

$y = \dfrac{2}{3}x$ Direct variation formula with $k = \dfrac{2}{3}$

$y = \dfrac{2}{3}(18) = 12$ Replace x with 18 and solve for y.

b. $w = \dfrac{k}{x}$ Inverse variation formula

$\dfrac{1}{3} = \dfrac{k}{15}$ Replace w with $\dfrac{1}{3}$ and x with 15.

$k = 5$ Solve for k.

$w = \dfrac{5}{x}$ Inverse variation formula with $k = 5$

$w = \dfrac{5}{25} = \dfrac{1}{5}$ Replace x with 25 and solve for w.

c. $z = kxy$ Joint variation formula

$18 = k(2)(3)$ Replace z with 18, x with 2, and y with 3.

$k = 3$ Solve for k.

$z = 3xy$ Joint variation formula with $k = 3$

$z = 3\left(\dfrac{2}{3}\right)\left(\dfrac{5}{8}\right) = \dfrac{5}{4}$ Replace x with $\dfrac{2}{3}$, y with $\dfrac{5}{8}$ and solve for z.

Exercises - Direct, Inverse, and Joint Variations

1

Which of the following tables shows a relationship in which y is directly proportional to x?

A)

x	-2	0	2
y	-1	1	3

B)

x	-2	0	2
y	5	0	-5

C)

x	-2	0	2
y	-3	1	5

D)

x	-2	0	2
y	3	1	-1

2

The distance it takes an automobile to stop varies directly as the square of its speed. If the stopping distance of a car traveling at 40 mph is 320 feet, what is the stopping distance of a car traveling at 50mph?

A) 360 ft

B) 420 ft

C) 500 ft

D) 580 ft

3

If y varies inversely as $\sqrt{x}$, and $y = 12$ when $x = 16$, what is the value of y when $x = 100$?

A) 1.2

B) 3

C) 4.8

D) 6.4

Questions 4 and 5 refer to the following information.

$$L = \frac{k}{d^2}$$

The formula above shows the brightness of the light of an object, which varies inversely as the square of the distance. L, measured in lumens, is the brightness of the light and d, measured in meters, is the distance from the object to the light source.

4

At distance 2 meters from a light source, the brightness of an object was measured at 9 lumens. What is the value of k?

A) 18

B) 24

C) 32

D) 36

5

The brightness of an object was measured d meters away from a light source. The brightness of the same object was measured $1.5d$ meters from the light source. What is the ratio of brightness of the object when it is close to the light source to when it is farther away from the light source?

A) $\dfrac{9}{4}$

B) $\dfrac{5}{2}$

C) $\dfrac{7}{4}$

D) $\dfrac{3}{2}$

14-4. Solving Word Problems Using Rational Equations

Work Problems

You can use the following formula to solve work problems.

Work rate × Time = Work done

Work rate means the amount of job done over time.

Example 1 □ Roy can finish a certain job in 12 hours and Chuck can finish the same job in 8 hours. How long will they take to finish the job together?

Solution □ Let x = the number of hours needed to do the job together.

Roy's work rate is $\dfrac{1}{12}$ job per hour and Chuck's work rate is $\dfrac{1}{8}$ job per hour.

	Work rate ×	Time	= Work done
Roy	$\dfrac{1}{12}$	x	$\dfrac{1}{12}x$
Chuck	$\dfrac{1}{8}$	x	$\dfrac{1}{8}x$

Roy's part of the job + Chuck's part of the job = Whole job

$$\frac{1}{12}x + \frac{1}{8}x = 1 \qquad\qquad \text{Translate wording into equation.}$$

Solving the above equation, we get $x = \dfrac{24}{5}$ or $4\dfrac{4}{5}$.

It will take them $4\dfrac{4}{5}$ hours to finish the job together.

Example 2 □ Pump A can fill a water tank in 6 hours and pump B can fill the same water tank in 10 hours. When the water tank was empty, both pumps were turned on for 2 hours and then pump A was turned off. How much longer did pump B have to run before the tank was filled?

Solution □ Let x = the number of hours needed for pump B to fill the tank after pump A was turned off. Let $x + 2$ = total number of hours for pump B to finish the job.

Pump A's work rate is $\dfrac{1}{6}$ job per hour and pump B's work rate is $\dfrac{1}{10}$ job per hour.

	Work rate ×	Time	= Work done
Pump A	$\dfrac{1}{6}$	2	$\dfrac{1}{6} \times 2$ or $\dfrac{1}{3}$
Pump B	$\dfrac{1}{10}$	$2 + x$	$\dfrac{1}{10}(2 + x)$

Pump A's part of the job + Pump B's part of the job = Whole job

$$\frac{1}{3} + \frac{1}{10}(2 + x) = 1 \qquad\qquad \text{Translate wording into equation.}$$

Solving the above equation, we get $x = \dfrac{14}{3}$ or $4\dfrac{2}{3}$.

It will take $4\dfrac{2}{3}$ hours for pump B to finish the job.

Exercises - Solving Word Problems Using Rational Equations

Questions 1 and 2 refer to the following information.

$$\frac{1}{4}+\frac{1}{6}=\frac{1}{x}$$

Working alone, a painter can paint a house in four days. Working alone, his assistant can paint the same house in six days. Working together, they can finish painting the house in x days. The equation above represents the situation described.

1

Which of the following describes what $\dfrac{1}{x}$ represents in the above equation?

A) The portion of the job that the painter can finish in one day.

B) The portion of the job that the assistant can finish in one day.

C) The portion of the job that the painter and assistant together can finish in one day.

D) The portion of the job that the painter and assistant together can finish in four days.

2

How many days will it take them to finish painting the house working together?

A) $1\dfrac{4}{5}$

B) $2\dfrac{2}{5}$

C) $2\dfrac{4}{5}$

D) $3\dfrac{1}{5}$

3

Three printers A, B, and C, working together at their respective constant rates, can finish a job in 4.5 hours. Printers A and B, working together, can finish the same job in 6 hours. How many hours will it take printer C, working alone, to finish the job?

A) 12.5

B) 14

C) 16.5

D) 18

4

Mike can do a job in 48 minutes. If his brother helps him, it takes them 32 minutes. How many minutes does it take Mike's brother to do the job alone?

A) 72

B) 80

C) 96

D) 102

5

James can do a job in 8 hours and Peter can do the same job in 5 hours. If they finished $\dfrac{13}{25}$ of the job by working together, how long did they work together?

A) 1 hour 24 minutes

B) 1 hour 36 minutes

C) 1 hour 48 minutes

D) 2 hours 8 minutes

Chapter 14 Practice Test

1

If $a \neq b$, which of the following is equivalent to $\dfrac{a}{a-b} + \dfrac{b}{b-a}$?

A) 1

B) $\dfrac{a+b}{a-b}$

C) $\dfrac{a+b}{(a-b)^2}$

D) $\dfrac{a^2+b^2}{(a-b)^2}$

2

If $x > 0$ and $y > 0$, which of the following is equivalent to $\dfrac{\dfrac{1}{x}-\dfrac{1}{y}}{\dfrac{1}{x^2}-\dfrac{1}{y^2}}$?

A) $\dfrac{xy}{x^2-y^2}$

B) $\dfrac{2xy}{x^2-y^2}$

C) $\dfrac{xy}{x+y}$

D) $\dfrac{xy}{x-y}$

3

$$\frac{(k+1)^2}{k} = 4k$$

What is the solution set of the equation above?

A) $\left\{-\dfrac{1}{3}\right\}$

B) $\{-1\}$

C) $\left\{-\dfrac{1}{3}, 1\right\}$

D) $\left\{\dfrac{1}{3}, -1\right\}$

4

$$\frac{3}{x} - \frac{x}{x+2} = \frac{2}{x+2}$$

What is the solution set of the equation above?

A) $\{2, -3\}$

B) $\{-2, 3\}$

C) $\{-2\}$

D) $\{3\}$

5

$$\frac{x}{x+1} + \frac{4}{x-4} = \frac{20}{x^2-3x-4}$$

What is the solution set of the equation above?

A) $\{-4\}$

B) $\{4\}$

C) $\{-4, 4\}$

D) There are no solutions to the equation.

6

If $x \neq \pm 1$, which of the following is equivalent

to $\dfrac{1+\dfrac{1}{x-1}}{1-\dfrac{1}{x+1}}$?

A) $\dfrac{x-1}{x+1}$

B) $\dfrac{x+1}{x-1}$

C) $\dfrac{x^2-1}{x^2+1}$

D) $\dfrac{x^2+1}{x^2-1}$

7

Working alone, Gary can load an empty truck in 3 hours. Working alone, his brother can load the same truck in x hours. If Gary and his brother worked together for t hours to load the empty truck, which of the following equations can be used to find out how much work was done during t hours?

A) $\dfrac{3}{t}+xt$

B) $\dfrac{3}{t}+\dfrac{x}{t}$

C) $3t+xt$

D) $\dfrac{1}{3}t+\dfrac{1}{x}t$

8

$$f(x)=\dfrac{5}{2(x-2)^2-3(x-2)-2}$$

What is one possible value of x, if function f is undefined?

9

If $x>0$, what is the solution to the equation $\dfrac{1}{2x}+\dfrac{3}{10x^2}=\dfrac{1}{5}$?

10

If $a \neq b$ and $\dfrac{ab}{a-b} \div \dfrac{ab^2}{b-a} = -\dfrac{1}{6}$, what is the value of b ?

11

If $\dfrac{a+\dfrac{1}{2}}{a-\dfrac{1}{2}}=2$, what is the value of a ?

Answer Key

Section 14-1

1. A   2. D   3. B   4. A   5. C

6. $\dfrac{3}{2}$

Section 14-2

1. C   2. D   3. D   4. A   5. 4

6. 9

Section 14-3

1. B   2. C   3. C   4. D   5. A

Section 14-4

1. C   2. B   3. D   4. C   5. B

Chapter 14 Practice Test

1. A   2. C   3. C   4. D   5. A

6. B   7. D   8. $\dfrac{3}{2}$ or 4   9. 3

10. 6   11. $\dfrac{3}{2}$

Answers and Explanations

Section 14-1

1. A

$$\frac{n^2}{n-4}+\frac{4n}{4-n}$$

$$=\frac{n^2}{n-4}-\frac{4n}{n-4} \qquad n-4=-(4-n)$$

$$=\frac{n^2-4n}{n-4} \qquad\qquad \text{Add the numerators.}$$

$$=\frac{n\,\cancel{(n-4)}}{\cancel{n-4}} \qquad\qquad \text{Factor and cancel.}$$

$$=n$$

2. D

$$\frac{a}{a^2-1}-\frac{1}{a+1}$$

$$=\frac{a}{(a+1)(a-1)}-\frac{1}{a+1} \qquad a^2-1=(a+1)(a-1)$$

$$=\frac{a}{(a+1)(a-1)}-\frac{1}{(a+1)}\cdot\frac{(a-1)}{(a-1)}$$

$$=\frac{a-(a-1)}{(a+1)(a-1)} \qquad\qquad \text{Add the numerators.}$$

$$=\frac{1}{(a+1)(a-1)}=\frac{1}{a^2-1}$$

3. B

$$\frac{y^2-1}{1+\dfrac{1}{y}}$$

$$=\frac{(y^2-1)y}{(1+\dfrac{1}{y})y} \qquad\qquad \begin{array}{l}\text{Multiply the numerator and}\\ \text{denominator by } y.\end{array}$$

$$=\frac{\cancel{(y+1)}(y-1)y}{\cancel{y+1}} \qquad\qquad \text{Distributive property}$$

$$=y(y-1) \qquad\qquad \text{Simplify.}$$

4. A

$$\frac{1-\dfrac{1}{x+1}}{1+\dfrac{1}{x^2-1}}$$

$$=\frac{(1-\dfrac{1}{x+1})}{(1+\dfrac{1}{x^2-1})}\cdot\frac{(x^2-1)}{(x^2-1)} \qquad \text{Multiply } x^2-1$$

$$=\frac{(x^2-1-\dfrac{x^2-1}{x+1})}{(x^2-1+1)} \qquad\qquad \text{Distributive property}$$

$$=\frac{x^2-1-(x-1)}{x^2} \qquad \frac{x^2-1}{x+1}=\frac{\cancel{(x+1)}(x-1)}{\cancel{x+1}}=x-1$$

$$=\frac{x^2-x}{x^2} \qquad\qquad \text{Simplify.}$$

$$=\frac{\cancel{x}(x-1)}{x^{\cancel{2}}}=\frac{x-1}{x} \qquad \text{Factor and cancel.}$$

5. C

$$\frac{x-3}{\dfrac{1}{x+2}-\dfrac{1}{2x-1}}$$

Multiply the numerator and the denominator
by $(x+2)(2x-1)$.

$$= \frac{(x-3)[(x+2)(2x-1)]}{(\frac{1}{x+2} - \frac{1}{2x-1})[(x+2)(2x-1)]}$$

$$= \frac{(x-3)(x+2)(2x-1)}{\frac{(x+2)(2x-1)}{x+2} - \frac{(x+2)(2x-1)}{2x-1}}$$

$$= \frac{(x-3)(x+2)(2x-1)}{(2x-1)-(x+2)}$$

$$= \frac{(x-3)(x+2)(2x-1)}{x-3}$$

$$= (x+2)(2x-1)$$

6. $\dfrac{3}{2}$

$$\frac{x^2 - xy}{2x} \div \frac{x-y}{3x^2}$$

$$= \frac{x^2 - xy}{2x} \times \frac{3x^2}{x-y} \qquad \text{Rewrite as multiplication.}$$

$$= \frac{x(x-y)}{2x} \times \frac{3x^2}{x-y} \qquad \text{Factor and cancel.}$$

$$= \frac{3}{2} x^2$$

So, if $\dfrac{x^2 - xy}{2x} \div \dfrac{x-y}{3x^2} = ax^2$, the value of a is $\dfrac{3}{2}$.

Section 14-2

1. C

$$\frac{x}{x-1} = \frac{x-2}{x+1}$$

$$x(x+1) = (x-1)(x-2) \qquad \text{Cross multiply.}$$

$$x^2 + x = x^2 - 3x + 2 \qquad \text{FOIL}$$

$$4x = 2 \qquad \text{Simplify.}$$

$$x = \frac{1}{2} \qquad \text{Divide.}$$

When x equals $\dfrac{1}{2}$, the denominator in the original equation does not have a value of 0.

The solution set is $\{\dfrac{1}{2}\}$.

2. D

$$\frac{x}{x-3} - 2 = \frac{4}{x-2}$$

Multiply each side by $(x-3)(x-2)$.

$$(x-3)(x-2)(\frac{x}{x-3} - 2) = (x-3)(x-2)(\frac{4}{x-2})$$

$$x(x-2) - 2(x-3)(x-2) = 4(x-3)$$

$$x^2 - 2x - 2(x^2 - 5x + 6) = 4x - 12$$

$$-x^2 + 8x - 12 = 4x - 12$$

$$x^2 - 4x = 0$$

$$x(x-4) = 0$$

$$x = 0 \text{ or } x = 4$$

When x equals 0 or 4, the denominator in the original equation does not have a value of 0. The solution set is $\{0, 4\}$.

3. D

$$\frac{1}{x} - \frac{2}{x-2} = \frac{-4}{x^2 - 2x}$$

$$x^2 - 2x = x(x-2).$$

So the LCD is $x(x-2)$.

Multiply each side by $x(x-2)$.

$$x(x-2)(\frac{1}{x} - \frac{2}{x-2}) = x(x-2)(\frac{-4}{x^2 - 2x})$$

$$(x-2) - 2x = -4$$

$$-x - 2 = -4$$

$$x = 2$$

When x equals 2, the denominator in the original equation has a value of 0.
So, the equation has no solution.

4. A

$$\frac{3}{x^2 - 3x} + \frac{1}{3-x} = 2$$

$$\frac{3}{x^2 - 3x} - \frac{1}{x-3} = 2 \qquad 3 - x = -(x-3)$$

$$x^2 - 3x = x(x-3). \text{ So the LCD is } x(x-3).$$

Multiply each side by $x(x-3)$.

$$x(x-3)(\frac{3}{x^2 - 3x} - \frac{1}{x-3}) = 2x(x-3)$$

$$3 - x = 2x^2 - 6x \qquad \text{Distributive property}$$

$$2x^2 - 5x - 3 = 0 \qquad \text{Make one side 0.}$$

$$(2x+1)(x-3) = 0 \qquad \text{Factor.}$$

$$x = -\frac{1}{2} \text{ or } x = 3$$

When x equals 3, the denominator in the original equation has a value of 0. Therefore,

3 cannot be a solution. The solution set is $\{-\dfrac{1}{2}\}$.

5. 4

If $f(x) = \dfrac{1}{(x-a)^2 - 4(x-a) + 4}$ is undefined,

the denominator $(x-a)^2 - 4(x-a) + 4$ is equal
to zero. If $x = 6$,
$(x-a)^2 - 4(x-a) + 4 = (6-a)^2 - 4(6-a) + 4 = 0$.
The expression $(6-a)^2 - 4(6-a) + 4$ is a perfect
square, which can be rewritten as $((6-a)-2)^2$.
The expression $((6-a)-2)^2 = 0$ is equal to zero
if $(6-a)-2 = 0$. Solving for a gives $a = 4$.

6. 9

The expression $g(x) = \dfrac{1}{(x+3)^2 - 24(x+3) + 144}$

is undefined when the denominator of $g(x)$ is
zero.
$(x+3)^2 - 24(x+3) + 144 = 0$
$((x+3)-12)^2 = 0$
$(x+3)-12 = 0$
$x = 9$

Section 14-3

1. B

The equation of direct variation is $y = kx$, and
the graph of direct variation always includes $(0,0)$.
Choice B is correct.

2. C

The distance it takes an automobile to stop varies
directly as the square of its speed. Thus, by the
definition of direct proportionality, $d = kx^2$,
in which d is the stopping distance in feet, x is
the speed of the car in miles per hour, and k is
a constant.

$d = kx^2$
$320 = k(40)^2$ $d = 320$, $x = 40$
$320 = 1600k$ Simplify.
$\dfrac{320}{1600} = k$ Divide each side by 1600.
$d = \dfrac{320}{1600} x^2$ Replace k with $\dfrac{320}{1600}$.
$d = \dfrac{320}{1600}(50)^2$ Substitute 50 for x.
$d = 500$

3. C

$y = \dfrac{k}{\sqrt{x}}$ Inverse variation equation

$12 = \dfrac{k}{\sqrt{16}}$ $y = 12$ when $x = 16$.

$12 = \dfrac{k}{4}$ or $k = 48$

$y = \dfrac{48}{\sqrt{x}}$ Replace k with 48.

$y = \dfrac{48}{\sqrt{100}}$ $x = 100$

$y = \dfrac{48}{10} = 4.8$

4. D

$L = \dfrac{k}{d^2}$

$9 = \dfrac{k}{2^2}$ $L = 9$ and $d = 2$

$36 = k$

5. A

$\dfrac{L \text{ measured at distance } d}{L \text{ measured at distance } 1.5d}$

$= \dfrac{\dfrac{36}{d^2}}{\dfrac{36}{(1.5d)^2}}$

$= \dfrac{36}{d^2} \cdot \dfrac{(1.5d)^2}{36} = \dfrac{2.25d^2}{d^2}$

$= 2.25 = 2\dfrac{1}{4} = \dfrac{9}{4}$

Section 14-4

1. C

Working together, they can finish painting the

house in x days. So $\dfrac{1}{x}$ is the portion of the house

painting job they can finish in one day.
Choice C is correct.

2. B

$\dfrac{1}{4} + \dfrac{1}{6} = \dfrac{1}{x}$

$$12x(\frac{1}{4}+\frac{1}{6})=12x(\frac{1}{x}) \qquad \text{LCD is } 12x$$

$3x+2x=12 \qquad$ Distributive property

$5x=12 \qquad$ Simplify.

$$x=\frac{12}{5}=2\frac{2}{5} \qquad \text{Divide each side by 5.}$$

3. D

Let a be the number of days it takes printer A to finish the job alone, let b be the number of days it takes printer B to finish the job alone, and let c be the number of days it takes printer C to finish the job alone. Then their respective work rates are $\frac{1}{a}$, $\frac{1}{b}$, and $\frac{1}{c}$. If three printers A, B, and C, working together at their respective constant rates, can finish a job in $4\frac{1}{2}$ hours, you can set up the equation $4\frac{1}{2}(\frac{1}{a}+\frac{1}{b}+\frac{1}{c})=1$. If printers, A and B, working together at their respective constant rates, can finish a job in 6 hours, you can set up the equation $6(\frac{1}{a}+\frac{1}{b})=1$.

Solving the two equations for $\frac{1}{a}+\frac{1}{b}$ gives

$$4\frac{1}{2}(\frac{1}{a}+\frac{1}{b}+\frac{1}{c})=1 \;\Rightarrow\; \frac{9}{2}(\frac{1}{a}+\frac{1}{b}+\frac{1}{c})=1$$

$$\Rightarrow \frac{1}{a}+\frac{1}{b}+\frac{1}{c}=\frac{2}{9} \;\Rightarrow\; \frac{1}{a}+\frac{1}{b}=\frac{2}{9}-\frac{1}{c} \text{ and}$$

$$6(\frac{1}{a}+\frac{1}{b})=1 \;\Rightarrow\; \frac{1}{a}+\frac{1}{b}=\frac{1}{6}.$$

Substituting $\frac{2}{9}-\frac{1}{c}$ for $\frac{1}{a}+\frac{1}{b}$ gives $\frac{2}{9}-\frac{1}{c}=\frac{1}{6}$. Multiply by $18c$ on each side of the equation and simplify.

$$18c(\frac{2}{9}-\frac{1}{c})=18c(\frac{1}{6})$$

$4c-18=3c$

$c=18$

4. C

Let b be the number of minutes for his brother to do the job alone. Since the part of the job Mike does in 32 minutes plus the part of the job his brother does in 32 minutes equals one whole job, you can set up the following equation.

$$32(\frac{1}{48}+\frac{1}{b})=1$$

$$48b\cdot 32(\frac{1}{48}+\frac{1}{b})=48b\cdot 1 \qquad \text{LCD is } 48b.$$

$32b+1536=48b \qquad$ Simplify.

$16b=1536$

$b=96$

5. B

If James can do a job in 8 hours, his work rate is $\frac{1}{8}$. If Peter can do the same job in 5 hours, his work rate is $\frac{1}{5}$.

Let $x=$ the number of hours they worked together.

$$\frac{1}{8}x+\frac{1}{5}x=\frac{13}{25}$$

$$200(\frac{1}{8}x+\frac{1}{5}x)=200\cdot\frac{13}{25} \qquad \text{LCD is } 200.$$

$25x+40x=104 \qquad$ Simplify.

$65x=104$

$$x=\frac{104}{65}=1.6$$

0.6 hours is 0.6×60 minutes, or 36 minutes. Therefore, it took 1 hour and 36 minutes for them to finish $\frac{13}{25}$ of the job.

Chapter 14 Practice Test

1. A

$$\frac{a}{a-b}+\frac{b}{b-a}$$

$$=\frac{a}{a-b}-\frac{b}{a-b} \qquad b-a=-(a-b)$$

$$=\frac{a-b}{a-b} \qquad \text{Add the numerators.}$$

$$=1$$

2. C

$$\frac{\dfrac{1}{x}-\dfrac{1}{y}}{\dfrac{1}{x^2}-\dfrac{1}{y^2}}$$

Multiply x^2y^2 by the numerator and the denominator.

$$= \frac{(\frac{1}{x} - \frac{1}{y})x^2y^2}{(\frac{1}{x^2} - \frac{1}{y^2})x^2y^2}$$

$$= \frac{xy^2 - x^2y}{y^2 - x^2} \qquad \text{Distributive property}$$

$$= \frac{xy\,\cancel{(y-x)}}{\cancel{(y-x)}(y+x)}$$

$$= \frac{xy}{(y+x)}$$

3. C

$$\frac{(k+1)^2}{k} = 4k$$

$(k+1)^2 = 4k^2$ Multiply by k on each side.

$k^2 + 2k + 1 = 4k^2$ FOIL

$0 = 3k^2 - 2k - 1$ Make one side 0.

$0 = (3k+1)(k-1)$ Factor.

$k = -\frac{1}{3}$ or $k = 1$

None of the solutions make the denominator zero, thus $\{-\frac{1}{3}, 1\}$ is the solution set.

Choice C is correct.

4. D

$$\frac{3}{x} - \frac{x}{x+2} = \frac{2}{x+2}$$

Multiply each side of the equation by $x(x+2)$.

$x(x+2)(\frac{3}{x} - \frac{x}{x+2}) = x(x+2)(\frac{2}{x+2})$

$3(x+2) - x^2 = 2x$ Distributive property

$3x + 6 - x^2 = 2x$ Distributive property

$0 = x^2 - x - 6$ Make one side 0.

$0 = (x+2)(x-3)$ Factor.

$x = -2$ or $x = 3$

When x equals -2, the denominator in the original equation has a value of 0. Therefore, -2 cannot be a solution.

The solution set is $\{3\}$.

5. A

$$\frac{x}{x+1} + \frac{4}{x-4} = \frac{20}{x^2 - 3x - 4}$$

$x^2 - 3x - 4 = (x+1)(x-4)$. So the LCD is $(x+1)(x-4)$. Multiply each side of the equation by $(x+1)(x-4)$.

$(x+1)(x-4)(\frac{x}{x+1} + \frac{4}{x-4})$

$= (x+1)(x-4)(\frac{20}{x^2 - 3x - 4})$

$x(x-4) + 4(x+1) = 20$ Distributive property

$x^2 - 4x + 4x + 4 = 20$

$x^2 = 16$

$x = 4$ or $x = -4$

When x equals 4, the denominator in the original equation has a value of 0. Therefore, 4 cannot be a solution.

The solution set is $\{-4\}$.

6. B

$$\frac{1 + \dfrac{1}{x-1}}{1 - \dfrac{1}{x+1}}$$

$$= \frac{(x+1)(x-1)(1 + \dfrac{1}{x-1})}{(x+1)(x-1)(1 - \dfrac{1}{x+1})} \qquad \text{Multiply by } (x+1)(x-1).$$

$$= \frac{(x+1)(x-1) + (x+1)}{(x+1)(x-1) - (x-1)} \qquad \text{Distributive property}$$

$$= \frac{x^2 - 1 + x + 1}{x^2 - 1 - x + 1} \qquad \text{FOIL}$$

$$= \frac{x^2 + x}{x^2 - x} \qquad \text{Simplify.}$$

$$= \frac{x(x+1)}{x(x-1)} \qquad \text{Factor.}$$

$$= \frac{x+1}{x-1} \qquad \text{Cancel and simplify.}$$

7. D

If working alone Gary can load the empty truck in 3 hours, his work rate is $\frac{1}{3}$. If working alone his brother can load the same truck in x hours, his work rate is $\frac{1}{x}$. If they work together for t

hours to load the empty truck, the amount of work done for t hours will be $t(\frac{1}{3}+\frac{1}{x})$, or $\frac{1}{3}t+\frac{1}{x}t$.

8. $\frac{3}{2}$ or 4

The expression $f(x)=\dfrac{5}{2(x-2)^2-3(x-2)-2}$ is undefined when the denominator of $f(x)$ is zero. Therefore, if $2(x-2)^2-3(x-2)-2$ is equal to 0, $f(x)$ is undefined.

$2(x-2)^2-3(x-2)-2=0$

Let $z=x-2$, then $2z^2-3z-2=0$.

$(2z+1)(z-2)=0$ Factor.

$2z+1=0$ or $z-2=0$ Zero Product Property

$z=-\dfrac{1}{2}$ or $z=2$

Now substitute $x-2$ for z.

$x-2=-\dfrac{1}{2}$ or $x-2=2$

The values of x that make f undefined are $\dfrac{3}{2}$ and 4.

9. 3

$\dfrac{1}{2x}+\dfrac{3}{10x^2}=\dfrac{1}{5}$

Multiply each side of the equation by $10x^2$.

$10x^2(\dfrac{1}{2x}+\dfrac{3}{10x^2})=10x^2(\dfrac{1}{5})$

$5x+3=2x^2$ Distributive property

$0=2x^2-5x-3$ Make one side 0.

$0=(2x+1)(x-3)$ Factor.

$x=-\dfrac{1}{2}$ or $x=3$

Since $x>0$, the only solution is 3.

10. 6

$\dfrac{ab}{a-b}\div\dfrac{ab^2}{b-a}=-\dfrac{1}{6}$

Rewrite as multiplication.

$\dfrac{ab}{a-b}\times\dfrac{b-a}{ab^2}=-\dfrac{1}{6}$

$\dfrac{\cancel{ab}}{\cancel{a-b}}\times\dfrac{-\cancel{(a-b)}}{\cancel{ab}^2}=-\dfrac{1}{6}$ $b-a=-(a-b)$

$\dfrac{-1}{b}=-\dfrac{1}{6}$

Therefore, the value of b is 6.

11. $\dfrac{3}{2}$

$\dfrac{a+\dfrac{1}{2}}{a-\dfrac{1}{2}}=2$

Multiply each side of the equation by $a-\dfrac{1}{2}$.

$a+\dfrac{1}{2}=2(a-\dfrac{1}{2})$

$a+\dfrac{1}{2}=2a-1$ Distributive property

$\dfrac{3}{2}=a$

CHAPTER 15
Trigonometric Functions

15-1. Trigonometric Ratios of Acute Angles

A ratio of the lengths of sides of a right triangle is called a **trigonometric ratio**. The six trigonometric ratios are **sine, cosine, tangent, cosecant, secant,** and **cotangent**.

Their abbreviations are sin, cos, tan, csc, sec, and cot, respectively. The six trigonometric ratios of any angle $0° < \theta < 90°$, sine, cosine, tangent, cosecant, secant, and cotangent, are defined as follows.

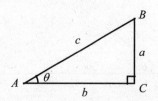

$$\sin\theta = \frac{\text{length of side opposite to } \theta}{\text{length of hypotenuse}} = \frac{a}{c} \qquad \csc\theta = \frac{1}{\sin\theta} = \frac{c}{a}$$

$$\cos\theta = \frac{\text{length of side adjacent to } \theta}{\text{length of hypotenuse}} = \frac{b}{c} \qquad \sec\theta = \frac{1}{\cos\theta} = \frac{c}{b}$$

$$\tan\theta = \frac{\text{length of side opposite to } \theta}{\text{length of side adjacent to } \theta} = \frac{a}{b} \qquad \cot\theta = \frac{1}{\tan\theta} = \frac{b}{a}$$

The sine and cosine are called **cofunctions**. In a right triangle ABC, $\angle A$ and $\angle B$ are complementary, that is, $m\angle A + m\angle B = 90$. Thus any trigonometric function of an acute angle is equal to the cofunction of the complement of the angle.

Complementary Angle Theorem

$$\sin\theta = \cos(90° - \theta) \qquad \cos\theta = \sin(90° - \theta)$$

If $\sin\angle A = \cos\angle B$, then $m\angle A + m\angle B = 90°$.

Trigonometric Identities

$$\tan\theta = \frac{\sin\theta}{\cos\theta} \qquad \sin^2\theta + \cos^2\theta = 1$$

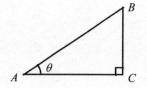

Example 1 □ In the right triangle shown at the right, find $\cos\theta$ and $\tan\theta$ if $\sin\theta = \frac{2}{3}$.

Solution □ $\sin^2\theta + \cos^2\theta = 1$ Trigonometric identity

$(\frac{2}{3})^2 + \cos^2\theta = 1$ Substitute $\frac{2}{3}$ for $\sin\theta$.

$\cos^2\theta = 1 - (\frac{2}{3})^2 = 1 - \frac{4}{9} = \frac{5}{9}$

$\cos\theta = \sqrt{\frac{5}{9}} = \frac{\sqrt{5}}{\sqrt{9}} = \frac{\sqrt{5}}{3}$

$\tan\theta = \frac{\sin\theta}{\cos\theta} = \frac{2/3}{\sqrt{5}/3} = \frac{2}{\sqrt{5}} = \frac{2\sqrt{5}}{\sqrt{5}\sqrt{5}} = \frac{2\sqrt{5}}{5}$

Example 2 □ In a right triangle, θ is an acute angle. If $\sin\theta = \frac{4}{9}$, what is $\cos(90° - \theta)$?

Solution □ By the complementary angle property of sine and cosine,

$\cos(90° - \theta) = \sin\theta = \frac{4}{9}$.

Exercises - Trigonometric Ratios of Acute Angles

Questions 1- 3 refer to the following information.

In the triangle shown below $AB = BC = 10$ and $AC = 12$.

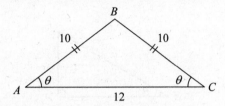

1

What is the value of $\cos\theta$?

A) 0.4

B) 0.6

C) 0.8

D) 1.2

2

What is the value of $\sin\theta$?

A) 0.4

B) 0.6

C) 0.8

D) 1.2

3

What is the value of $\tan\theta$?

A) $\dfrac{3}{4}$

B) $\dfrac{4}{3}$

C) $\dfrac{5}{4}$

D) $\dfrac{5}{3}$

4

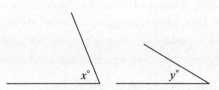

Note: Figures not drawn to scale.

In the figures above $y < x < 90$ and $\cos x° = \sin y°$. If $x = 3a - 14$ and $y = 50 - a$, what is the value of a ?

A) 16

B) 21

C) 24

D) 27

5

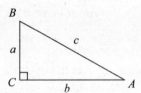

Given the right triangle ABC above, which of the following is equal to $\dfrac{a}{c}$?

  I. $\sin A$

  II. $\cos B$

  III. $\tan A$

A) I only

B) II only

C) I and II only

D) II and III only

15-2. The Radian Measure of an Angle

One **radian** is the measure of a central angle θ whose intercepted arc has a length equal to the circle's radius. In the figure at the right, if length of the arc $AB = OA$, then $m\angle AOB = 1$ radian .

Since the circumference of the circle is $2\pi r$ and a complete revolution has degree measure $360°$,

2π radians $= 360°$, or π radians $= 180°$.

The conversion formula π radians $= 180°$ can be used to convert radians to degrees and vice versa.

$1 \text{ radian} = \dfrac{180°}{\pi} \approx 57.3°$ and $1° = \dfrac{\pi}{180}$ radians

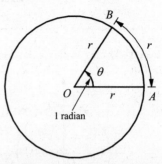

The measure of a central angle θ is 1 radian, if the length of the arc AB is equal to the radius of the circle.

On a coordinate plane, an angle may be drawn by two rays that share a fixed endpoint at the origin. The beginning ray, called the **initial side** of the angle and the final position, is called the **terminal side** of the angle. An angle is in **standard position** if the vertex is located at the origin and the initial side lies along the positive x-axis. Counterclockwise rotations produce **positive angles** and clockwise rotations produce **negative angles**. When two angles have the same initial side and the same terminal side, they are called **coterminal angles**.

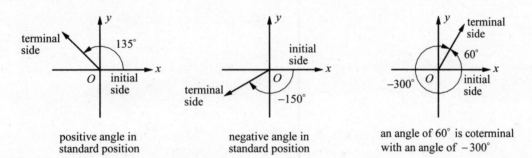

positive angle in standard position

negative angle in standard position

an angle of $60°$ is coterminal with an angle of $-300°$

You can find an angle that is coterminal to a given angle by adding or subtracting integer multiples of $360°$ or 2π radians. In fact, the sine and cosine functions repeat their values every $360°$ or 2π radians, and tangent functions repeat their values every $180°$ or π radians.

Periodic Properties of the Trigonometric Functions

$\sin(\theta \pm 360°) = \sin\theta$ $\qquad$ $\cos(\theta \pm 360°) = \cos\theta$ $\qquad$ $\tan(\theta \pm 180°) = \tan\theta$

Example 1 $\square$ Change the degree measure to radian measure and change the radian measure to degree measure.

a. $45°$ $\hspace{4cm}$ b. $\dfrac{2\pi}{3}$ radians

Solution $\square$ a. $45° = 45 \cdot \dfrac{\pi}{180}$ radians $= \dfrac{\pi}{4}$ radians

b. $\dfrac{2\pi}{3}$ radians $= \dfrac{2\pi}{3}$ radians$\left(\dfrac{180°}{\pi \text{ radians}}\right) = 120°$

Exercises - The Radian Measure of an Angle

1

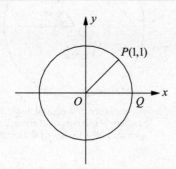

In the xy-plane above, O is the center of the circle, and the measure of $\angle POQ$ is $k\pi$ radians. What is the value of k?

A) $\dfrac{1}{6}$

B) $\dfrac{1}{4}$

C) $\dfrac{1}{3}$

D) $\dfrac{1}{2}$

2

Which of the following is equal to $\cos(\dfrac{\pi}{8})$?

A) $\cos(\dfrac{3\pi}{8})$

B) $\cos(\dfrac{7\pi}{8})$

C) $\sin(\dfrac{3\pi}{8})$

D) $\sin(\dfrac{7\pi}{8})$

3

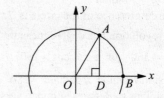

In the xy-plane above, O is the center of the circle and the measure of $\angle AOD$ is $\dfrac{\pi}{3}$. If the radius of circle O is 6 what is the length of AD?

A) 3

B) $3\sqrt{2}$

C) 4.5

D) $3\sqrt{3}$

4

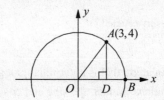

In the figure above, what is the value of $\cos \angle AOD$?

A) $\dfrac{3}{5}$

B) $\dfrac{3}{4}$

C) $\dfrac{4}{5}$

D) $\dfrac{4}{3}$

15-3. Trigonometric Functions and the Unit Circle

Suppose $P(x, y)$ is a point on the circle $x^2 + y^2 = r^2$ and θ is an angle in standard position with terminal side OP, as shown at the right. We define sine of θ and cosine of θ as

$$\sin\theta = \frac{y}{r} \qquad\qquad \cos\theta = \frac{x}{r}.$$

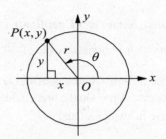

The circle $x^2 + y^2 = 1$ is called the **unit circle**. This circle is the easiest one to work with because $\sin\theta$ and $\cos\theta$ are simply the y-coordinates and the x-coordinates of the points where the terminal side of θ intersects the circle.

$$\sin\theta = \frac{y}{r} = \frac{y}{1} = y \qquad \cos\theta = \frac{x}{r} = \frac{x}{1} = x.$$

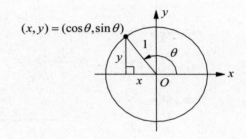

Angles in standard position whose measures are multiples of $30°$ ($\dfrac{\pi}{6}$ radians) or multiples

of $45°$ ($\dfrac{\pi}{4}$ radians) are called **familiar angles**. To obtain the trigonometric values of sine, cosine,

and tangent of the familiar angles, use $30°$-$60°$-$90°$ triangle ratio or the $45°$-$45°$-$90°$ triangle ratio.

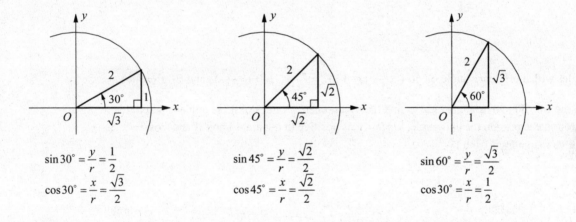

$$\sin 30° = \frac{y}{r} = \frac{1}{2}$$
$$\cos 30° = \frac{x}{r} = \frac{\sqrt{3}}{2}$$

$$\sin 45° = \frac{y}{r} = \frac{\sqrt{2}}{2}$$
$$\cos 45° = \frac{x}{r} = \frac{\sqrt{2}}{2}$$

$$\sin 60° = \frac{y}{r} = \frac{\sqrt{3}}{2}$$
$$\cos 30° = \frac{x}{r} = \frac{1}{2}$$

The **reference angle** associated with θ is the acute angle formed by the x-axis and the terminal side of the angle θ. A reference angle can be used to evaluate trigonometric functions for angles greater than $90°$.

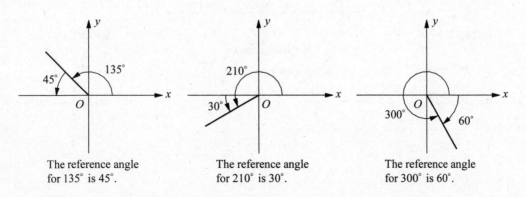

The reference angle
for $135°$ is $45°$.

The reference angle
for $210°$ is $30°$.

The reference angle
for $300°$ is $60°$.

Familiar Angles in a Coordinate Plane

Angles with a reference angle of $30°(=\dfrac{\pi}{6})$ are $150°(=\dfrac{5\pi}{6})$, $210°(=\dfrac{7\pi}{6})$, and $330°(=\dfrac{11\pi}{6})$.

Use the $30°$-$60°$-$90°$ triangle ratio to find the trigonometric values of these angles and put the appropriate signs. On the unit circle, $\sin\theta = y$ is positive in quadrant I and II and $\cos\theta = x$ is positive in quadrant I and IV.

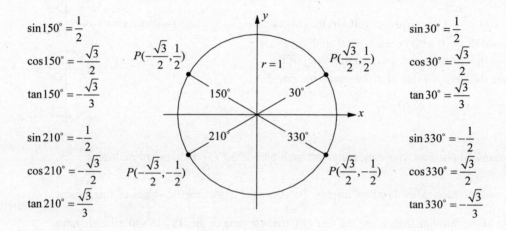

$$\sin 150° = \frac{1}{2}$$
$$\cos 150° = -\frac{\sqrt{3}}{2}$$
$$\tan 150° = -\frac{\sqrt{3}}{3}$$
$$\sin 210° = -\frac{1}{2}$$
$$\cos 210° = -\frac{\sqrt{3}}{2}$$
$$\tan 210° = \frac{\sqrt{3}}{3}$$

$$\sin 30° = \frac{1}{2}$$
$$\cos 30° = \frac{\sqrt{3}}{2}$$
$$\tan 30° = \frac{\sqrt{3}}{3}$$
$$\sin 330° = -\frac{1}{2}$$
$$\cos 330° = \frac{\sqrt{3}}{2}$$
$$\tan 330° = -\frac{\sqrt{3}}{3}$$

Angles with a reference angle of $60°(=\dfrac{\pi}{3})$ are $120°(=\dfrac{2\pi}{3})$, $240°(=\dfrac{4\pi}{3})$, and $300°(=\dfrac{5\pi}{3})$.

Use the $30°$-$60°$-$90°$ triangle ratio to find the trigonometric values of these angles and put the appropriate signs. On the unit circle, $\sin\theta = y$ is positive in quadrant I and II and $\cos\theta = x$ is positive in quadrant I and IV.

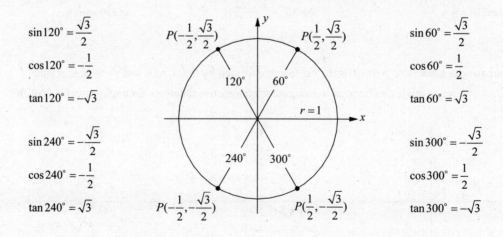

$$\sin 120° = \frac{\sqrt{3}}{2}$$
$$\cos 120° = -\frac{1}{2}$$
$$\tan 120° = -\sqrt{3}$$
$$\sin 240° = -\frac{\sqrt{3}}{2}$$
$$\cos 240° = -\frac{1}{2}$$
$$\tan 240° = \sqrt{3}$$

$$\sin 60° = \frac{\sqrt{3}}{2}$$
$$\cos 60° = \frac{1}{2}$$
$$\tan 60° = \sqrt{3}$$
$$\sin 300° = -\frac{\sqrt{3}}{2}$$
$$\cos 300° = \frac{1}{2}$$
$$\tan 300° = -\sqrt{3}$$

Angles with a reference angle of $45°(=\dfrac{\pi}{4})$ are $135°(=\dfrac{3\pi}{4})$, $225°(=\dfrac{5\pi}{4})$, and $315°(=\dfrac{7\pi}{4})$,

Use the $45°$-$45°$-$90°$ triangle ratio to find the trigonometric values of these angles and put the appropriate signs. On the unit circle, $\sin\theta = y$ is positive in quadrant I and II and $\cos\theta = x$ is positive in quadrant I and IV.

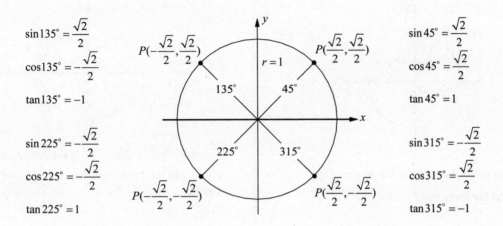

$\sin 135° = \dfrac{\sqrt{2}}{2}$

$\cos 135° = -\dfrac{\sqrt{2}}{2}$

$\tan 135° = -1$

$\sin 225° = -\dfrac{\sqrt{2}}{2}$

$\cos 225° = -\dfrac{\sqrt{2}}{2}$

$\tan 225° = 1$

$\sin 45° = \dfrac{\sqrt{2}}{2}$

$\cos 45° = \dfrac{\sqrt{2}}{2}$

$\tan 45° = 1$

$\sin 315° = -\dfrac{\sqrt{2}}{2}$

$\cos 315° = \dfrac{\sqrt{2}}{2}$

$\tan 315° = -1$

For the angles $0°$, $90° = \dfrac{\pi}{2}$, $180° = \pi$, and $270° = \dfrac{3\pi}{2}$, $\sin\theta$ is equal to the y value of the point $P(x,y)$ and $\cos\theta$ is equal to the x value of the point $P(x,y)$. The points $P(1,0)$, $P(0,1)$, $P(-1,0)$, and $P(0,-1)$ on the unit circle corresponds to $\theta = 0° = 0$, $\theta = 90° = \dfrac{\pi}{2}$, $\theta = 180° = \pi$, and $\theta = 270° = \dfrac{3\pi}{2}$ respectively.

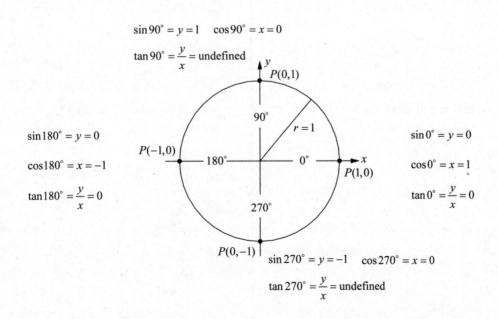

$\sin 90° = y = 1 \quad \cos 90° = x = 0$

$\tan 90° = \dfrac{y}{x} = $ undefined

$\sin 180° = y = 0$

$\cos 180° = x = -1$

$\tan 180° = \dfrac{y}{x} = 0$

$\sin 0° = y = 0$

$\cos 0° = x = 1$

$\tan 0° = \dfrac{y}{x} = 0$

$\sin 270° = y = -1 \quad \cos 270° = x = 0$

$\tan 270° = \dfrac{y}{x} = $ undefined

Exercises - The Trigonometric Functions and the Unit Circle

Questions 1 and 2 refer to the following information.

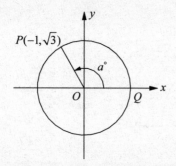

In the xy- plane above, O is the center of the circle, and the measure of $\angle POQ$ is $a°$.

1

What is the cosine of $a°$?

A) $-\dfrac{1}{2}$

B) $\sqrt{3}$

C) $-\dfrac{1}{\sqrt{3}}$

D) $\dfrac{\sqrt{3}}{2}$

2

What is the cosine of $(a+180)°$?

A) $-\sqrt{3}$

B) $-\dfrac{\sqrt{3}}{2}$

C) $\dfrac{1}{2}$

D) $\dfrac{1}{\sqrt{3}}$

Questions 3 and 4 refer to the following information.

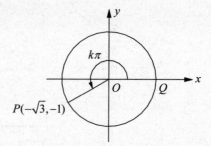

In the xy- plane above, O is the center of the circle, and the measure of the angle shown is $k\pi$ radians.

3

What is the value of k ?

A) $\dfrac{5}{6}$

B) $\dfrac{7}{6}$

C) $\dfrac{4}{3}$

D) $\dfrac{5}{3}$

4

What is the value of $\tan(k\pi)$?

A) $-\sqrt{3}$

B) -1

C) $-\dfrac{1}{\sqrt{3}}$

D) $\dfrac{1}{\sqrt{3}}$

Chapter 15 Practice Test

1

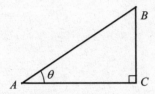

Note: Figure not drawn to scale.

In the right triangle shown above, if $\tan \theta = \dfrac{3}{4}$, what is $\sin \theta$?

A) $\dfrac{1}{3}$

B) $\dfrac{1}{2}$

C) $\dfrac{4}{5}$

D) $\dfrac{3}{5}$

2

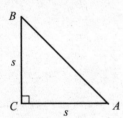

In the isosceles right triangle shown above, what is $\tan \angle A$?

A) s

B) $\dfrac{1}{s}$

C) 1

D) $\dfrac{s}{\sqrt{2}}$

Questions 1 and 2 refer to the following information.

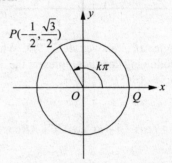

In the xy- plane above, O is the center of the circle, and the measure of $\angle POQ$ is $k\pi$ radians.

3

What is the value of k ?

A) $\dfrac{1}{3}$

B) $\dfrac{1}{2}$

C) $\dfrac{2}{3}$

D) $\dfrac{3}{4}$

4

What is $\cos(k+1)\pi$?

A) $\dfrac{1}{\sqrt{3}}$

B) $\dfrac{1}{2}$

C) $\dfrac{\sqrt{3}}{2}$

D) $\sqrt{3}$

5

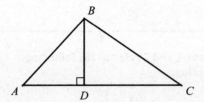

In triangle ABC above, $\overline{AC} \perp \overline{BD}$. Which of the following does not represent the area of triangle ABC?

A) $\dfrac{1}{2}(AB\cos\angle A + BC\cos\angle C)(AB\cos\angle ABD)$

B) $\dfrac{1}{2}(AB\cos\angle A + BC\cos\angle C)(BC\sin\angle C)$

C) $\dfrac{1}{2}(AB\sin\angle ABD + BC\sin\angle CBD)(AB\sin\angle A)$

D) $\dfrac{1}{2}(AB\sin\angle ABD + BC\sin\angle CBD)(BC\cos\angle C)$

6

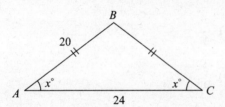

In the isosceles triangle above, what is the value of $\sin x°$?

A) $\dfrac{1}{2}$

B) $\dfrac{3}{5}$

C) $\dfrac{2}{3}$

D) $\dfrac{4}{5}$

7

In triangle ABC, the measure of $\angle C$ is $90°$, $AC = 24$, and $BC = 10$. What is the value of $\sin A$?

8

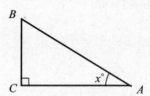

In the right triangle ABC above, the cosine of $x°$ is $\dfrac{3}{5}$. If $BC = 12$, what is the length of AC?

9

If $\sin(5x-10)° = \cos(3x+16)°$, what is the value of x?

Answer Key

Section 15-1

1. B   2. C   3. B   4. D   5. C

Section 15-2

1. B   2. C   3. D   4. A

Section 15-3

1. A   2. C   3. B   4. D

Chapter 15 Practice Test

1. D   2. C   3. C   4. B   5. D

6. D   7. $\dfrac{5}{13}$ 8. 9   9. 10.5

Answers and Explanations

Section 15-1

1. B

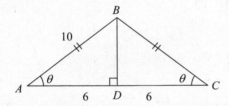

Draw a perpendicular segment from B to the opposite side AC. Let the perpendicular segment intersect side AC at D. Because the triangle is isosceles, a perpendicular segment from the vertex to the opposite side bisects the base and creates two congruent right triangles.

Therefore, $AD = \dfrac{1}{2}AC = \dfrac{1}{2}(12) = 6$.

In right $\triangle ABD$,

$\cos\theta = \dfrac{\text{adjacent}}{\text{hypotenuse}} = \dfrac{AD}{AB} = \dfrac{6}{10} = 0.6$.

2. C

$AB^2 = BD^2 + AD^2$ Pythagorean Theorem

$10^2 = BD^2 + 6^2$

$100 = BD^2 + 36$

$64 = BD^2$

$8 = BD$

$\sin\theta = \dfrac{\text{opposite}}{\text{hypotenuse}} = \dfrac{BD}{AB} = \dfrac{8}{10} = 0.8$

3. B

$\tan\theta = \dfrac{\text{opposite}}{\text{adjacent}} = \dfrac{BD}{AD} = \dfrac{8}{6} = \dfrac{4}{3}$

4. D

If x and y are acute angles and $\cos x° = \sin y°$, $x + y = 90$ by the complementary angle theorem.

$(3a - 14) + (50 - a) = 90$ $x = 3a - 14$, $y = 50 - a$

$2a + 36 = 90$ Simplify.

$2a = 54$

$a = 27$

5. C

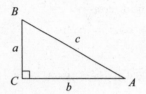

I. $\sin A = \dfrac{\text{opposite of } \angle A}{\text{hypotenuse}} = \dfrac{a}{c}$

Roman numeral I is true.

II. $\cos B = \dfrac{\text{adjacent of } \angle B}{\text{hypotenuse}} = \dfrac{a}{c}$

Roman numeral II is true.

III. $\tan A = \dfrac{\text{opposite of } \angle A}{\text{adjacent of } \angle A} = \dfrac{a}{b}$

Roman numeral III is false.

Section 15-2

1. B

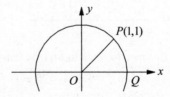

The graph shows $P(x, y) = P(1, 1)$. Thus, $x = 1$ and $y = 1$. Use the distance formula to find the length of radius OA.

$OA = \sqrt{x^2 + y^2} = \sqrt{1^2 + 1^2} = \sqrt{2}$

$\sin\theta = \dfrac{\text{opposite}}{\text{hypotenuse}} = \dfrac{1}{\sqrt{2}}$ or $\sin\theta = \dfrac{\sqrt{2}}{2}$

Therefore, the measure of $\angle POQ$ is $45°$,

which is equal to $45(\dfrac{\pi}{180}) = \dfrac{\pi}{4}$ radians.

Thus, $k = \dfrac{1}{4}$.

2. C

Use the complementary angle theorem.

$\cos(\theta) = \sin(90° - \theta)$, or $\cos(\theta) = \sin(\dfrac{\pi}{2} - \theta)$

Therefore, $\cos(\dfrac{\pi}{8}) = \sin(\dfrac{\pi}{2} - \dfrac{\pi}{8}) = \sin(\dfrac{3\pi}{8})$.

All the other answer choices have values

different from $\cos(\dfrac{\pi}{8})$.

3. D

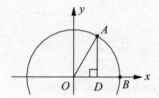

In $\triangle OAD$, $\sin\dfrac{\pi}{3} = \sin 60° = \dfrac{AD}{OA} = \dfrac{AD}{6}$.

Since $\sin 60° = \dfrac{\sqrt{3}}{2}$, you get $\dfrac{AD}{6} = \dfrac{\sqrt{3}}{2}$.

Therefore, $2AD = 6\sqrt{3}$ and $AD = 3\sqrt{3}$.

4. A

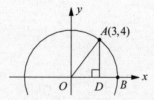

Use the distance formula to find the length of OA.

$OA = \sqrt{x^2 + y^2} = \sqrt{3^2 + 4^2} = \sqrt{25} = 5$

$\cos\angle AOD = \dfrac{OD}{OA} = \dfrac{3}{5}$

Section 15-3

1. A

Draw segment PR, which is perpendicular to
the x-axis. In right triangle POR, $x = -1$

and $y = \sqrt{3}$. To find the length of OP, use the
Pythagorean theorem.

$OP^2 = PR^2 + OR^2 = (\sqrt{3})^2 + (-1)^2 = 4$

Which gives $OP = 2$.

$\cos a° = \dfrac{x}{OP} = \dfrac{-1}{2}$

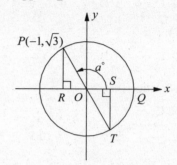

2. C

Since the terminal side of $(a + 180)°$ is OT, the

value of $\cos(a + 180)°$ is equal to $\dfrac{OS}{OT}$.

$\dfrac{OS}{OT} = \dfrac{1}{2}$

3. B

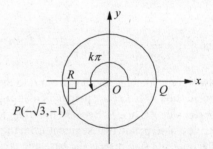

Draw segment PR, which is perpendicular to
the x-axis. In right triangle POR, $x = -\sqrt{3}$
and $y = -1$. To find the length of OP, use the
Pythagorean theorem.

$OP^2 = PR^2 + OR^2 = (-1)^2 + (\sqrt{3})^2 = 4$

Which gives $OP = 2$.

Since $\sin\angle POR = \dfrac{y}{OP} = \dfrac{-1}{2}$, the measure of

$\angle POR$ is equal to $30°$, or $\dfrac{\pi}{6}$ radian.

$k\pi = \pi + \dfrac{\pi}{6} = \dfrac{7}{6}\pi$

Therefore, $k = \dfrac{7}{6}$

4. D

$$\tan(k\pi) = \tan(\frac{7}{6}\pi) = \frac{y}{x} = \frac{-1}{-\sqrt{3}} = \frac{1}{\sqrt{3}}$$

Chapter 15 practice Test

1. D

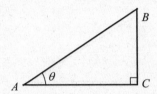

Note: Figure not drawn to scale.

In $\triangle ABC$, $\tan\theta = \dfrac{\text{opposite}}{\text{adjacent}} = \dfrac{BC}{AC}$.

If $\tan\theta = \dfrac{3}{4}$, then $BC = 3$ and $AC = 4$.

By the Pythagorean theorem,

$AB^2 = AC^2 + BC^2 = 4^2 + 3^2 = 25$, thus

$AB = \sqrt{25} = 5$.

$\sin\theta = \dfrac{BC}{AB} = \dfrac{3}{5}$

2. C

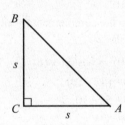

$$\tan\angle A = \frac{\text{opposite side of } \angle A}{\text{adjacent side of } \angle A} = \frac{s}{s} = 1$$

$$= \frac{s}{s} = 1$$

3. C

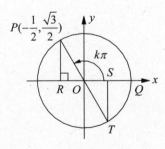

Draw segment PR, which is perpendicular to

the x-axis. In right triangle POR, $x = -\dfrac{1}{2}$

and $y = \dfrac{\sqrt{3}}{2}$. To find the length of OP, use the

Pythagorean theorem.

$$OP^2 = PR^2 + OR^2 = (\frac{\sqrt{3}}{2})^2 + (\frac{-1}{2})^2 = \frac{3}{4} + \frac{1}{4} = 1$$

Which gives $OP = 1$. Thus, triangle OPR is

$30°\text{-}60°\text{-}90°$ triangle and the measure of $\angle POR$

is $60°$, which is $\dfrac{\pi}{3}$ radian. Therefore, the measure

of $\angle POQ$ is $\pi - \dfrac{\pi}{3}$, or $\dfrac{2\pi}{3}$ radian. If $\angle POQ$ is

$k\pi$ radians then k is equal to $\dfrac{2}{3}$.

4. B

Since the terminal side of $(k+1)\pi$ is OT, the

value of $\cos(k+1)\pi$ is equal to $\dfrac{OS}{OT}$.

$$\frac{OS}{OT} = \frac{1}{2}$$

5. D

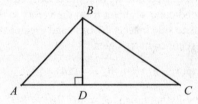

Area of triangle $ABC = \dfrac{1}{2}(AC)(BD)$

Check each answer choice.

A) $\dfrac{1}{2}(AB\cos\angle A + BC\cos\angle C)(AB\cos\angle ABD)$

$$= \frac{1}{2}(AB \cdot \frac{AD}{AB} + BC \cdot \frac{CD}{BC})(AB \cdot \frac{BD}{AB})$$

$$= \frac{1}{2}(AD + CD)(BD) = \frac{1}{2}(AC)(BD)$$

B) $\dfrac{1}{2}(AB\cos\angle A + BC\cos\angle C)(BC\sin\angle C)$

$$= \frac{1}{2}(AB \cdot \frac{AD}{AB} + BC \cdot \frac{CD}{BC})(BC \cdot \frac{BD}{BC})$$

$$= \frac{1}{2}(AD + CD)(BD) = \frac{1}{2}(AC)(BD)$$

C) $\frac{1}{2}(AB\sin\angle ABD + BC\sin\angle CBD)(AB\sin\angle A)$

$= \frac{1}{2}(AB\cdot\frac{AD}{AB} + BC\cdot\frac{CD}{BC})(AB\cdot\frac{BD}{AB})$

$= \frac{1}{2}(AD + CD)(BD) = \frac{1}{2}(AC)(BD)$

D) $\frac{1}{2}(AB\sin\angle ABD + BC\sin\angle CBD)(BC\cos\angle C)$

$= \frac{1}{2}(AB\cdot\frac{AD}{AB} + BC\frac{CD}{BC})(BC\cdot\frac{CD}{BC})$

$= \frac{1}{2}(AD + CD)(CD) = \frac{1}{2}(AC)(CD)$

Which does not represent the area of triangle ABC.

Choice D is correct.

6. D

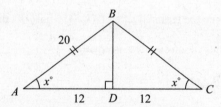

Draw segment BD, which is perpendicular to side AC. Because the triangle is isosceles, a perpendicular segment from the vertex to the opposite side bisects the base and creates two congruent right triangles.

Therefore, $AD = \frac{1}{2}AC = \frac{1}{2}(24) = 12$.

By the Pythagorean theorem, $AB^2 = BD^2 + AD^2$. Thus, $20^2 = BD^2 + 12^2$.

$BD^2 = 20^2 - 12^2 = 256$

$BD = \sqrt{256} = 16$

In right $\triangle ABD$,

$\sin x° = \frac{\text{adjacent}}{\text{hypotenuse}} = \frac{BD}{AB} = \frac{16}{20} = \frac{4}{5}$.

7. $\frac{5}{13}$

Sketch triangle ABC.

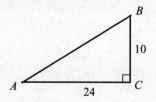

$AB^2 = BC^2 + AC^2$

$AB^2 = 10^2 + 24^2 = 676$

$AB = \sqrt{676} = 26$

$\sin A = \frac{10}{26} = \frac{5}{13}$

8. 9

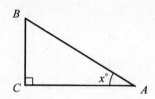

$\cos x° = \frac{AC}{AB} = \frac{3}{5}$

Let $AC = 3x$ and $AB = 5x$.

$AB^2 = BC^2 + AC^2$ Pythagorean Theorem

$(5x)^2 = 12^2 + (3x)^2$ $BC = 12$

$25x^2 = 144 + 9x^2$

$16x^2 = 144$

$x^2 = 9$

$x = \sqrt{9} = 3$

Therefore, $AC = 3x = 3(3) = 9$

9. 10.5

According to the complementary angle theorem, $\sin\theta = \cos(90 - \theta)$.

If $\sin(5x - 10)° = \cos(3x + 16)°$,

$3x + 16 = 90 - (5x - 10)$.

$3x + 16 = 90 - 5x + 10$

$3x + 16 = 100 - 5x$

$8x = 84$

$x = 10.5$

IV. Geometry

CHAPTER 16
Lines and Angles

16-1. Lines, Segments, and Rays

A **line** is a straight arrangement of points and extends in two directions without ending.

Written as: line ℓ, line PQ, or $\overleftrightarrow{PQ}$.

A line is often named by a lower-case script letter. If the names of two points on a line are known, then the line can be named by those points.

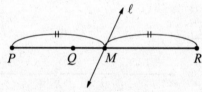

A **segment** is a part of a line and consists of two endpoints and all points in between.

Written as: segment PQ, or $\overline{PQ}$.

A **ray** is a part of a line. It has one endpoint and extends forever in one direction.

Written as: ray PQ or $\overrightarrow{PQ}$.

Two rays $\overrightarrow{RP}$ and $\overrightarrow{RQ}$ are called opposite rays if points R, P, and Q are collinear and R is between P and Q.

The length of $\overline{PQ}$, written as PQ, is the distance between the point P and point Q.

Segment Addition Postulate

If Q is between P and R, then $PQ + QR = PR$.

Definition of Midpoint

If M is the **midpoint** of $\overline{PR}$, then $PM = MR = \dfrac{1}{2}PR$.

A **segment bisector** is a line or a segment that intersects a segment at its midpoint.

Line ℓ is a segment bisector.

Example 1 □ Points A, B, M and C lie on the line as shown below. Point M is the midpoint of $\overline{AC}$.

a. Which ray is opposite to ray BC?

b. If $BM = 6$ and $AB = \dfrac{2}{3}MC$, what is the length of AM?

Solution □ a. Ray BA

b. Let $AB = x$.

$AM = AB + BM = x + 6$ Segment addition postulate

$AM = MC$ Definition of midpoint

$x + 6 = \dfrac{3}{2}x$ Substitution. If $AB = \dfrac{2}{3}MC$, $MC = \dfrac{3}{2}AB = \dfrac{3}{2}x$.

$x = 12$ Solve for x.

$AM = x + 6 = 12 + 6 = 18$ Substitute and simplify.

Exercises - Lines, Segments, and Rays

1

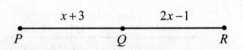

In the figure above, Q is the midpoint of PR. If $PQ = x + 3$ and $QR = 2x - 1$, what is the length of segment PR?

A) 4

B) 7

C) 11

D) 14

2

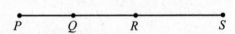

Note: Figure not drawn to scale.

On the segment PS above, $PR = 12$, $QS = 16$, and $QR = \dfrac{1}{3} PS$. What is the length of PS?

A) 19

B) 20

C) 21

D) 22

3

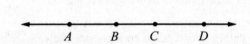

In the figure above, which of the following are opposite rays?

A) Ray AB and Ray CD

B) Ray CA and Ray CD

C) Ray DA and Ray AD

D) Ray CA and Ray BD

4

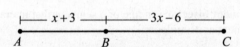

Note: Figure not drawn to scale.

In the figure above, $AB = \dfrac{2}{3} BC$. What is the length of AC?

A) 15

B) 18

C) 21

D) 25

16-2. Angles

Angles are classified according to their measures.

An **acute angle** measures between 0 and 90.   Ex. $\angle POQ$ and $\angle QOR$

A **right angle** measures 90.   Ex. $\angle POR$ and $\angle SOR$

An **obtuse angle** measures between 90 and 180.   Ex. $\angle QOS$

A **straight angle** measures 180.   Ex. $\angle POS$

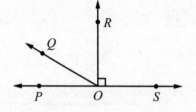

Angle Addition Postulate

If C is in the interior of $\angle AOB$, then $m\angle AOB = m\angle AOC + m\angle COB$.

An **angle bisector** divides an angle into two congruent angles.

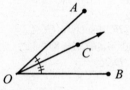

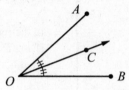

$m\angle AOB = m\angle AOC + m\angle COB$ If $\overrightarrow{OC}$ is the angle bisector of $\angle AOB$,

then $m\angle AOC = m\angle COB = \dfrac{1}{2}m\angle AOB$.

Special Pairs of Angles

When two lines intersect, they form two pairs of **vertical angles**.

Vertical angles are congruent.

$\angle 1 \cong \angle 3 \ (m\angle 1 = m\angle 3) \quad \angle 2 \cong \angle 4 \ (m\angle 2 = m\angle 4)$

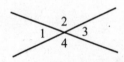

Two angles whose measures have a sum of 180
are called **supplementary angles**.

Two angles whose measures have a sum of 90
are called **complementary angles**.

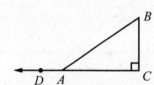

$\angle DAB$ and $\angle BAC$ are supplementary.
$\angle B$ and $\angle BAC$ are complementary.

Example 1   □   In the figure shown at the right, $m\angle POQ = 55$.
Find the each of the following.

a. $m\angle SOT$ b. $m\angle ROT$ c. $m\angle POT$ d. $m\angle POR$

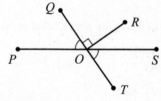

Solution   □   a. $m\angle SOT = m\angle POQ = 55$ Vertical angles are congruent.

b. $m\angle QOR + m\angle ROT = 180$ Straight angle measures 180.
$\quad 90 + m\angle ROT = 180$ $m\angle QOR = 90$
$\quad m\angle ROT = 90$ Solve for $m\angle ROT$.

c. $m\angle POQ + m\angle POT = 180$ Straight angle measures 180.
$\quad 55 + m\angle POT = 180$ $m\angle POQ = 55$
$\quad m\angle POT = 125$ Solve for $m\angle POT$.

d. $m\angle POR = m\angle POQ + m\angle QOR$ Angle Addition Postulate
$\quad m\angle POR = 55 + 90 = 145$ Substitution

Exercises - Angles

1

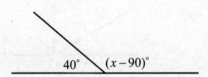

In the figure above, what is the value of x ?

A) 140

B) 160

C) 190

D) 230

2

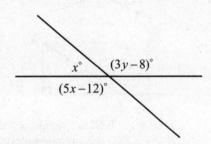

Note: Figure not drawn to scale.

In the figure above, what is the values of y ?

A) 52

B) 60

C) 68

D) 76

3

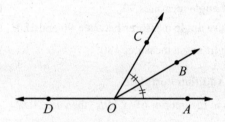

Note: Figure not drawn to scale.

In the figure above, ray OB bisects $\angle COA$.
If $m\angle DOB = 11x + 6$ and $m\angle COA = 8x - 12$,
what is the measure of $\angle DOC$?

A) 92

B) 96

C) 102

D) 108

4

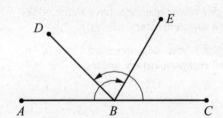

Note: Figure not drawn to scale.

In the figure above, $m\angle ABE = 120°$ and
$m\angle CBD = 135°$. What is the measure of $\angle DBE$?

A) 63

B) 68

C) 75

D) 79

16-3. Parallel and Perpendicular Lines

For two parallel lines ℓ and m which are cut by the transversal t :

1) **Corresponding Angles** are equal in measure.

$m\angle 1 = m\angle 5 \quad m\angle 2 = m\angle 6$

$m\angle 3 = m\angle 7 \quad m\angle 4 = m\angle 8$

2) **Alternate Interior Angles** are equal in measure.

$m\angle 3 = m\angle 5 \quad m\angle 4 = m\angle 6$

3) **Alternate Exterior Angles** are equal in measure.

$m\angle 1 = m\angle 7 \quad m\angle 2 = m\angle 8$

4) **Consecutive(Same Side) Interior Angles** are supplementary.

$m\angle 3 + m\angle 6 = 180° \quad m\angle 4 + m\angle 5 = 180°$

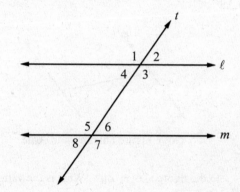

Theorem

In a plane, if a line is perpendicular to one of two parallel lines, it is also perpendicular to the other.

If $t \perp \ell$ and $\ell \parallel m$, then $t \perp m$.

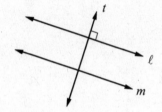

Example 1 □ In the figure below, $\ell \parallel m$, $r \perp t$ and $m\angle 1 = 32$. Lines ℓ, r, and t intersect at one point. Find $m\angle 2$, $m\angle 3$, $m\angle 4$, and $m\angle 5$.

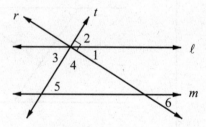

Solution □	$m\angle 1 + m\angle 2 = 90$	A right angle measures 90.
	$32 + m\angle 2 = 90$	Substitution
	$m\angle 2 = 58$	Solve for $m\angle 2$.
	$m\angle 2 = m\angle 3 = 58$	Vertical angles are $\cong$.
	$m\angle 1 + m\angle 4 + m\angle 3 = 180$	A straight angle measures 180.
	$32 + m\angle 4 + 58 = 180$	Substitution
	$m\angle 4 = 90$	Solve for $m\angle 4$.
	$m\angle 3 = m\angle 5 = 58$	Alternate Interior $\angle s$ are $\cong$.
	$m\angle 1 = m\angle 6 = 32$	Corresponding $\angle s$ are $\cong$.

Exercises - Parallel and Perpendicular Lines

1

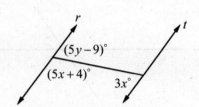

Note: Figure not drawn to scale

In the figure above, $r \parallel t$. What is the value of $x + y$?

A) 37

B) 40

C) 43

D) 46

2

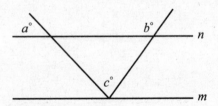

In the figure above, $m \parallel n$. If $a = 50$ and $b = 120$, what is the value of c?

A) 50

B) 60

C) 70

D) 80

3

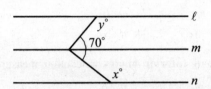

Note: Figure not drawn to scale.

In the figure above, lines ℓ, m, and n are parallel. What is the value of $x + y$?

A) 160

B) 200

C) 230

D) 290

4

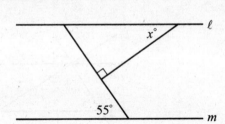

In the figure above, $\ell \parallel m$. What is the value of x?

A) 30

B) 35

C) 40

D) 45

Chapter 16 Practice Test

1

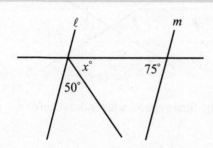

Note: Figure not drawn to scale.

In the figure above, $\ell \parallel m$. What is the value of x?

A) 45

B) 50

C) 55

D) 60

2

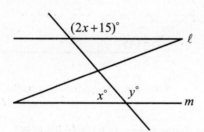

Note: Figure not drawn to scale.

In the figure above, $\ell \parallel m$. What is the value of y?

A) 120

B) 125

C) 130

D) 135

3

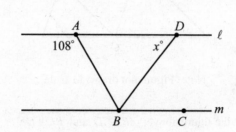

Note: Figure not drawn to scale.

In the figure above, lines ℓ and m are parallel and $\overline{BD}$ bisects $\angle ABC$. What is the value of x?

A) 54

B) 60

C) 68

D) 72

4

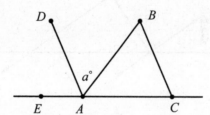

In the figure above, $\overline{DA} \parallel \overline{BC}$ and $\overline{AB}$ bisects $\angle DAC$. What is the measure of $\angle BCA$ in terms of a?

A) $180 - a$

B) $2a - 180$

C) $180 - 2a$

D) $2a - 90$

5

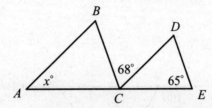

Note: Figure not drawn to scale.

In the figure above, $\overline{AB} \parallel \overline{CD}$ and $\overline{BC} \parallel \overline{DE}$.
What is the value of x?

A) 47

B) 51

C) 55

D) 57

6

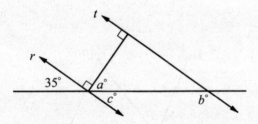

In the figure above, $r \parallel t$. What is the value
of $a+b$?

A) 160

B) 175

C) 185

D) 200

7

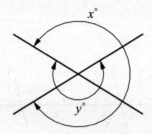

In the figure above, what is the value of $x+y$?

8

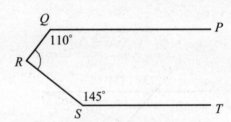

Note: Figure not drawn to scale.

In the figure above, $\overline{PQ}$ is parallel to $\overline{ST}$.
What is the measure of $\angle QRS$?

Answer Key

Section 16-1

1. D   2. C   3. B   4. D

Section 16-2

1. D   2. A   3. B   4. C

Section 16-3

1. A   2. C   3. D   4. B

Chapter 16 Practice Test

1. C   2. B   3. A   4. C   5. A
6. D   7. 540   8. 105

Answers and Explanations

Section 16-1

1. D

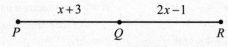

$PQ = QR$	Definition of Midpoint
$x+3 = 2x-1$	Substitution
$x+3-x = 2x-1-x$	Subtract x from each side.
$3 = x-1$	Simplify.
$4 = x$	
$PR = PQ+QR$	Segment Addition Postulate
$\quad = x+3+2x-1$	Substitution
$\quad = 3x+2$	
$\quad = 3(4)+2 = 14$	$x = 4$

2. C

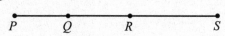

Note: Figure not drawn to scale.

Let $PS = x$, then $QR = \dfrac{1}{3}PS = \dfrac{1}{3}x$.

$PR = PQ+QR$	Segment Addition Postulate
$12 = PQ+\dfrac{1}{3}x$	$PR = 12$ and $QR = \dfrac{1}{3}x$
$PQ = 12-\dfrac{1}{3}x$	Solve for PQ.
$QS = QR+RS$	Segment Addition Postulate

$16 = \dfrac{1}{3}x+RS$	$QS = 16$ and $QR = \dfrac{1}{3}x$
$RS = 16-\dfrac{1}{3}x$	Solve for RS.
$PS = PQ+QR+RS$	Segment Addition Postulate
$x = (12-\dfrac{1}{3}x)+\dfrac{1}{3}x+(16-\dfrac{1}{3}x)$	Substitution
$x = 28-\dfrac{1}{3}x$	Simplify.
$\dfrac{4}{3}x = 28$	Add $\dfrac{1}{3}x$ to each side.
$\dfrac{3}{4}\cdot\dfrac{4}{3}x = \dfrac{3}{4}\cdot 28$	Multiply $\dfrac{3}{4}$ by each side.
$x = 21$	

Therefore, $PS = x = 21$.

3. B

Ray CA and Ray CD are opposite rays, because points A, C, and D are collinear and C is between A and D.

4. D

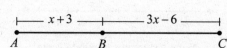

Note: Figure not drwan to scale.

$AB = \dfrac{2}{3}BC$	Given
$x+3 = \dfrac{2}{3}(3x-6)$	Substitution
$x+3 = 2x-4$	Simplify.
$7 = x$	Solve for x.
$AC = AB+BC$	Segment Addition Postulate
$\quad = x+3+3x-6$	Substitution
$\quad = 4x-3$	Simplify.
$\quad = 4(7)-3$	$x = 7$
$\quad = 25$	

Section 16-2

1. D

$40+x-90 = 180$	Straight $\angle$ measures 180.
$x-50 = 180$	Simplify.
$x-50+50 = 180+50$	Add 50 to each side.
$x = 230$	

2. A

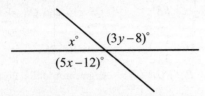

Note: Figure not drawn to scale.

$x + 5x - 12 = 180$	Straight $\angle$ measures 180.
$6x - 12 = 180$	
$6x = 192$	
$x = 32$	
$x + 3y - 8 = 180$	Straight $\angle$ measures 180.
$32 + 3y - 8 = 180$	$x = 32$
$24 + 3y = 180$	Simplify.
$24 + 3y - 24 = 180 - 24$	
$3y = 156$	
$y = 52$	

3. B

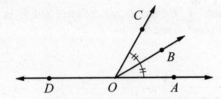

Note: Figure not drawn to scale.

$m\angle BOA = \dfrac{1}{2} m\angle COA$ Definition of $\angle$ bisector

$m\angle BOA = \dfrac{1}{2}(8x - 12)$ Substitution

$m\angle BOA = 4x - 6$	Simplify.
$m\angle DOB + m\angle BOA = 180$	Straight $\angle$ measures 180.
$11x + 6 + 4x - 6 = 180$	Substitution
$15x = 180$	Simplify.
$x = 12$	

Thus, $m\angle COA = 8x - 12 = 8(12) - 12 = 84$.

$m\angle DOC + m\angle COA = 180$	Straight $\angle$ measures 180.
$m\angle DOC + 84 = 180$	$m\angle COA = 84$
$m\angle DOC = 96$	

4. C

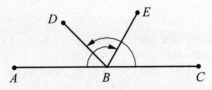

Note: Figure not drawn to scale.

Let $m\angle DBE = x$

$m\angle ABE$

$= m\angle ABD + m\angle DBE$	Angle Addition Postulate
$120 = m\angle ABD + x$	Substitution
$120 - x = m\angle ABD$	
$m\angle ABD + m\angle CBD = 180$	Straight $\angle$ measures 180.
$120 - x + 135 = 180$	Substitution
$255 - x = 180$	Simplify.
$x = 75$	

Therefore, $m\angle DBE = x = 75$.

Section 16-3

1. A

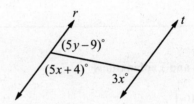

Note: Figure not drawn to scale

$5x + 4 + 3x = 180$	If $r \parallel t$, consecutive interior $\angle s$ are supplementary.
$8x + 4 = 180$	Simplify.
$8x = 176$	
$x = 22$	
$5x + 4 + 5y - 9 = 180$	Straight $\angle$ measures 180.
$5x - 5 + 5y = 180$	Simplify.
$5(22) - 5 + 5y = 180$	$x = 22$
$110 - 5 + 5y = 180$	Simplify.
$105 + 5y = 180$	Simplify.
$5y = 75$	Simplify.
$y = 15$	

Therefore, $x + y = 22 + 15 = 37$.

2. C

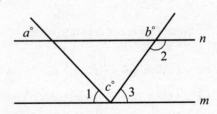

$m\angle 1 = a$	If $m \parallel n$, corresponding $\angle s$ are $\cong$.
$m\angle 1 = 50$	$a = 50$
$m\angle 2 = b$	Vertical $\angle s$ are $\cong$.
$m\angle 2 = 120$	$b = 120$

$m\angle 2 + m\angle 3 = 180$ If $m \parallel n$, consecutive interior
                                  $\angle s$ are supplementary.

$120 + m\angle 3 = 180$ $m\angle 2 = 120$

$m\angle 3 = 60$

$m\angle 1 + c + m\angle 3 = 180$ Straight $\angle$ measures 180.

$50 + c + 60 = 180$ $m\angle 1 = 50$ and $m\angle 3 = 60$

$c + 110 = 180$ Simplify.

$c = 70$

3. D

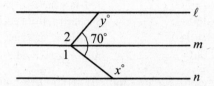

Note: Figure not drawn to scale.

$m\angle 1 = x$ If $m \parallel n$, alternate interior
                    $\angle s$ are $\cong$.

$m\angle 2 = y$ If $\ell \parallel m$, alternate interior
                    $\angle s$ are $\cong$.

$m\angle 1 + m\angle 2 + 70 = 360$ There are $360°$ in a circle.

$x + y + 70 = 360$ $m\angle 1 = x$ and $m\angle 2 = y$

$x + y = 290$

4. B

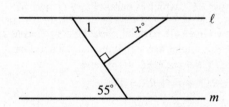

$m\angle 1 = 55$ If $\ell \parallel m$, alternate interior
                    $\angle s$ are $\cong$.

$m\angle 1 + x = 90$ The acute $\angle s$ of a right
                    triangle are complementary.

$55 + x = 90$ $m\angle 1 = 55$

$x = 35$

Chapter 16 Practice Test

1. C

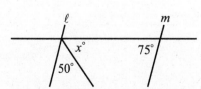

Note: Figure not drawn to scale.

$50 + x + 75 = 180$ If $\ell \parallel m$, consecutive interior
                                 $\angle s$ are supplementary.

$125 + x = 180$ Simplify.

$x = 55$

2. B

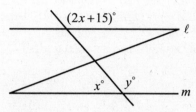

Note: Figure not drwan to scale.

$y = 2x + 15$ If $\ell \parallel m$, consecutive interior
                    $\angle s$ are supplementary.

$x + y = 180$ Straight $\angle$ measures 180.

$x + (2x + 15) = 180$ $y = 2x + 15$

$3x + 15 = 180$ Simplify.

$3x = 165$

$x = 55$

Therefore, $y = 2x + 15 = 2(55) + 15 = 125$.

3. A

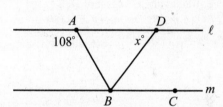

Note: Figure not drawn to scale.

$m\angle ABC = 108$ If $\ell \parallel m$, alternate interior
                    $\angle s$ are $\cong$.

$m\angle DBC = \frac{1}{2}m\angle ABC$ Definition of $\angle$ bisector

$m\angle DBC = \frac{1}{2}(108)$ $m\angle ABC = 108$

$m\angle DBC = 54$ Simplify.

$x = m\angle DBC$ If $\ell \parallel m$, alternate interior
                    $\angle s$ are $\cong$.

$x = 54$ $m\angle DBC = 54$

4. C

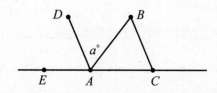

$m\angle BAC = m\angle DAB$ Definition of $\angle$ bisector

$m\angle BAC = a$ $m\angle DAB = a$

Since straight angles measure 180,

$m\angle DAE + m\angle DAB + m\angle BAC = 180$.

$m\angle DAE + a + a = 180$ $m\angle DAB = m\angle BAC = a$

$m\angle DAE = 180 - 2a$ Subtract $2a$.

$m\angle BCA = m\angle DAE$ If $DA \parallel BC$, corresponding $\angle s$ are $\cong$.

$m\angle BCA = 180 - 2a$ $m\angle DAE = 180 - 2a$

5. A

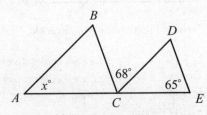

Note: Figure not drawn to scale.

$m\angle BCA = m\angle DEC$ If $DE \parallel BC$, corresponding $\angle s$ are $\cong$.

$m\angle BCA = 65$ $m\angle DEC = 65$

$m\angle DCE = x$ If $AB \parallel CD$, corresponding $\angle s$ are $\cong$.

Since straight angles measure 180,

$m\angle BCA + m\angle BCD + m\angle DCE = 180$.

$65 + 68 + x = 180$ Substitution

$133 + x = 180$ Simplify.

$x = 47$

6. D

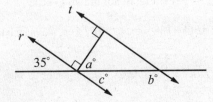

$c = 35$ Vertical $\angle s$ are $\cong$.

$a + c = 90$ $\angle a$ and $\angle c$ are complementary.

$a + 35 = 90$ $c = 35$

$a = 55$

$b + c = 180$ If $r \parallel t$, consecutive interior $\angle s$ are supplementary.

$b + 35 = 180$ $c = 35$

$b = 145$

Therefore, $a + b = 55 + 145 = 200$.

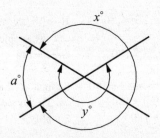

Draw $\angle a$.

$x + a = 360$ $360°$ in a circle.

$x = 360 - a$ Subtract a from each side.

$y - a = 180$ Straight $\angle$ measures 180.

$y = 180 + a$ Add a to each side.

Therefore, $x + y = (360 - a) + (180 + a) = 540$.

8. 105

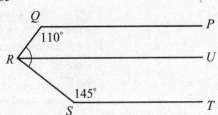

Note: Figure not drawn to scale.

Draw $\overline{RU}$, which is parallel to $\overline{PQ}$ and $\overline{ST}$.

If two lines are parallel, then the consecutive interior angles are supplementary. Therefore, $m\angle PQR + m\angle QRU = 180$ and $m\angle RST + m\angle URS = 180$.

$110 + m\angle QRU = 180$ $m\angle PQR = 110$

$m\angle QRU = 70$ Subtract 110.

$145 + m\angle URS = 180$ $m\angle RST = 145$

$m\angle URS = 35$ Subtract 145.

By the Angle Addition Postulate, $m\angle QRS = m\angle QRU + m\angle URS$.

Substituting 70 for $m\angle QRU$ and 35 for $m\angle QRU$ gives $m\angle QRS = 70 + 35 = 105$.

7. 540

CHAPTER 17
Triangles

17-1. Angles of a Triangle

Angle Sum Theorem

The angle sum of a triangle is $180°$.

$$m\angle A + m\angle B + m\angle C = 180°$$

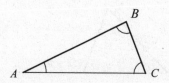

Exterior Angle Theorem

The measure of an **exterior angle** of a triangle is equal to the sum of the measures of the two remote interior angles.

$$m\angle BCD = m\angle A + m\angle B$$

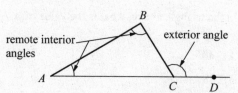

Isosceles Triangle Theorem

If two sides of a triangle are congruent, the angles opposite of those sides are congruent.

If $AB = BC$, then $m\angle C = m\angle A$.
The converse is also true.

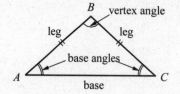

Isosceles Triangle Theorem - Corollary

If a line bisects the vertex angle of an isosceles triangle, the line is the perpendicular bisector of the base.

If $AB = BC$ and $m\angle ABD = m\angle CBD$,
then $\overline{BD} \perp \overline{AC}$ and $AD = CD$.

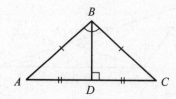

Example 1 ☐ a. In $\triangle ABC$ shown below, $AB = BC$, $m\angle BCD = 110$ and $m\angle BDE = 140$.
Find $m\angle 1$, $m\angle 2$, $m\angle 3$, and $m\angle 4$.

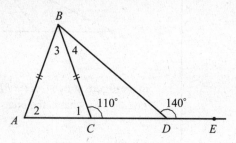

Solution ☐	$m\angle 1 + m\angle BCD = 180$	Straight angle equals $180°$.
	$m\angle 1 + 110 = 180$	Substitution
	$m\angle 1 = 180 - 110 = 70$	Subtraction
	$m\angle 2 = m\angle 1 = 70$	Isosceles Triangle Theorem
	$m\angle 3 + m\angle 2 = 110$	Exterior Angle Theorem
	$m\angle 3 + 70 = 110$	Substitution
	$m\angle 3 = 40$	Subtraction
	$m\angle 4 + 110 = 140$	Exterior Angle Theorem
	$m\angle 4 = 30$	Subtraction

Exercises - Angles of a Triangle

1

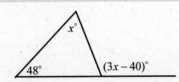

In the triangle above, what is the value of x?

A) 44

B) 48

C) 52

D) 56

2

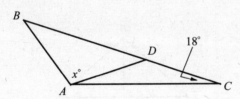

In $\triangle ABC$ above, if $AB = AD = DC$, what is the value of x?

A) 92

B) 96

C) 102

D) 108

3

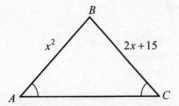

In $\triangle ABC$ above, $m\angle A = m\angle C$. If $x > 0$, what is the value of x?

4

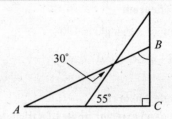

Note: Figure not drawn to scale.

In the figure above, $AC \perp BC$. What is the measure of $\angle ABC$?

A) 50

B) 55

C) 60

D) 65

5

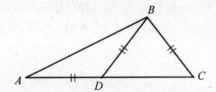

In the figure above, $AD = BD = BC$. If $m\angle A = 26$, what is the measure of $m\angle DBC$?

A) 68

B) 72

C) 76

D) 82

17-2. Pythagorean Theorem and Special Right Triangles

A triangle with a right angle is called a **right triangle**.
The side opposite to the right angle is called the **hypotenuse**
and the other two sides are called **legs**.
In a right triangle the acute angles are complementary.
In triangle shown at right, $m\angle A + m\angle B = 90$.

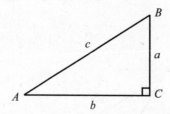

The **Pythagorean theorem** states that in a right triangle,
the sum of the squares of the lengths of the legs equals
the square of the length of the hypotenuse.

In right triangle ABC at the right, $a^2 + b^2 = c^2$.
The converse is also true.

The Pythagorean theorem can be used to determine the ratios
of the lengths of the sides of two special right triangles.

In a **45°-45°-90°** triangle, the hypotenuse is $\sqrt{2}$ times
as long as a leg. An isosceles right triangle is also called
a 45°-45°-90° triangle.

In a **30°-60°-90°** triangle, the hypotenuse is twice as long
as the shorter leg, and the longer leg is $\sqrt{3}$ times as long
as the shorter leg.

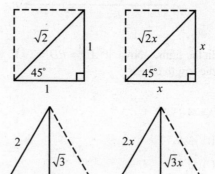

Example 1   □   In the figure below, find the value of x.

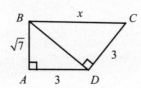

Solution   □ $BD^2 = (\sqrt{7})^2 + 3^3 = 16$ Pythagorean Theorem

               $x^2 = BD^2 + 3^2$ Pythagorean Theorem

               $x^2 = 16 + 9 = 25$ Substitution

               $x = \sqrt{25} = 5$

Example 2   □   In the figures below, find the values of x and y.

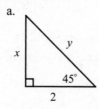

Solution   □   a. Since a 45°-45°-90° triangle is an isosceles right triangle, $x = 2$.

              In a 45°-45°-90° triangle, hypotenuse $= \sqrt{2} \cdot$ leg $\Rightarrow y = 2\sqrt{2}$

            b. In a 30°-60°-90° triangle, longer leg $= \sqrt{3} \cdot$ shorter leg $\Rightarrow 3 = \sqrt{3}x \Rightarrow x = \dfrac{3}{\sqrt{3}} = \sqrt{3}$

              hypotenuse $= 2 \cdot$ shorter leg $\Rightarrow y = 2\sqrt{3}$

Exercises - Pythagorean Theorem and Special Right Triangles

1

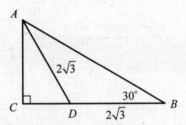

In the figure above, if $AD = BD = 2\sqrt{3}$, what is the length of AB?

A) $4\sqrt{3}$

B) $3\sqrt{6}$

C) 6

D) $6\sqrt{2}$

2

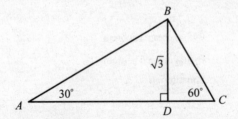

In $\triangle ABC$ above, $BD = \sqrt{3}$. What is the perimeter of $\triangle ABC$?

A) $2\sqrt{2}+6$

B) $2\sqrt{3}+6$

C) $2\sqrt{6}+6$

D) $3\sqrt{2}+6$

3

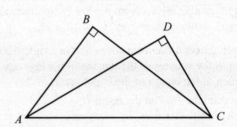

Note: Figure not drawn to scale.

In the figure above, $AB = 6$, $BC = 8$, and $CD = 5$. What is the length of AD?

A) $4\sqrt{3}$

B) $5\sqrt{2}$

C) $5\sqrt{3}$

D) $6\sqrt{2}$

4

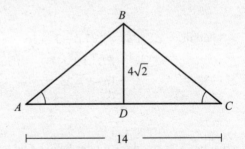

Note: Figure not drawn to scale.

In the figure above, $\angle A \cong \angle C$ and $\overline{BD}$ bisects $\overline{AC}$. What is the perimeter of $\triangle ABC$?

A) 32

B) 36

C) $14+10\sqrt{2}$

D) $14+12\sqrt{2}$

17-3. Similar Triangles and Proportional Parts

AA Similarity Postulate

If two angles of one triangle are congruent to two angles of another triangle, the triangles are similar.

If two triangles are similar, their corresponding angles are congruent and their corresponding sides are proportional.

If two triangles are similar, their perimeters are proportional to the measures of the corresponding sides.

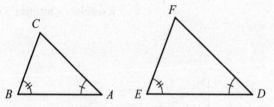

If $\angle A \cong \angle D$ and $\angle B \cong \angle E$, then $\angle C \cong \angle F$.

Therefore $\triangle ABC \sim \triangle DEF$, and

$$\frac{AB}{DE} = \frac{BC}{EF} = \frac{AC}{DF} = \frac{\text{perimeter of } \triangle ABC}{\text{perimeter of } \triangle DEF}.$$

Triangle Proportionality Theorem

If a line parallel to one side of a triangle intersects the other two sides, it divides those sides proportionally.

In $\triangle ABC$, if $\overline{AC} \parallel \overline{DE}$ then $\triangle ABC \sim \triangle DBE$ by AA Similarity.

It follows that $\dfrac{AB}{DB} = \dfrac{CB}{EB} = \dfrac{AC}{DE}$. Also $\dfrac{BD}{DA} = \dfrac{BE}{EC}$, $\dfrac{BA}{DA} = \dfrac{BC}{EC}$,

$\dfrac{BD}{DE} = \dfrac{BA}{AC}$, and $\dfrac{BE}{DE} = \dfrac{BC}{AC}$.

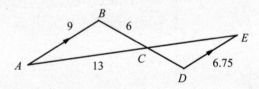

If D and E are the midpoints of $\overline{AB}$ and $\overline{BC}$, $\overline{AC} \parallel \overline{DE}$ and $DE = \dfrac{1}{2} AC$.

Example 1   □   In the figure below, $\overline{AB} \parallel \overline{DE}$. Find CD and CE.

Solution   □
$m\angle A = m\angle E$ Alternate Interior $\angle s$ are $\cong$.
$m\angle BCA = m\angle DCE$ Vertical $\angle s$ are $\cong$.
$\triangle ABC \sim \triangle EDC$ AA Similarity

Therefore $\dfrac{AB}{ED} = \dfrac{BC}{DC} \Rightarrow \dfrac{9}{6.75} = \dfrac{6}{DC} \Rightarrow DC = 4.5$

$\dfrac{AB}{ED} = \dfrac{AC}{EC} \Rightarrow \dfrac{9}{6.75} = \dfrac{13}{EC} \Rightarrow EC = 9.75$

Example 2   □   In the figure at right, $\overline{AC} \parallel \overline{DE}$.

Find the length of $\overline{DA}$ and $\overline{AC}$.

Solution   □
$\dfrac{BD}{DA} = \dfrac{BE}{EC} \Rightarrow \dfrac{6}{DA} = \dfrac{8}{12} \Rightarrow DA = 9$

$\dfrac{BD}{DE} = \dfrac{BA}{AC} \Rightarrow \dfrac{6}{10} = \dfrac{6+9}{AC} \Rightarrow AC = 25$

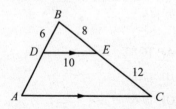

Exercises - Similar Triangles and Proportional Parts

1

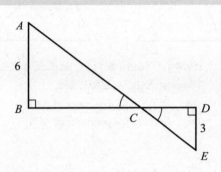

In the figure above, if $AB = 6$, $DE = 3$, and $BD = 12$, what is the length of AE?

A) 12

B) $9\sqrt{2}$

C) $8\sqrt{3}$

D) 15

2

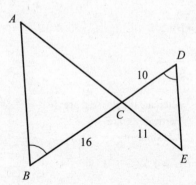

Note: Figure not drawn to scale.

In the figure above, $\angle B \cong \angle D$. If $BC = 16$, $CD = 10$, and $CE = 11$, what is the length of AE?

A) 16.8

B) 17.2

C) 17.6

D) 18.4

Questions 3 and 4 refer to the following information.

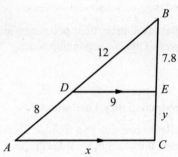

In the figure above, $\overline{DE} \parallel \overline{AC}$.

3

What is the value of x?

A) 12.5

B) 15

C) 16.5

D) 18

4

What is the value of y?

A) 5.2

B) 5.6

C) 6.0

D) 6.4

17-4. Area of a Triangle

The **area** A of a triangle equals half the product of a base and the height to that base.

$$A = \frac{1}{2}b \cdot h$$

Area of equilateral triangle with side length of a.

$$A = \frac{1}{2}(a)(\frac{\sqrt{3}}{2}a) = \frac{\sqrt{3}}{4}a^2$$

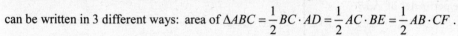

Any side of a triangle can be used as a base. The height that corresponds to the base is the perpendicular line segment from the opposite vertex to the base. The area of $\triangle ABC$ at the right

can be written in 3 different ways: area of $\triangle ABC = \frac{1}{2}BC \cdot AD = \frac{1}{2}AC \cdot BE = \frac{1}{2}AB \cdot CF$.

The **perimeter** P of a triangle is the sum of the lengths of all three sides.
$$P = AB + BC + CA$$

Ratios of Areas of Two Triangles

1. If two triangles are similar with corresponding sides in a ratio of $a:b$, then the ratio of their areas equals $a^2 : b^2$.

2. If two triangles have equal heights, then the ratio of their areas equals the ratio of their bases.

3. If two triangles have equal bases, then the ratio of their areas equals the ratio of their heights.

Example 1   □   In the figure below, if $AC = 6$, $BD = 4$, and $AB = 8$, what is the length of CE?

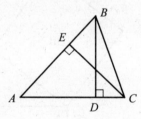

Solution   □   Area of $\triangle ABC = \frac{1}{2}AC \cdot BD = \frac{1}{2}AB \cdot CE$.

$$\Rightarrow \frac{1}{2}(6)(4) = \frac{1}{2}(8)(CE) \Rightarrow CE = 3$$

Example 2   □   In the figure below, $AD = 5$ and $DC = 3$. Find the ratio of the area of $\triangle ABD$ to the area of $\triangle CBD$.

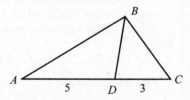

Solution   □   The two triangles have the same height, so the ratio of the areas of the two triangles is equal to the ratio of their bases.

$$\frac{\text{area of } \triangle ABD}{\text{area of } \triangle CBD} = \frac{AD}{CD} = \frac{5}{3}$$

Exercises - Area of a Triangle

1

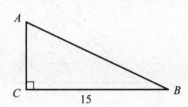

In the figure above, the area of right triangle *ABC* is 60. What is the perimeter of △*ABC*?

A) 34

B) 36

C) 38

D) 40

2

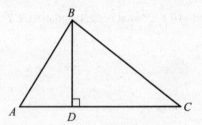

In triangle *ABC* above, if *BD* was increased by 50 percent and *AC* was reduced by 50 percent, how would the area of △*ABC* change?

A) The area of △*ABC* would be decreased by 25 percent.

B) The area of △*ABC* would be increased by 25 percent.

C) The area of △*ABC* would not change.

D) The area of △*ABC* would be decreased by 50 percent.

3

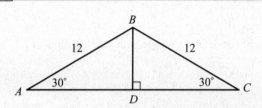

In the figure above, what is the area of △*ABC*?

A) $24\sqrt{3}$

B) $30\sqrt{3}$

C) $36\sqrt{3}$

D) $48\sqrt{3}$

4

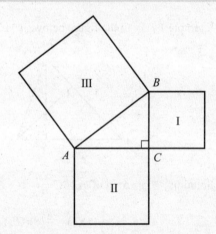

The figure above shows right triangle △*ABC* and three squares. If the area of square region I is 80 square inches and the area of square region II is 150 square inches, which of the following is true about the area of square region III?

A) Less than 230 square inches.

B) More than 230 square inches.

C) Equal to 230 square inches.

D) It cannot be determined from the information given.

Chapter 17 Practice Test

1

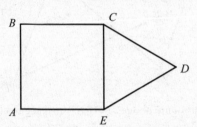

In the figure above, CDE is an equilateral triangle and $ABCD$ is a square with an area of $4x^2$. What is the area of triangle CDE in terms of x?

A) $\dfrac{\sqrt{3}}{2}x^2$

B) $\sqrt{3}x^2$

C) $\dfrac{3\sqrt{3}}{2}x^2$

D) $2\sqrt{3}x^2$

2

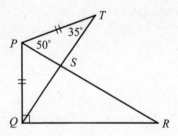

In the figure above, $\overline{PQ} \perp \overline{QR}$ and $\overline{PQ} \cong \overline{PT}$. What is the measure of $\angle R$?

A) 30

B) 35

C) 40

D) 45

3

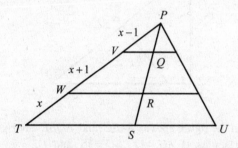

Note: Figure not drawn to scale.

In the figure above, $\overline{VQ} \parallel \overline{WR} \parallel \overline{TS}$.
If $PS = 15$, what is the length of $\overline{RS}$?

A) 4.5

B) 5

C) 6

D) 6.5

4

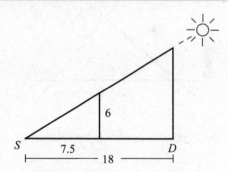

Note: Figure not drawn to scale.

A person 6 feet tall stands so that the ends of his shadow and the shadow of the pole coincide. The length of the person's shadow was measured 7.5 feet and the length of the pole's shadow, SD, was measured 18 feet. How tall is the pole?

A) 12.8

B) 13.6

C) 14.4

D) 15.2

5

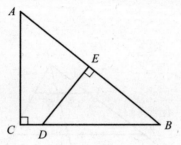

In the figure above, $\triangle ABC$ and $\triangle DBE$ are right triangles. If $AC = 12$, $BC = 15$, and $DE = 8$, what is the length of BE?

A) 8.5

B) 9

C) 9.5

D) 10

6

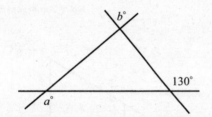

In the figure above, what is the value of $a - b$?

A) 50

B) 55

C) 60

D) 65

7

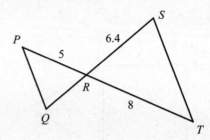

In the figure above, $\overline{PQ} \parallel \overline{ST}$ and segment PT intersects segment QS at R. What is the length of segment QS?

8

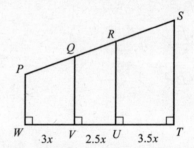

In the figure above, if $PS = 162$, what is the length of segment QR?

9

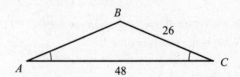

In the figure above, what is the area of the isosceles triangle ABC?

Answer Key

Section 17-1

1. A   2. D   3. 5   4. D   5. C

Section 17-2

1. C   2. B   3. C   4. A

Section 17-3

1. D   2. C   3. B   4. A

Section 17-4

1. D   2. A   3. C   4. C

Chapter 17 Practice Test

1. B   2. A   3. B   4. C   5. D
6. A   7. 10.4   8. 45   9. 240

Answers and Explanations

Section 17-1

1. A

$3x - 40 = x + 48$ Exterior Angle Theorem
$3x - 40 - x = x + 48 - x$ Subtract x from each side.
$2x - 40 = 48$ Simplify.
$2x = 88$ Add 40 to each side.
$x = 44$

2. D

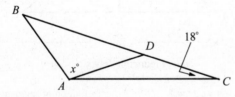

$AD = DC$ Given
$m\angle DAC = m\angle DCA = 18$ Isosceles $\triangle$ Theorem
$m\angle BDA$ Exterior $\angle$ Theorem
$= m\angle DCA + m\angle DAC$
$m\angle BDA = 18 + 18$ $m\angle DAC = m\angle DCA = 18$
$m\angle BDA = 36$ Simplify.
$AB = AD$ Given
$m\angle DBA = m\angle BDA = 36$ Isosceles $\triangle$ Theorem

In triangle ABD, the angle sum is 180.

Thus, $x + 36 + 36 = 180$.
Solving the equation for x gives $x = 108$.

3. 5

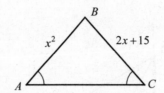

$m\angle A = m\angle C$ Given
$AB = BC$ Isosceles $\triangle$ Theorem
$x^2 = 2x + 15$ Substitution
$x^2 - 2x - 15 = 0$ Make one side 0.
$(x + 3)(x - 5) = 0$ Factor.
$x + 3 = 0$ or $x - 5 = 0$ Zero Product Property
$x = -3$ or $x = 5$
Since $x > 0$, the value of x is 5.

4. D

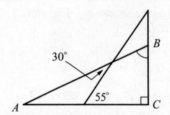

$m\angle A + 30 = 55$ Exterior Angle Theorem
$m\angle A = 25$
$m\angle A + m\angle B = 90$ The acute $\angle s$ of a right
                        $\triangle$ are complementary.
$25 + m\angle B = 90$ $m\angle A = 25$.
$m\angle B = 65$

5. C

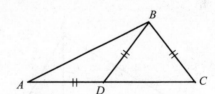

$AD = BD$ Given
$m\angle ABD = m\angle A$ Isosceles $\triangle$ Theorem
$m\angle A = 26$ Given
$m\angle ABD = 26$ $m\angle A = 26$
$m\angle BDC$ Exterior $\angle$ Theorem
$= m\angle A + m\angle ABD$
$m\angle BDC = 26 + 26 = 52$ $m\angle A = m\angle ABD = 26$
$BD = BC$ Given
$m\angle C = m\angle BDC$ Isosceles $\triangle$ Theorem
$m\angle C = 52$ $m\angle BDC = 52$
$m\angle C + m\angle BDC + m\angle DBC = 180$ Angle Sum
                                  Theorem
$52 + 52 + m\angle DBC = 180$ $m\angle C = m\angle BDC = 52$
$m\angle DBC = 76$

Section 17-2

1. C

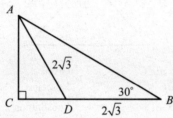

$AD = BD$ Given
$m\angle BAD = m\angle B = 30$ Isosceles $\triangle$ Theorem
$m\angle ADC = m\angle BAD + m\angle B$ Exterior $\angle$ Theorem
$m\angle ADC = 30 + 30 = 60$ $m\angle BAD = m\angle B = 30$
$\triangle ADC$ is a $30°$-$60°$-$90°$ triangle.

In a $30°$-$60°$-$90°$ triangle, the hypotenuse is twice as long as the shorter leg. Therefore,
$AD = 2CD$
$2\sqrt{3} = 2CD$
$\sqrt{3} = CD$.

$BC = BD + CD = 2\sqrt{3} + \sqrt{3} = 3\sqrt{3}$
Triangle ABC is also a $30°$-$60°$-$90°$ triangle.
In a $30°$-$60°$-$90°$ triangle, the longer leg is $\sqrt{3}$ times as long as the shorter leg. Therefore,
$BC = \sqrt{3}AC$
$3\sqrt{3} = \sqrt{3}AC$
$3 = AC$.

$AB = 2AC = 2 \times 3 = 6$

2. B

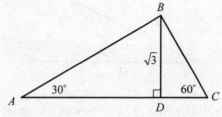

In the figure above, $\triangle ABD$ and $\triangle BCD$ are $30°$-$60°$-$90°$ triangles.
In a $30°$-$60°$-$90°$ triangle, the hypotenuse is twice as long as the shorter leg and the longer leg is $\sqrt{3}$ times as long as the shorter leg. In $\triangle ABD$,
$AB = 2BD = 2\sqrt{3}$
$AD = \sqrt{3}BD = \sqrt{3} \cdot \sqrt{3} = 3$.
In $\triangle BCD$,
$BD = \sqrt{3}CD$
$\sqrt{3} = \sqrt{3}CD$

$1 = CD$
$BC = 2CD = 2 \cdot 1 = 2$

perimeter of $\triangle ABC$
$= AB + BC + AC$
$= 2\sqrt{3} + 2 + (3 + 1)$
$= 2\sqrt{3} + 6$

3. C

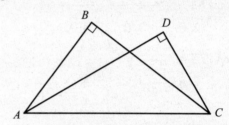

Note: Figure not drawn to scale.

$AC^2 = AB^2 + BC^2$ Pythagorean Theorem
$AC^2 = 6^2 + 8^2 = 100$
$AC^2 = AD^2 + CD^2$ Pythagorean Theorem
$100 = AD^2 + 5^2$ $AC^2 = 100$, $CD = 5$
$100 - 25 = AD^2$
$75 = AD^2$
$\sqrt{75} = AD$
$5\sqrt{3} = AD$

4. A

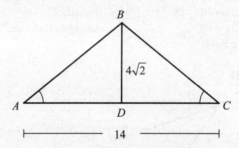

Note: Figure not drawn to scale.

$AD = CD = 7$ Definition of segment
                     bisector

$AB^2 = BD^2 + AD^2$ Pythagorean Theorem
$AB^2 = (4\sqrt{2})^2 + 7^2$ Substitution
    $= 32 + 49 = 81$

$AB = \sqrt{81} = 9$ Square root both sides.

$AB = BC$ Isosceles Triangle Theorem
Perimeter of $\triangle ABC$
$= AB + BC + AC$
$= 9 + 9 + 14 = 32$

Section 17-3

1. D

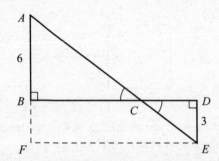

Draw $\overline{EF}$, which is parallel and congruent to $\overline{BD}$. Extend $\overline{AB}$ to point F. Since $\overline{EF} \parallel \overline{BD}$, $\angle F$ is a right angle.

$BD = EF = 12$ and $DE = BF = 3$
$AF = AB + BF = 6 + 3 = 9$
$AE^2 = AF^2 + EF^2$ Pythagorean Theorem
$ = 9^2 + 12^2$
$ = 225$
$AE = \sqrt{225} = 15$

2. C

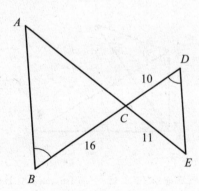

Note: Figure not drawn to scale.

$\angle B \cong \angle D$ Given
$\angle ACB \cong \angle ECD$ Vertical $\angle s$ are $\cong$.
$\triangle ACB \sim \triangle ECD$ AA similarity

If two triangles are similar, their corresponding sides are proportional.

$\dfrac{BC}{DC} = \dfrac{AC}{EC}$

$\dfrac{16}{10} = \dfrac{AC}{11}$

$10AC = 16 \times 11$
$AC = 17.6$

3. B

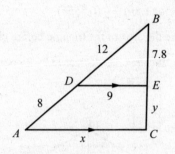

$\dfrac{BD}{DE} = \dfrac{BA}{AC} \Rightarrow \dfrac{12}{9} = \dfrac{20}{x} \Rightarrow 12x = 9 \cdot 20$
$\Rightarrow x = 15$

4. A

$\dfrac{BD}{DA} = \dfrac{BE}{EC} \Rightarrow \dfrac{12}{8} = \dfrac{7.8}{y} \Rightarrow 12y = 8 \times 7.8$
$\Rightarrow y = 5.2$

Section 17-4

1. D

Area of triangle $ABC = \dfrac{1}{2} BC \cdot AC$

$ = \dfrac{1}{2}(15)AC = 60$

$\Rightarrow 7.5 AC = 60 \Rightarrow AC = 8$

$AB^2 = AC^2 + BC^2$ Pythagorean Theorem
$AB^2 = 8^2 + 15^2$
$ = 289$
$AB = \sqrt{289} = 17$

Perimeter of $\triangle ABC = AB + BC + AC$
$= 17 + 15 + 8 = 40$

2. A

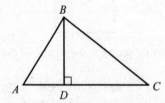

Let $BD = h$ and let $AC = b$.
If BD was increased by 50 percent, the new BD will be $h + 0.5h$, or $1.5h$.
If AC was reduced by 50 percent, the new AC will be $b - 0.5b$, or $0.5b$.

The new area of $\triangle ABC = \dfrac{1}{2}(\text{new } AC) \times (\text{new } BD)$

$$=\frac{1}{2}(0.5b)(1.5h)=\frac{1}{2}(0.75bh)$$

Because the area of the triangle before change was $\frac{1}{2}(bh)$, the area has decreased by 25 percent.

3. C

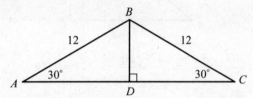

$\triangle ABD$ and $\triangle CBD$ are 30°-60°-90° triangles. In a 30°-60°-90° triangle, the hypotenuse is twice as long as the shorter leg and the longer leg is $\sqrt{3}$ times as long as the shorter leg.

$AB = 2BD$
$12 = 2BD$
$6 = BD$
$AD = \sqrt{3}BD$
$AD = \sqrt{3}(6) = 6\sqrt{3}$
$AC = 2AD = 12\sqrt{3}$

Area of $\triangle ABC = \frac{1}{2}AC \cdot BD = \frac{1}{2}(12\sqrt{3})(6)$

$= 36\sqrt{3}$

4. C

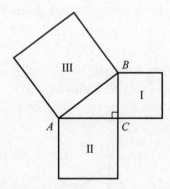

The area of a square is the square of the length of any side.

The area of square region I $= BC^2 = 80$.

The area of square region II $= AC^2 = 150$.

The area of square region III $= AB^2$

$AB^2 = BC^2 + AC^2$ Pythagorean Theorem
$ = 80 + 150 = 230$

Therefore, the area of square region III is 230.

Chapter 17 Practice Test

1. B

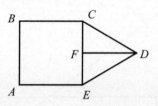

If the area of square $ABCD$ is $4x^2$, the length of the side of square $ABCD$ is $2x$.

Drawing $\overline{DF}$, a perpendicular bisector of $\overline{CE}$, makes two 30°-60°-90° triangles, $\triangle CDF$ and $\triangle EDF$.

$CE = 2x$
$CF = \frac{1}{2}CE = \frac{1}{2}(2x) = x$
$DF = \sqrt{3}CF = \sqrt{3}x$

Area of $\triangle CDE = \frac{1}{2}CE \cdot DF = \frac{1}{2}(2x)(\sqrt{3}x)$

$= \sqrt{3}x^2$

2. A

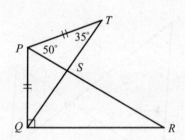

$\overline{PQ} \cong \overline{PT}$	Given
$m\angle PQT = m\angle T = 35$	Isosceles $\triangle$ Theorem
$m\angle PQT + m\angle T + m\angle QPT$	Angle Sum Theorem
$= 180$	
$35 + 35 + m\angle QPT = 180$	Substitution
$m\angle QPT = 110$	
$m\angle QPT$	Angle Addition Postulate
$= m\angle QPR + m\angle RPT$	
$110 = m\angle QPR + 50$	Substitution
$60 = m\angle QPR$	
$\overline{PQ} \perp \overline{QR}$	Given
$m\angle PQR = 90$	Definition of Right $\angle$
$m\angle PQR + m\angle QPR + m\angle R$	Angle Sum Theorem
$= 180$	
$90 + 60 + m\angle R = 180$	Substitution
$m\angle R = 30$	

3. **B**

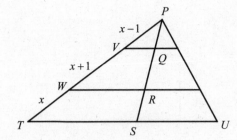

Note: Figure not drawn to scale.

Since $\overline{VQ} \parallel \overline{WR} \parallel \overline{TS}$, $\dfrac{PT}{PS} = \dfrac{x}{RS}$.

$\dfrac{(x-1)+(x+1)+x}{15} = \dfrac{x}{RS}$ Substitution

$\dfrac{3x}{15} = \dfrac{x}{RS}$ Simplify.

$3x(RS) = 15x$ Cross Products

$RS = 5$

4. **C**

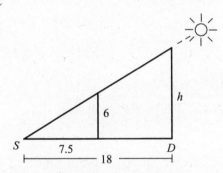

Note: Figure not drawn to scale.

Let $h =$ the length of the pole.

$\dfrac{6}{7.5} = \dfrac{h}{18}$

$7.5h = 6 \times 18$ Cross Products

$h = 14.4$

5. **D**

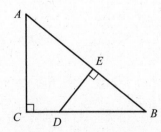

$m\angle C = m\angle BED$ All right $\angle s$ are equal.
$m\angle B = m\angle B$ Reflexive Property
$\triangle ABC \sim \triangle DBE$ AA Similarity Postulate

$\dfrac{AC}{BC} = \dfrac{DE}{BE}$ AA Similarity Postulate

$\dfrac{12}{15} = \dfrac{8}{BE}$ Substitution

$12BE = 15 \times 8$ Cross Products

$BE = 10$

6. **A**

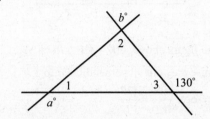

$m\angle 1 + m\angle 2 + m\angle 3 = 180$ Angle Sum Theorem

$a + m\angle 1 = 180$ Straight $\angle$ measures 180.

$m\angle 1 = 180 - a$

$m\angle 2 = b$ Vertical $\angle s$ are $\cong$.

$130 + m\angle 3 = 180$ Straight $\angle$ measures 180.

$m\angle 3 = 50$

$180 - a + b + 50 = 180$ Substitution

$230 - a + b = 180$

$-a + b = -50$

$a - b = 50$

7. **10.4**

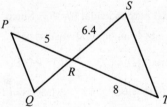

$\overline{PQ} \parallel \overline{ST}$ Given

$m\angle P = m\angle T$ If $\overline{PQ} \parallel \overline{ST}$, alternate interior $\angle s$ are $\cong$.

$m\angle PRQ = m\angle TRS$ Vertical $\angle s$ are $\cong$.

$\triangle PRQ \sim \triangle TRS$ AA Similarity Postulate

$\dfrac{PR}{TR} = \dfrac{RQ}{RS}$ AA Similarity Postulate

$\dfrac{5}{8} = \dfrac{RQ}{6.4}$ Substitution

$8RQ = 5 \times 6.4$ Cross Products

$RQ = 4$

$QS = SR + RQ = 6.4 + 4 = 10.4$

8. 45

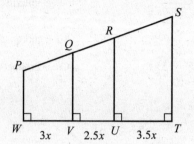

In the figure above, $\overline{PW} \parallel \overline{QV} \parallel \overline{RU} \parallel \overline{ST}$,

because they are all perpendicular to $\overline{TW}$.

Therefore, $\dfrac{PS}{WT} = \dfrac{QR}{VU}$.

$\dfrac{162}{3x + 2.5x + 3.5x} = \dfrac{QR}{2.5x}$ Substitution

$\dfrac{162}{9x} = \dfrac{QR}{2.5x}$ Simplify.

$9x(QR) = 162(2.5x)$ Cross Products

$9x(QR) = 405x$ Simplify.

$QR = 45$

9. 240

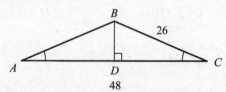

Draw $\overline{BD}$ perpendicular to $\overline{AC}$. Since $\triangle ABC$ is
an isosceles triangle, $\overline{BD}$ bisects $\overline{AC}$.

Therefore, $AD = CD = \dfrac{1}{2} AC = \dfrac{1}{2}(48) = 24$.

$CD^2 + BD^2 = BC^2$ Pythagorean Theorem

$24^2 + BD^2 = 26^2$

$576 + BD^2 = 676$

$BD^2 = 100$

$BD = 10$

Area of $\triangle ABC = \dfrac{1}{2}(AC)(BD)$.

$\qquad\qquad = \dfrac{1}{2}(48)(10)$

$\qquad\qquad = 240$

CHAPTER 18
Polygons and Quadrilaterals

18-1. Parallelograms

A **parallelogram** ($\square$) is a quadrilateral with two pairs of parallel opposite sides.

In $\square ABCD$, $\overline{AB} \parallel \overline{CD}$ and $\overline{BC} \parallel \overline{AD}$.

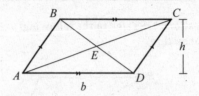

Properties of Parallelogram

Opposite sides are congruent.	$\overline{AB} \cong \overline{CD}$ and $\overline{BC} \cong \overline{AD}$
Opposite angles are congruent.	$\angle BAD \cong \angle BCD$ and $\angle ABC \cong \angle ADC$
Consecutive angles are supplementary.	$m\angle ABC + m\angle BAD = 180$ and $m\angle ADC + m\angle BCD = 180$
The diagonals bisect each other.	$AE = CE$ and $BE = DE$

A **rhombus** is a parallelogram with four sides of equal measure. The diagonals of a rhombus are perpendicular to each other, and each diagonal of a rhombus bisects a pair of opposite angles.

In rhombus $ABCD$, $AB = BC = CD = DA$, $AC \perp BD$, $m\angle 1 = m\angle 2 = m\angle 5 = m\angle 6$, and $m\angle 3 = m\angle 4 = m\angle 7 = m\angle 8$.

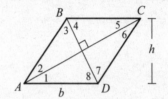

Theorem

The area of a parallelogram equals the product of a base and the height to that base. $A = b \cdot h$

The area of a rhombus is half the product of the lengths of its diagonals (d_1 and d_2). $A = \dfrac{1}{2} d_1 \cdot d_2$

Example 1 □ Find the values of the variables in the parallelogram shown at the right.

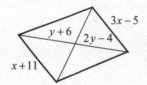

Solution □ $x + 11 = 3x - 5$ Opposite sides of $\square$ are $\cong$.

              $16 = 2x \implies x = 8$

              $y + 6 = 2y - 4$ The diagonals of $\square$ bisect each other.

              $y = 10$

Example 2 □ Find the area of parallelogram $PQRS$ shown at the right.

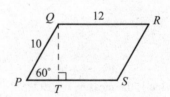

Solution □ Notice that $\triangle PQT$ is a $30°$-$60°$-$90°$ triangle.

$$PT = \frac{1}{2}PQ = \frac{1}{2}(10) = 5$$

$$QT = \sqrt{3}PT = \sqrt{3}(5) = 5\sqrt{3}$$

Area of $PQRS = b \cdot h = 12 \cdot 5\sqrt{3} = 60\sqrt{3}$

Exercise - Parallelograms

Questions 1-5 refer to the following information.

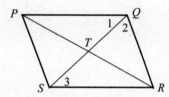

In $\square PQRS$ above, $PT = x + 2y$, $ST = 8x - y$, $PR = 32$, $TQ = 26$, $m\angle 1 = 6a$, $m\angle 2 = 10a$, $m\angle 3 = a^2 - 7$ and $m\angle PRS = 4a$.

1

What is the value of x ?

2

What is the value of y ?

3

What is the measure of $\angle PQR$?

4

What is the measure of $\angle QRS$?

5

What is the measure of $\angle QTR$?

6

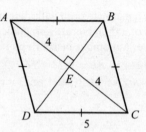

What is the area of rhombus $ABCD$ above?

7

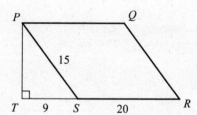

In the figure above, $PQRS$ is a parallelogram and PTS is a right triangle. What is the area of the parallelogram $PQRS$?

18-2. Rectangles, Squares, and Trapezoids

A **rectangle** is a quadrilateral with four right angles. The diagonals of a rectangle are congruent and bisect each other. The diagonals divide the rectangle into four triangles of equal area.

In rectangle $ABCD$, $AE = BE = CE = DE$.

Area of $\triangle ABE =$ Area of $\triangle BCE =$ Area of $\triangle CDE =$ Area of $\triangle DAE$

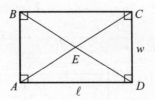

If a quadrilateral is both a rhombus and a rectangle, it is a **square**. A square has four right angles and four congruent sides. The diagonals of a square are congruent and bisect each other.

In square $ABCD$, $AB = BC = CD = DA$, $\overline{AB} \perp \overline{BC} \perp \overline{CD} \perp \overline{DA}$, and $AE = CE = BE = DE$.

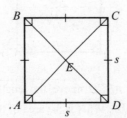

A **trapezoid** is a quadrilateral with exactly one pair of parallel sides.

The **midsegment** of a trapezoid is parallel to the bases and the length of the midsegment is the average of the lengths of the bases. Trapezoid $ABCD$ with median $\overline{MN}$, $\overline{AD} \parallel \overline{MN} \parallel \overline{BC}$ and $MN = \frac{1}{2}(b_1 + b_2)$.

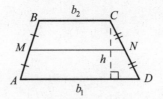

If the legs of a trapezoid are congruent, the trapezoid is an **isosceles trapezoid**. The diagonals of an isosceles trapezoid are congruent. Each pair of base angles of an isosceles trapezoid is congruent. For isosceles trapezoid $ABCD$ at the right,

$AC = BD$, $m\angle BAD = m\angle CDA$, and $m\angle ABC = m\angle BCD$.

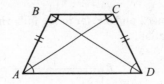

Theorems - Areas of Rectangle, Square, and Trapezoid

The area of a rectangle is the product of its base and height. $\qquad A = b \cdot h$

The area of a square is the square of the length of a side. $\qquad A = s^2$

The area of a trapezoid is half the product of its height and sum of the bases. $\qquad A = \frac{1}{2}h(b_1 + b_2)$

Example 1 □ Find the areas of the quadrilaterals shown below.

a.

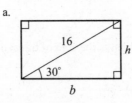

b.

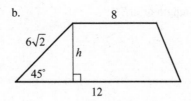

Solution □ a. The quadrilateral is a rectangle.

$h = \frac{1}{2}(16) = 8$, $b = h \cdot \sqrt{3} = 8\sqrt{3}$ Use the 30°-60°-90° Δ ratio.

$A = b \cdot h = 8\sqrt{3} \cdot 8 = 64\sqrt{3}$ Area formula for rectangle

b. The quadrilateral is a trapezoid.

$h \cdot \sqrt{2} = 6\sqrt{2} \Rightarrow h = 6$ Use the 45°-45°-90° Δ ratio.

$A = \frac{1}{2}h(b_1 + b_2) = \frac{1}{2}(6)(8 + 12) = 60$ Area formula for trapezoid

Exercise - Rectangles, Squares, and Trapezoids

1

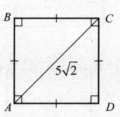

In square *ABCD* above, the length of diagonal *AC* is $5\sqrt{2}$. What is the area of the square?

Questions 2 and 3 refer to the following information.

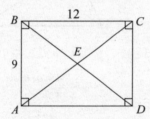

In the figure above, *ABCD* is a rectangle.

2

What is the length of *AE* ?

3

What is the area of $\triangle CED$?

4

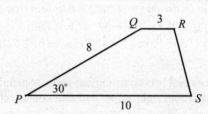

What is the area of trapezoid *PQRS* above?

A) 20

B) 24

C) 26

D) 32

5

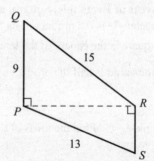

What is the area of trapezoid *PQRS* above?

A) 64

B) 72

C) 76

D) 84

18-3. Regular Polygons

A **regular polygon** is a convex polygon with all sides congruent and all angles congruent.
A polygon is **inscribed in a circle** and the circle is **circumscribed about the polygon** where each vertex
of the polygon lies on the circle. The **radius of a regular polygon** is the distance from the center to a vertex
of the polygon. A **central angle of a regular polygon** is an angle formed by two radii drawn to consecutive
vertices. The **apothem of a regular polygon** is the distance from the center to a side.

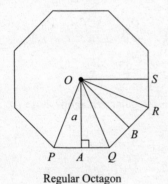

Center: O

Radius: OP, OQ, OR, $\cdots$

Central Angle: $\angle POQ$, $\angle QOR$, $\cdots$

Interior Angle: $\angle PQR$, $\angle QRS$, $\cdots$

Apothem: OA, OB, $\cdots$ (Denoted with letter a.)

Regular Octagon

Theorems - Angles and Areas of Regular Polygons

The sum of the measures of the interior angles of an n-sided polygon is $(n-2)180$.

The measure of each interior angle of a regular n-sided polygon is $\dfrac{(n-2)180}{n}$.

The sum of the measures of the exterior angles of any polygon is 360.

The area of a regular polygon is half the product of the apothem a, and the perimeter p. $A = \dfrac{1}{2}ap$

Regular Polygons Inscribed in Circles

Equilateral Triangle	Square	Regular Pentagon	Regular Hexagon	Regular Octagon
Central angle $= 120°$	Central angle $= 90°$	Central angle $= 72°$	Central angle $= 60°$	Central angle $= 45°$
Interior angle $= 60°$	Interior angle $= 90°$	Interior angle $= 108°$	Interior angle $= 120°$	Interior angle $= 135°$

Example 1 $\square$ A regular hexagon with the length of side of 4 is
shown at the right.
Find the area of the regular hexagon.

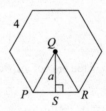

Solution $\square$ $m\angle PQR = 360 \div 6 = 60$

$m\angle PQS = \dfrac{1}{2}m\angle PQR = \dfrac{1}{2}(60) = 30$

$PS = \dfrac{1}{2}PR = \dfrac{1}{2}(4) = 2$

$a = \sqrt{3} \cdot PS = 2\sqrt{3}$ 30°-60°-90° triangle ratio is used.

$A = \dfrac{1}{2}ap = \dfrac{1}{2}(2\sqrt{3})(24) = 24\sqrt{3}$ $A = \dfrac{1}{2}ap$

Exercise - Regular Polygons

Questions 1 - 4 refer to the following information.

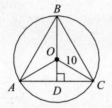

The figure above is an equilateral inscribed in a circle with radius 10.

1

What is the measure of $\angle AOC$?

2

What is the length of OD?

3

What is the length of BD?

4

What is the area of $\triangle ABC$?

A) $45\sqrt{3}$

B) $50\sqrt{3}$

C) $60\sqrt{3}$

D) $75\sqrt{3}$

Questions 5 - 7 refer to the following information.

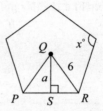

The figure above is a regular pentagon whose radius is 6.

5

What is the value of x?

6

What is the measure of $\angle RQS$?

7

Which of the following equations can be used to find the value of a?

A) $\sin \angle RQS = \dfrac{a}{6}$

B) $\cos \angle RQS = \dfrac{a}{6}$

C) $\sin \angle RQS = \dfrac{6}{a}$

D) $\cos \angle RQS = \dfrac{6}{a}$

Chapter 18 Practice Test

1

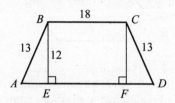

What is the area of the isosceles trapezoid above?

A) 238

B) 252

C) 276

D) 308

2

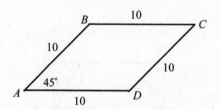

What is the area of rhombus $ABCD$ above?

A) $20\sqrt{2}$

B) $25\sqrt{2}$

C) $50\sqrt{2}$

D) $100\sqrt{2}$

3

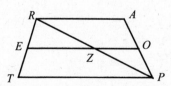

In the figure above, $\overline{EO}$ is the midsegment of trapezoid $TRAP$ and $\overline{RP}$ intersect $\overline{EO}$ at point Z. If $RA = 15$ and $EO = 18$, what is the length of $\overline{EZ}$?

4

A rectangle has a length that is 6 meters more than twice its width. What is the perimeter of the rectangle if the area of the rectangle is 1,620 square meters?

5

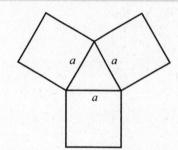

The figure above shows an equilateral triangle with sides of length a and three squares with sides of length a. If the area of the equilateral triangle is $25\sqrt{3}$, what is the sum of the areas of the three squares?

A) 210

B) 240

C) 270

D) 300

6

The perimeter of a rectangle is $5x$ and its length is $\dfrac{3}{2}x$. If the area of the rectangle is 294, what is the value of x?

7

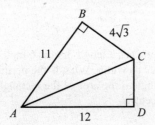

In the figure above, what is the area of the region *ABCD* ?

A) $22\sqrt{3}+30$

B) $22\sqrt{3}+36$

C) $22\sqrt{3}+42$

D) $22\sqrt{3}+48$

8

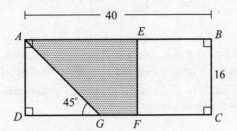

In the figure above, *ABCD* is a rectangle and *BCFE* is a square. If $AB = 40$, $BC = 16$, and $m\angle AGD = 45$, what is the area of the shaded region?

A) 240

B) 248

C) 256

D) 264

9

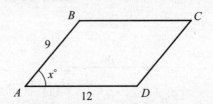

The figure above shows parallelogram *ABCD*. Which of the following equations represents the area of parallelogram *ABCD* ?

A) $12\cos x° \times 9\sin x°$

B) $12 \times 9\tan x°$

C) $12 \times 9\cos x°$

D) $12 \times 9\sin x°$

10

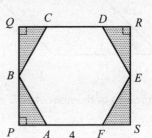

In the figure above, *ABCDEF* is a regular hexagon with side lengths of 4. *PQRS* is a rectangle. What is the area of the shaded region?

A) $8\sqrt{3}$

B) $9\sqrt{3}$

C) $10\sqrt{3}$

D) $12\sqrt{3}$

Answer Key

Section 18-1

1. 4   2. 6   3. 112   4. 68   5. 70
6. 24   7. 240

Section 18-2

1. 25   2. 7.5   3. 27   4. C   5. D

Section 18-3

1. 120   2. 5   3. 15   4. D   5. 108
6. 36   7. B

Chapter 18 Practice Test

1. C   2. B   3. 10.5   4. 174   5. D
6. 14   7. A   8. C   9. D   10. A

Answers and Explanations

Section 18-1

1. 4

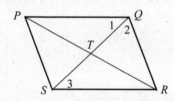

$$PT = \frac{1}{2}PR$$ Diagonals of ▱ bisect each other.

$$x + 2y = \frac{1}{2}(32) = 16$$ Substitution

$$ST = TQ$$ Diagonals of ▱ bisect each other.

$$8x - y = 26$$ Substitution

$$2(8x - y) = 2(26)$$ Multiply each side by 2.

$$16x - 2y = 52$$ Simplify.

Add $x + 2y = 16$ and $16x - 2y = 52$.

$$16x - 2y = 52$$
$$+\quad x + 2y = 16$$
$$\overline{\qquad\qquad\qquad}$$
$$17x = 68$$
$$x = 4$$

2. 6

Substitute 4 for x into the equation $x + 2y = 16$.

$$4 + 2y = 16$$

$$2y = 12$$
$$y = 6$$

3. 112

$$m\angle 3 = m\angle 1$$ If $\overline{PQ} \parallel \overline{RS}$, Alternate Interior $\angle s$ are $\cong$.

$$a^2 - 7 = 6a$$ Substitution

$$a^2 - 6a - 7 = 0$$ Make one side 0.

$$(a - 7)(a + 1) = 0$$ Factor.

$$a = 7 \text{ or } a = -1$$

Discard $a = -1$, because the measure of angles in parallelogram are positive.

$$m\angle 1 = 6a = 6(7) = 42$$
$$m\angle 2 = 10a = 10(7) = 70$$
$$m\angle PQR = m\angle 1 + m\angle 2$$
$$= 42 + 70$$
$$= 112$$

4. 68

Since $\overline{PQ} \parallel \overline{RS}$, consecutive interior angles are supplementary. Thus, $m\angle PQR + m\angle QRS = 180$.

$$112 + m\angle QRS = 180 \qquad m\angle PQR = 112$$
$$m\angle QRS = 68$$

5. 70

$$m\angle QTR = m\angle PRS + m\angle 3$$ Exterior Angle Theorem
$$m\angle 3 = m\angle 1 = 42$$
$$m\angle PRS = 4a$$ Given
$$= 4(7) = 28$$ $a = 7$
$$m\angle QTR = 28 + 42$$ Substitution
$$= 70$$

6. 24

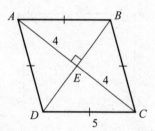

$$CE^2 + DE^2 = CD^2$$ Pythagorean Theorem
$$4^2 + DE^2 = 5^2$$

$$DE^2 = 9$$
$$DE = 3$$

Area of $ABCD = \frac{1}{2}AC \cdot BD = \frac{1}{2}(8)(6) = 24$

7. 240

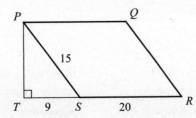

$$PT^2 + ST^2 = PS^2 \qquad \text{Pythagorean Theorem}$$
$$PT^2 + 9^2 = 15^2$$
$$PT^2 = 15^2 - 9^2 = 144$$
$$PT = \sqrt{144} = 12$$

Area of $PQRS = SR \times PT = 20 \times 12 = 240$.

Section 18-2

1. 25

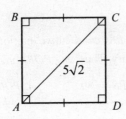

Let $AD = CD = s$.
$$AD^2 + CD^2 = (5\sqrt{2})^2 \qquad \text{Pythagorean Theorem}$$
$$s^2 + s^2 = 50$$
$$2s^2 = 50$$
$$s^2 = 25$$

Area of $ABCD = s^2 = 25$.

2. 7.5

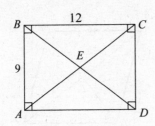

$$AC^2 = AB^2 + BC^2 \qquad \text{Pythagorean Theorem}$$
$$AC^2 = 9^2 + 12^2 = 225 \qquad \text{Substitution}$$
$$AC = \sqrt{225} = 15$$
$$AE = \frac{1}{2}AC \qquad \begin{array}{l}\text{Diagonals of rectangle} \\ \text{bisect each other.}\end{array}$$
$$= \frac{1}{2}(15) = 7.5$$

3. 27

Area of rectangle $ABCD = 12 \times 9 = 108$.
In a rectangle, diagonals divide the rectangle into four triangles of equal area. Therefore,

Area of $\triangle CED = \dfrac{1}{4}$ the area of rectangle $ABCD$

$$= \frac{1}{4}(108) = 27.$$

4. C

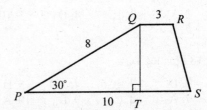

Draw $\overline{QT}$, which is perpendicular to $\overline{PS}$, to make triangle PQT, a $30°$-$60°$-$90°$ triangle.

In a $30°$-$60°$-$90°$ triangle, the hypotenuse is twice as long as the shorter leg. Therefore,

$$QT = \frac{1}{2}PQ = \frac{1}{2}(8) = 4.$$

Area of trapezoid $PQRS = \dfrac{1}{2}(PS + QR) \cdot QT$

$$= \frac{1}{2}(10 + 3) \cdot 4 = 26$$

5. D

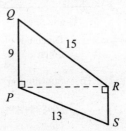

$$PR^2 + PQ^2 = QR^2 \qquad \text{Pythagorean Theorem}$$
$$PR^2 + 9^2 = 15^2 \qquad \text{Substitution}$$
$$PR^2 = 15^2 - 9^2 = 144$$
$$PR = \sqrt{144} = 12$$
$$12^2 + RS^2 = 13^2 \qquad \text{Pythagorean Theorem}$$
$$RS^2 = 13^2 - 12^2 = 25$$
$$RS = \sqrt{25} = 5$$

Area of trapezoid $PQRS$

$$= \frac{1}{2}(PQ + RS) \cdot PR = \frac{1}{2}(9 + 5) \cdot 12$$

$$= 84$$

Section 18-3

1. 120

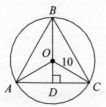

$$m\angle AOB = m\angle BOC = m\angle AOC = \frac{1}{3}(360) = 120$$

2. 5

$$m\angle COD = \frac{1}{2}m\angle AOC = \frac{1}{2}(120) = 60$$

Since triangle COD is a $30°$-$60°$-$90°$ triangle, the hypotenuse is twice as long as the shorter leg.

Therefore, $OD = \frac{1}{2}CO = \frac{1}{2}(10) = 5$.

3. 15

In a circle all radii are equal in measure. Therefore, $AO = BO = CO = 10$.
$$BD = BO + OD = 10 + 5 = 15$$

4. D

In a $30°$-$60°$-$90°$ triangle, the longer leg is $\sqrt{3}$ times as long as the shorter leg. Therefore,
$$CD = \sqrt{3}OD = 5\sqrt{3}$$
$$AC = 2CD = 10\sqrt{3}$$

Area of $\triangle ABC$
$$= \frac{1}{2}(AC)(BD) = \frac{1}{2}(10\sqrt{3})(15) = 75\sqrt{3}$$

5. 108

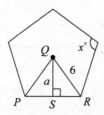

The measure of each interior angle of a regular n-sided polygon is $\frac{(n-2)180}{n}$. Therefore,

$$x = \frac{(5-2)180}{5} = 108.$$

6. 36

$$m\angle PQR = \frac{360}{5} = 72$$

$$m\angle RQS = \frac{1}{2}m\angle PQR = \frac{1}{2}(72) = 36$$

7. B

In triangle RQS, QR is the hypotenuse and QS is adjacent to $\angle RQS$. Therefore the cosine ratio can be used to find the value of a.

$$\cos\angle RQS = \frac{\text{adjacent to } \angle RQS}{\text{hypotenuse}} = \frac{a}{6}$$

Chapter 18 Practice Test

1. C

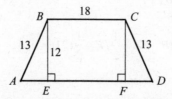

$$AE^2 + BE^2 = AB^2 \qquad \text{Pythagorean Theorem}$$
$$AE^2 + 12^2 = 13^2$$
$$AE^2 = 13^2 - 12^2 = 25$$
$$AE = \sqrt{25} = 5$$

Also $DF = 5$.
$$AD = AE + EF + DF = 5 + 18 + 5 = 28$$

Area of trapezoid $= \frac{1}{2}(AD + BC) \cdot BF$

$$= \frac{1}{2}(28 + 18) \cdot 12 = 276$$

2. B

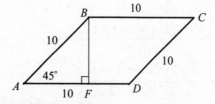

Draw $\overline{BF}$ perpendicular to $\overline{AD}$ to form a $45°$-$45°$-$90°$ triangle.

In a $45°$-$45°$-$90°$ triangle, the hypotenuse is $\sqrt{2}$ times as long as a leg. Therefore, $\sqrt{2}BF = AB$.

$\sqrt{2}BF = 10$ Substitution

$BF = \dfrac{10}{\sqrt{2}} = \dfrac{10 \cdot \sqrt{2}}{\sqrt{2} \cdot \sqrt{2}} = \dfrac{10\sqrt{2}}{2} = 5\sqrt{2}$

Area of rhombus $ABCD$

$= \dfrac{1}{2} AD \cdot BF = \dfrac{1}{2}(10)(5\sqrt{2}) = 25\sqrt{2}$

3. 10.5

The length of the midsegment of a trapezoid is the average of the lengths of the bases. Therefore,

$EO = \dfrac{1}{2}(TP + RA)$.

$18 = \dfrac{1}{2}(TP + 15)$ Substitution

$2 \times 18 = 2 \times \dfrac{1}{2}(TP + 15)$

$36 = TP + 15$

$21 = TP$

In $\triangle TRP$, $EZ = \dfrac{1}{2}TP = \dfrac{1}{2}(21) = 10.5$.

4. 174

Let $w =$ the width of the rectangle in meters, then $2w + 6 =$ the length of the rectangle in meters.
Area of rectangle = length × width

$= (2w + 6) \times w = 2w^2 + 6w$.

Since the area of the rectangle is 1,620 square meters, you can set up the following equation.

$2w^2 + 6w = 1620$

$2w^2 + 6w - 1620 = 0$ Make one side 0.

$2(w^2 + 3w - 810) = 0$ Common factor is 2.

Use the quadratic formula to solve the equation, $w^2 + 3w - 810 = 0$.

$w = \dfrac{-b \pm \sqrt{b^2 - 4ac}}{2a}$

$= \dfrac{-3 \pm \sqrt{3^2 - 4(1)(-810)}}{2(1)}$

$= \dfrac{-3 \pm \sqrt{3249}}{2} = \dfrac{-3 \pm 57}{2}$

Since the width is positive, $w = \dfrac{-3 + 57}{2} = 27$.

The length is $2w + 6 = 2(27) + 6 = 60$.

The perimeter of the rectangle is
2(length + width) = 2(60 + 27) = 174

5. D

Area of an equilateral triangle with side length of $a = \dfrac{\sqrt{3}}{4}a^2$. Since the area of the equilateral triangle is given as $25\sqrt{3}$, you can set up the following equation.

$\dfrac{\sqrt{3}}{4}a^2 = 25\sqrt{3}$

$a^2 = 25\sqrt{3} \cdot \dfrac{4}{\sqrt{3}} = 100$

The area of each square is a^2, or 100, so the sum of the areas of the three squares is 3×100, or 300.

6. 14

Let $w =$ the width of the rectangle.
The perimeter of the rectangle is given as $5x$.
Perimeter of rectangle = 2(length + width)

$5x = 2(\dfrac{3}{2}x + w)$

$5x = 3x + 2w$

$2x = 2w$

$x = w$

Area of rectangle = length × width = 294

$\dfrac{3}{2}x \cdot x = 294$

$x^2 = 294 \cdot \dfrac{2}{3} = 196$

$x = \sqrt{196} = 14$

7. A

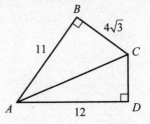

$AC^2 = AB^2 + BC^2$ Pythagorean Theorem

$AC^2 = 11^2 + (4\sqrt{3})^2$ Substitution

$AC^2 = 121 + 48 = 169$

$AC = \sqrt{169} = 13$

$AC^2 = AD^2 + CD^2$ Pythagorean Theorem

$169 = 12^2 + CD^2$ Substitution

$25 = CD^2$

$5 = CD$

The area of region $ABCD$ is the sum of the area of $\triangle ABC$ and the area of $\triangle ADC$.

Area of the region $ABCD$

$= \dfrac{1}{2}(11)(4\sqrt{3}) + \dfrac{1}{2}(12)(5)$

$= 22\sqrt{3} + 30$

8. C

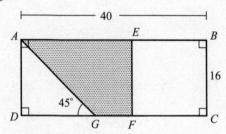

Since $BCFE$ is a square,

$BC = BE = CF = EF = 16$.

$AE = AB - BE$

$\quad = 40 - 16 = 24$

Triangle AGD is a $45°$-$45°$-$90°$ triangle.

In a $45°$-$45°$-$90°$ triangle, the length of the two legs are equal in measure. Therefore,

$AD = DG = 16$.

$FG = DC - DG - CF$

$\quad = 40 - 16 - 16 = 8$

Area of the shaded region

$= \dfrac{1}{2}(AE + FG) \cdot EF$

$= \dfrac{1}{2}(24 + 8) \cdot 16 = 256$

9. D

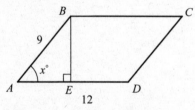

Draw $\overline{BE}$ perpendicular to $\overline{AD}$.

In $\triangle ABE$, $\sin x° = \dfrac{BE}{9}$.

Therefore, $BE = 9 \sin x°$.

Area of parallelogram $ABCD$

$= AD \times BE = 12 \times 9 \sin x°$

10. A

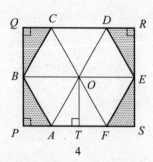

Draw the diagonals of a regular hexagon, $\overline{AD}$, $\overline{BE}$, and $\overline{CF}$.

$BE = BO + OE = 8$ and $QR = BE = 8$

Since $ABCDEF$ is a regular hexagon, the diagonals intersect at the center of the hexagon. Let the point of intersection be O. The diagonals divide the hexagon into 6 equilateral triangles with side lengths of 4. Area of each equilateral triangle with side lengths of 4 is $\dfrac{\sqrt{3}}{4}(4)^2 = 4\sqrt{3}$.

Draw $\overline{OT}$ perpendicular to $\overline{PS}$.

Triangle AOT is a $30°$-$60°$-$90°$ triangle.

Therefore, $AT = \dfrac{1}{2}AO = \dfrac{1}{2}(4) = 2$ and

$OT = \sqrt{3}AT = 2\sqrt{3}$.

In rectangle $PQRS$, $RS = 2OT = 2(2\sqrt{3}) = 4\sqrt{3}$.

Area of rectangle $PQRS = QR \times RS$

$= 8 \times 4\sqrt{3} = 32\sqrt{3}$.

Area of regular hexagon $ABCDEF$

$= 6 \times$ area of the equilateral triangle

$= 6 \times 4\sqrt{3} = 24\sqrt{3}$

Area of shaded region

$=$ area of rectangle $-$ area of hexagon

$= 32\sqrt{3} - 24\sqrt{3} = 8\sqrt{3}$.

CHAPTER 19
Circles

19-1. Arcs, Angles, and Tangents

In a plane, a **circle** is the set of all points equidistant from a given point called the **center**. It follows from the definition of a circle that **all radii are equal in measure**.

A circle is usually named by its center. The circle at the right is called circle O. (symbolized as $\odot O$)

A **chord** is a segment whose endpoints lie on a circle.

A **secant** is a line that contains a chord.

A **tangent** is a line in the plane of a circle, and intersects the circle at exactly one point: the **point of tangency**.

A **central angle** is an angle whose vertex is the center of the circle.

An arc is a part of a circle. The measure of a **minor arc** is the measure of its central angle. The measure of a minor arc is less than 180.

The measure of a **semicircle** is 180.

The measure of a **major arc** is 360 minus the measure of its minor arc.

Arc Addition Postulate

The measure of an arc formed by two adjacent arcs is the sum of the measure of the two arcs. $m\overarc{PQR} = m\overarc{PQ} + m\overarc{QR}$

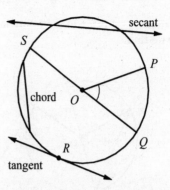

$\angle POQ$ and $\angle POS$ are central angles.

$\overarc{PQ}, \overarc{QR}, \overarc{RS},$ and $\overarc{SP}$ are minor arcs.

$\overarc{QPS}$ and $\overarc{QRS}$ are semicircles.

$\overarc{PQS}$ and $\overarc{SPR}$ are major arcs.

$m\overarc{QPS} = m\overarc{QRS} = 180$

$m\overarc{PQS} = 360 - m\overarc{SP}$

Theorems - Tangent Lines

If a line is tangent to a circle, then the line is perpendicular to the radius at the point of tangency.

$\overline{PA} \perp \overline{OA}$ and $\overline{PB} \perp \overline{OB}$

Tangents to a circle from the same exterior point are congruent.

$PA = PB$

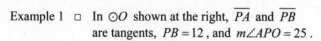

Example 1   □   In $\odot O$ shown at the right, $\overline{PA}$ and $\overline{PB}$ are tangents, $PB = 12$, and $m\angle APO = 25$.

a. Find the measure of $\angle POA$.
b. Find the length of PA.
c. Find the radius of $\odot O$.

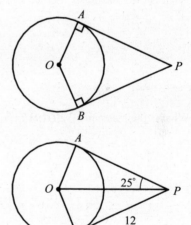

Solution   □   a. $\overline{PA} \perp \overline{OA}$

$m\angle PAO = 90$
$m\angle POA + m\angle APO + m\angle PAO = 180$
$m\angle POA + 25 + 90 = 180$
$m\angle POA = 65$

If a line is tangent to a circle, then the line is $\perp$ to the radius at the point of tangency.
Definition of $\perp$ lines
Angle Sum Theorem
Substitution

b. $PA = PB = 12$

Tangents to a circle from the same exterior point are $\cong$.

c. $\tan 25° = \dfrac{OA}{PA} = \dfrac{OA}{12}$

$OA = 12 \tan 25° \approx 5.6$

Exercises - Arcs, Angles, and Tangents

Questions 1 - 4 refer to the following information.

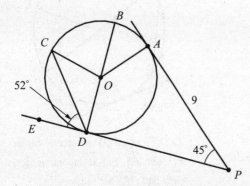

In the figure above, $\overline{BD}$ is a diameter, and $\overline{PA}$ and $\overline{PD}$ are tangents to circle O. $m\angle CDE = 52$, $m\angle APD = 45$, and $AP = 9$.

1

What is the measure of $\angle ODC$?

2

What is the measure of $\angle OCD$?

3

What is the measure of $\angle AOD$?

4

What is the length of PD?

5

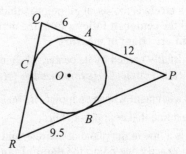

In the figure above, $\odot O$ is inscribed in ΔPQR. If $PA = 12$, $QA = 6$, and $RB = 9.5$, what is the perimeter of ΔPQR?

A) 46

B) 49

C) 52

D) 55

6

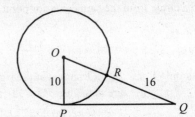

In the figure above, $\overline{OP}$ is a radius and $\overline{PQ}$ is tangent to circle O. If the radius of circle O is 10 and $QR = 16$, what is the length of $\overline{PQ}$?

A) 16

B) 20

C) 24

D) 28

19-2. Arc Lengths and Areas of Sectors

Circumference of a circle: $C = 2\pi r$ or $C = \pi d$

Area of circle: $\qquad A = \pi r^2$

A **sector** of a circle is a region bound by two radii and an arc of the circle.
The shaded region of the circle at the right is called sector AOB.

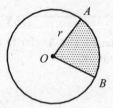

Length of $\overset{\frown}{AB} = 2\pi r \cdot \dfrac{m\angle AOB}{360}$

Area of sector $AOB = \pi r^2 \cdot \dfrac{m\angle AOB}{360}$

The distance traveled by a wheel $= 2\pi r \times$ number of revolutions

Example 1 □ In circle O shown at the right, $\overline{AB}$ is
tangent to the circle.

a. Find the area of the shaded region.

b. Find the perimeter of the shaded region.

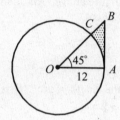

Solution □ a. $m\angle OAB = 90$ Line tangent to a circle is $\perp$ to the radius.

$m\angle OBA = 45$ Acute angles of a right $\triangle$ are complementary.

$OA = AB = 12$ Legs of isosceles triangle are $\cong$.

Area of $\triangle OAB = \dfrac{1}{2}(12)(12) = 72$

Area of sector $AOC = \pi(12)^2 \cdot \dfrac{45}{360} = 18\pi$.

Area of shaded region $= 72 - 18\pi$ Answer

b. Length of $\overset{\frown}{AC} = 2\pi(12) \cdot \dfrac{45}{360} = 3\pi$

Length of $BC = OB - OC = 12\sqrt{2} - 12$ In a $45°$-$45°$-$90°$ $\triangle$, the hypotenuse is $\sqrt{2}$ times as long as a leg.

Perimeter of shaded region

$= $ length of $\overset{\frown}{AC} + BC + AB$

$= 3\pi + (12\sqrt{2} - 12) + 12 = 3\pi + 12\sqrt{2}$ Answer

Example 2 □ The radius of a bicycle wheel is 12 inches. What is the number of revolutions
the wheel makes to travel 1 mile? (1 mile $= 5,280$ ft)

Solution □ Let $x = $ number of revolutions.

The distance traveled by a wheel $= 2\pi r \times$ number of revolutions

1 mile $= 2\pi(12$ in$) \times x$

$1 \times 5280 \times 12$ in $= 2\pi(12$ in$)x$ 1 mile $= 5280$ ft $= 5280 \times 12$ in

$x = \dfrac{5280 \times 12}{2\pi \times 12} = \dfrac{2640}{\pi} \approx 840$ Answer

Exercises - Arc Lengths and Areas of Sectors

Questions 1 and 2 refer to the following information.

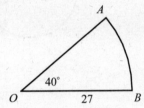

In the figure above, $\overset{\frown}{AB}$ is an arc of a circle with radius 27 cm.

1

If the length of arc AB is $k\pi$, what is the value of k?

2

If the area of sector OAB is $n\pi$, what is the value of n?

3

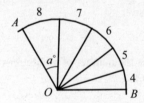

The figure above shows arcs of length 8, 7, 6, 5, and 4. If $m\overset{\frown}{AB} = 120$, what is the degree measure of angle a?

4

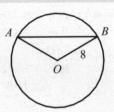

In the figure above, the radius of the circle is 8 and $m\angle AOB = 120°$. What is the length of $\overline{AB}$?

A) $8\sqrt{2}$

B) $8\sqrt{3}$

C) $12\sqrt{2}$

D) $12\sqrt{3}$

5

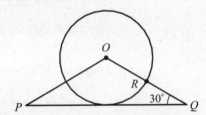

In the figure above, $OP = OQ$ and $\overline{PQ}$ is tangent to circle O. If the radius of circle O is 8, what is the length of $\overline{QR}$?

A) $10(\sqrt{2}-1)$

B) 6

C) $10(\sqrt{3}-1)$

D) 8

19-3. Inscribed Angles

An **inscribed angle** is an angle whose vertex is on a circle and whose sides contain chords of the circle.

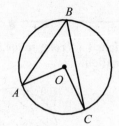

Theorem - Inscribed Angle

The measure of an inscribed angle is half the measure of its intercepted arc and half the measure of its central angle.

$$m\angle B = \frac{1}{2} m\widehat{AC} = \frac{1}{2} m\angle AOC$$

Corollaries to the Inscribed Angle Theorem

Corollary 1	**Corollary 2**	**Corollary 3**
Two inscribed angles that intercept the same arc are congruent.	An angle inscribed in a semicircle is a right angle.	If a quadrilateral is inscribed in a circle, its opposite angles are supplementary.

$\angle A \cong \angle B$

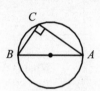

$\angle C$ is a right angle.

$\angle A$ is supp. to $\angle C$
$\angle B$ is supp. to $\angle D$

Example 1   □   a. In the figure below, find the values of x and y.

b. In the figure below, AC is a diameter and $m\widehat{AB} = 72$.
Find the values of a, b, and c.

c. In the figure below, find the values of p and q.

a.
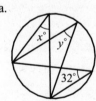

b.
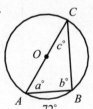

c.

Solution   □   a. $x = y = 32$ Inscribed $\angle s$ that intercept the same arc are $\cong$.

b. $c = 72 \div 2 = 36$ The measure of an inscribed $\angle$ is half the measure of its intercepted arc.

$b = 90$ An $\angle$ inscribed in a semicircle is a right $\angle$.
$a + c = 90$ The acute $\angle s$ of a right $\triangle$ are complementary.
$a = 90 - 36 = 54$ Substitute $c = 36$ and solve for a.

c. $p + 76 = 180$ If a quad. is inscribed in a circle, its opposite $\angle s$ are supplementary.

$p = 104$ Solve for p.
$q + 94 = 180$ If a quad. is inscribed in a circle, its opposite $\angle s$ are supplementary.

$q = 86$ Solve for q.

Exercises - Inscribed Angles

Questions 1 - 4 refer to the following information.

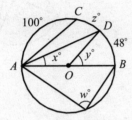

In circle O above, $\overline{AB}$ is a diameter.

1

What is the value of y ?

2

What is the value of x ?

3

What is the value of w ?

4

What is the value of z ?

Questions 5 and 6 refer to the following information.

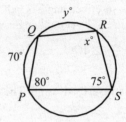

In the figure above, a quadrilateral is inscribed in a circle.

5

What is the value of x ?

A) 70

B) 80

C) 90

D) 100

6

What is the value of y ?

A) 75

B) 80

C) 85

D) 90

19-4. Arcs and Chords

Theorems

Theorem 1	**Theorem 2**	**Theorem 3**
In the same circle or in congruent circles, congruent arcs have congruent chords.	If a diameter is $\perp$ to a chord, it bisects the chord and its arc.	In the same circle or in congruent circles, chords equidistant to the center(s) are congruent.

If $\overarc{AB} \cong \overarc{CD}$, then $\overline{AB} \cong \overline{CD}$. The converse is also true.

If diameter $\overline{CD} \perp \overline{AB}$, then $\overline{AE} \cong \overline{BE}$ and $\overarc{AC} \cong \overarc{BC}$.

If $OE = OF$, then $\overline{AB} \cong \overline{CD}$. The converse is also true.

Example 1 □ a. In the figure below, if $m\overarc{AB} = m\overarc{CD} = 110$ and $CD = 15$, what is the length of $\overline{AB}$?

b. In the figure below, $\overline{AB} \perp \overline{CD}$. If $AB = 20$ and $CD = 16$, what is the length of $\overline{OE}$?

c. In the figure below, $OE = OF = 9$ and $BE = 12$. What is the length of $\overline{CD}$?

a.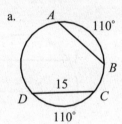

b.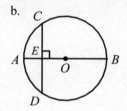

c.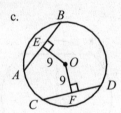

Solution □ a. $AB = CD = 15$ In the same circle, $\cong$ arcs have $\cong$ chords.

b. $DE = \dfrac{1}{2}CD = 8$ If a diameter is $\perp$ to a chord, it bisects the chord.

$OD = OB = \dfrac{1}{2}AB = 10$ In a circle, all radii are $\cong$.

$OD^2 = DE^2 + OE^2$ Pythagorean Theorem

$10^2 = 8^2 + OE^2$ Substitution

$OE^2 = 36$

$OE = 6$ Simplify.

c. $AB = 2BE = 2(12) = 24$ If a diameter is $\perp$ to a chord, it bisects the chord.

$CD = AB = 24$ In the same circle, chords equidistant to the center are $\cong$.

Exercises - Arcs and Chords

1

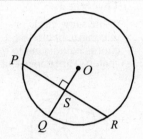

In circle O above, if the radius is 13 and $PR = 24$, what is the length of QS ?

A) 6

B) 7

C) 8

D) 9

3

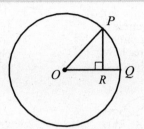

In circle O above, the area of the circle is 9π and $PR = \sqrt{5}$. What is the length of QR ?

A) 1

B) $\sqrt{2}$

C) $\sqrt{3}$

D) 2

2

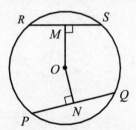

In the circle above, if $RS = 6$, $OM = 5$, and $ON = 4$, what is the length of PQ ?

A) $4\sqrt{2}$

B) 6

C) $6\sqrt{2}$

D) $6\sqrt{3}$

4

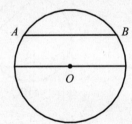

In the figure above, the radius of the circle is 12. If the length of chord $\overline{AB}$ is 18, what is the distance between the chord and the diameter?

A) $2\sqrt{10}$

B) $3\sqrt{7}$

C) $4\sqrt{5}$

D) $6\sqrt{2}$

19-5. Circles in the Coordinate Plane

Equation of a Circle

The equation of a circle with center (h, k) and radius r is

$(x - h)^2 + (y - k)^2 = r^2$.

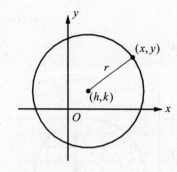

Example 1 □ a. Write an equation of a circle with center $(-3, 2)$ and $r = 2$.

b. Find the center and radius of a circle with the equation $x^2 + y^2 - 4x + 6y - 12 = 0$.

c. Write an equation of a circle that is tangent to the y-axis and has center $(4, 3)$.

d. Write an equation of a circle whose endpoints of its diameter are at $(-4, 8)$ and $(2, -4)$.

Solution □ a. $(x - h)^2 + (y - k)^2 = r^2$ Use the standard form of an equation of a circle.

$(x - (-3))^2 + (y - 2)^2 = 2^2$ Substitute $(-3, 2)$ for (h, k) and 2 for r .

$(x + 3)^2 + (y - 2)^2 = 4$ Simplify.

b. $x^2 + y^2 - 4x + 6y = 12$ Isolate the constant onto one side.

$x^2 - 4x + 4 + y^2 + 6y + 9 = 12 + 4 + 9$ Add $(-4 \cdot \frac{1}{2})^2 = 4$ and $(6 \cdot \frac{1}{2})^2 = 9$ to each side.

$(x - 2)^2 + (y + 3)^2 = 25$ Factor.

The center is $(2, -3)$ and $r = \sqrt{25} = 5$.

c. To visualize the circle, draw a sketch. Since the circle has its center at $(4, 3)$ and is tangent to the y-axis, its radius is 4 units.

The equation is $(x - 4)^2 + (y - 3)^2 = 16$.

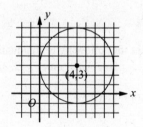

d. The center of a circle is the midpoint of its diameter.

$(h, k) = (\dfrac{-4 + 2}{2}, \dfrac{8 + (-4)}{2}) = (-1, 2)$

Use the distance formula to find the diameter of the circle.

$d = \sqrt{(2 - (-4))^2 + (-4 - 8)^2} = \sqrt{6^2 + 12^2} = \sqrt{180} = 6\sqrt{5}$

$r = \dfrac{1}{2}(6\sqrt{5}) = 3\sqrt{5}$

The equation of the circle is $(x + 1)^2 + (y - 2)^2 = (3\sqrt{5})^2$ or $(x + 1)^2 + (y - 2)^2 = 45$.

Exercises - Circles in the Coordinate Plane

1

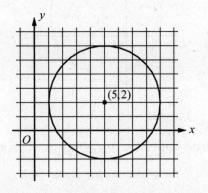

Which of the following equations represents the equation of the circle shown in the xy- plane above?

A) $(x+5)^2 +(y+2)^2 = 4$

B) $(x-5)^2 +(y-2)^2 = 4$

C) $(x+5)^2 +(y+2)^2 = 16$

D) $(x-5)^2 +(y-2)^2 = 16$

2

Which of the following is an equation of a circle in the xy- plane with center $(-2,0)$ and a radius with endpoint $(0,\frac{3}{2})$?

A) $x^2 +(y-\frac{3}{2})^2 = \frac{5}{2}$

B) $x^2 +(y-\frac{3}{2})^2 = \frac{25}{4}$

C) $(x+2)^2 + y^2 = \frac{25}{4}$

D) $(x-2)^2 + y^2 = \frac{25}{4}$

3

$$x^2 +12x + y^2 -4y +15 = 0$$

The equation of a circle in the xy- plane is shown above. Which of the following is true about the circle?

A) center $(-6,2)$, radius $= 5$

B) center $(6,-2)$, radius $= 5$

C) center $(-6,2)$, radius $= \sqrt{15}$

D) center $(6,-2)$, radius $= \sqrt{15}$

4

Which of the following represents an equation of a circle whose diameter has endpoints $(-8,4)$ and $(2,-6)$?

A) $(x-3)^2 +(y-1)^2 = 50$

B) $(x+3)^2 +(y+1)^2 = 50$

C) $(x-3)^2 +(y-1)^2 = 25$

D) $(x+3)^2 +(y+1)^2 = 25$

5

$$x^2 +2x + y^2 -4y -9 = 0$$

The equation of a circle in the xy- plane is shown above. If the area of the circle is $k\pi$, what is the value of k ?

Chapter 19 Practice Test

1

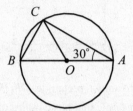

In the figure above, O is the center of the circle and $\overline{AB}$ is a diameter. If the length of $\overline{AC}$ is $4\sqrt{3}$ and $m\angle BAC = 30$, what is the area of circle O?

A) 12π

B) 16π

C) 18π

D) 24π

2

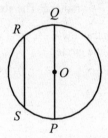

In the circle above, chord $\overline{RS}$ is parallel to diameter $\overline{PQ}$. If the length of $\overline{RS}$ is $\dfrac{3}{4}$ of the length of $\overline{PQ}$ and the distance between the chord and the diameter is $2\sqrt{7}$, what is the radius of the circle?

A) 6

B) $3\sqrt{7}$

C) 8

D) $4\sqrt{7}$

3

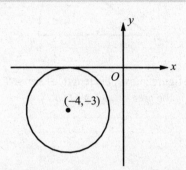

In the figure above, the circle is tangent to the x-axis and has center $(-4,-3)$. Which of the following equations represents the equation of the circle shown in the xy-plane above?

A) $(x+4)^2 + (y+3)^2 = 9$

B) $(x-4)^2 + (y-3)^2 = 9$

C) $(x+4)^2 + (y+3)^2 = 3$

D) $(x-4)^2 + (y-3)^2 = 3$

4

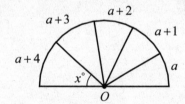

The figure above shows a semicircle with the lengths of the adjacent arcs a, $a+1$, $a+2$, $a+3$, and $a+4$. If the value of x is 42, what is the value of a?

A) 7

B) 8

C) 9

D) 10

5

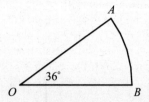

In the figure above, the length of arc $\overset{\frown}{AB}$ is π. What is the area of sector OAB?

A) 2π

B) $\dfrac{5}{2}\pi$

C) 3π

D) $\dfrac{7}{2}\pi$

6

$$x^2 - 4x + y^2 - 6x - 17 = 0$$

What is the area of the circle in the xy-plane above?

A) 20π

B) 24π

C) 26π

D) 30π

7

Which of the following is the equation of a circle that has a diameter of 8 units and is tangent to the graph of $y = 2$?

A) $(x+1)^2 + (y+2)^2 = 16$

B) $(x-1)^2 + (y-2)^2 = 16$

C) $(x+2)^2 + (y+1)^2 = 16$

D) $(x-2)^2 + (y-1)^2 = 16$

8

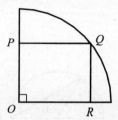

In the figure above, rectangle $OPQR$ is inscribed in a quarter circle that has a radius of 9. If $PQ = 7$, what is the area of rectangle $OPQR$?

A) $24\sqrt{2}$

B) $26\sqrt{2}$

C) $28\sqrt{2}$

D) $30\sqrt{2}$

9

In a circle with center O, the central angle has a measure of $\dfrac{2\pi}{3}$ radians. The area of the sector formed by central angle AOB is what fraction of the area of the circle?

10

A wheel with a radius of 2.2 feet is turning at a constant rate of 400 revolutions per minute on a road. If the wheel traveled $k\pi$ miles in one hour what is the value of k? (1 mile = 5,280 feet)

Answer Key

Section 19-1

1. 38   2. 38   3. 135   4. 9   5. D
6. C

Section 19-2

1. 6   2. 81   3. 32   4. B   5. D

Section 19-3

1. 48   2. 24   3. 90   4. 32   5. D
6. B

Section 19-4

1. C   2. C   3. A   4. B

Section 19-5

1. D   2. C   3. A   4. B   5. 14

Chapter 19 Practice Test

1. B   2. C   3. A   4. D   5. B
6. D   7. A   8. C   9. $\frac{1}{3}$ 10. 20

Answers and Explanations

Section 19-1

1. 38

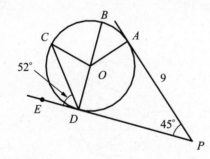

$\overline{PD} \perp \overline{OD}$ Tangent to a ⊙ is ⊥ to radius.
$m\angle ODE = 90$ A right ∠ measures 90.
$m\angle ODC = 90 - 52$
$\qquad = 38$

2. 38

$OC = OD$ In a ⊙ all radii are ≅.
$m\angle OCD = m\angle ODC$ Isosceles Triangle Theorem
$\qquad = 38$

3. 135

If a line is tangent to a circle, the line is ⊥ to the radius at the point of tangency. Therefore, $m\angle ODP = m\angle OAP = 90$.
The sum of the measures of interior angles of quadrilateral is 360. Therefore,
$m\angle AOD + m\angle ODP + m\angle OAP + m\angle P = 360$.

$m\angle AOD + 90 + 90 + 45 = 360$ Substitution
$m\angle AOD + 225 = 360$ Simplify.
$m\angle AOD = 135$

4. 9

Tangents to a circle from the same exterior point are congruent. Therefore,

$PD = PA = 9$.

5. D

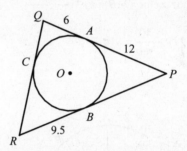

Since tangents to a circle from the same exterior point are congruent, $QA = QC = 6$, $PA = PB = 12$, and $RB = RC = 9.5$. Therefore,
Perimeter of $\triangle PQR = 2(6 + 12 + 9.5) = 55$

6. C

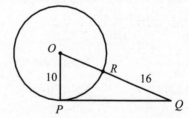

$OR = OP = 10$ In a ⊙ all radii are ≅.
$OQ = OR + RQ$ Segment Addition Postulate
$\quad = 10 + 16 = 26$
$PQ^2 + OP^2 = OQ^2$ Pythagorean Theorem
$PQ^2 + 10^2 = 26^2$ Substitution
$PQ^2 = 26^2 - 10^2 = 576$
$PQ = \sqrt{576} = 24$

Section 19-2

1. 6

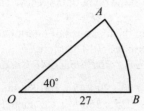

Length of arc $AB = 2\pi r \cdot \dfrac{m\angle AOB}{360}$

$= 2\pi(27) \cdot \dfrac{40}{360} = 6\pi$

Thus, $k = 6$.

2. 81

Area of sector $OAB = \pi r^2 \cdot \dfrac{m\angle AOB}{360}$

$= \pi(27)^2 \cdot \dfrac{40}{360} = 81\pi$

Thus, $n = 81$.

3. 32

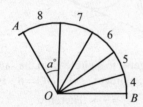

The length of arc $AB = 8 + 7 + 6 + 5 + 4 = 30$
In a circle, the lengths of the arcs are proportional
to the degree measures of the corresponding arcs.

Therefore, $\dfrac{\text{length of arc } AB}{120°} = \dfrac{8}{a°}$.

$\dfrac{30}{120} = \dfrac{8}{a}$ Substitution

$30a = 120 \times 8$ Cross Products

$a = 32$

4. B

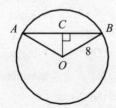

Draw $\overline{OC}$ perpendicular to $\overline{AB}$. Since $\triangle AOB$
is an isosceles triangle, $\overline{OC}$ bisects $\angle AOB$.

$m\angle AOC = m\angle BOC = \dfrac{1}{2}m\angle AOB = \dfrac{1}{2}(120) = 60$.

$\triangle BOC$ is a $30°$-$60°$-$90°$ triangle.

In a $30°$-$60°$-$90°$ triangle, the hypotenuse is twice
as long as the shorter leg and the longer leg is $\sqrt{3}$
times as long as the shorter leg.

$OC = \dfrac{1}{2}OB = \dfrac{1}{2}(8) = 4$

$BC = \sqrt{3} \cdot OC = 4\sqrt{3}$

$AB = 2BC = 2 \times 4\sqrt{3} = 8\sqrt{3}$

5. D

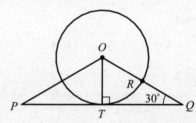

Let T be a point of tangency. Then $\overline{PQ} \perp \overline{OT}$,
because a line tangent to a circle is $\perp$ to the
radius at the point of tangency.

$\triangle OQT$ is a $30°$-$60°$-$90°$ triangle.

$OT = OR = 8$ In a $\odot$ all radii are $\cong$.

In a $30°$-$60°$-$90°$ triangle, the hypotenuse is twice
as long as the shorter leg. Therefore,

$OQ = 2OT = 2(8) = 16$

$QR = OQ - OR = 16 - 8 = 8$

Section 19-3

1. 48

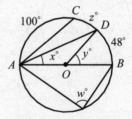

The measure of a minor arc is the measure
of its central angle. Therefore, $y = 48$.

2. 24

The measure of an inscribed angle is half the
measure of its intercepted arc.

Therefore, $x = \dfrac{1}{2}(48) = 24$.

3. 90

An angle inscribed in a semicircle is a right angle. Therefore, $w = 90$.

4. 32

The measure of a semicircle is 180, thus $m\widehat{ACB} = 180$.
The measure of an arc formed by two adjacent arcs is the sum of the measure of the two arcs, thus

$m\widehat{ACB} = m\widehat{AC} + m\widehat{CD} + m\widehat{DB}$
$180 = 100 + z + 48$ Substitution
$180 = 148 + z$ Simplify.
$32 = z$

5. D

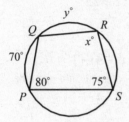

If a quadrilateral is inscribed in a circle, its opposite angles are supplementary. Therefore,
$x + 80 = 180$.
$x = 100$

6. B

The measure of an inscribed angle is half the measure of its intercepted arc. Therefore,

$m\angle RSP = \frac{1}{2}(m\widehat{PQ} + m\widehat{QR})$.

$75 = \frac{1}{2}(70 + y)$ Substitution

$2 \cdot 75 = 2 \cdot \frac{1}{2}(70 + y)$ Multiply each side by 2.

$150 = 70 + y$ Simplify.

$80 = y$

Section 19-4

1. C

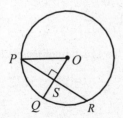

If a diameter is $\perp$ to a chord, it bisects the chord and its arc. Therefore,

$PS = \frac{1}{2}PR = \frac{1}{2}(24) = 12$.

The radius of the circle is 13, thus $OP = OQ = 13$.

Draw $\overline{OP}$.

$OS^2 + PS^2 = OP^2$ Pythagorean Theorem
$OS^2 + 12^2 = 13^2$ Substitution
$OS^2 = 13^2 - 12^2 = 25$
$OS = \sqrt{25} = 5$
$QS = OQ - OS$
     $= 13 - 5$
     $= 8$

2. C

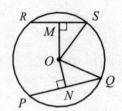

Draw $\overline{OS}$ and $\overline{OQ}$.

If a diameter is $\perp$ to a chord, it bisects the chord and its arc. Therefore,

$MS = \frac{1}{2}RS = \frac{1}{2}(6) = 3$ and $PQ = 2NQ$.

$OS^2 = MS^2 + OM^2$ Pythagorean Theorem
$OS^2 = 3^2 + 5^2$ Substitution
$OS^2 = 34$
$OS = \sqrt{34}$
$OQ = OS = \sqrt{34}$ In a $\odot$ all radii are $\cong$.
$OQ^2 = ON^2 + NQ^2$ Pythagorean Theorem
$(\sqrt{34})^2 = 4^2 + NQ^2$ Substitution
$34 = 16 + NQ^2$
$18 = NQ^2$
$NQ = \sqrt{18} = 3\sqrt{2}$
$PQ = 2NQ = 2(3\sqrt{2}) = 6\sqrt{2}$

3. A

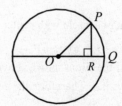

Area of the circle $= \pi r^2 = 9\pi$.

$\Rightarrow r^2 = 9 \Rightarrow r = 3$

Therefore, $OP = OQ = 3$.

$OR^2 + PR^2 = OP^2$ $\qquad$ Pythagorean Theorem

$OR^2 + (\sqrt{5})^2 = 3^2$ $\qquad$ Substitution

$OR^2 + 5 = 9$ $\qquad$ Simplify.

$OR^2 = 9 - 5 = 4$

$OR = \sqrt{4} = 2$

$QR = OQ - OR = 3 - 2 = 1$

4. B

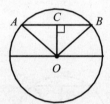

Draw $\overline{OA}$ and $\overline{OB}$. Draw $\overline{OC} \perp$ to $\overline{AB}$.
OC is the distance between the chord and
the diameter.

$BC = \dfrac{1}{2} AB = \dfrac{1}{2}(18) = 9$

$OC^2 + BC^2 = OB^2$ $\qquad$ Pythagorean Theorem

$OC^2 + 9^2 = 12^2$ $\qquad$ Substitution

$OC^2 = 12^2 - 9^2 = 63$

$OC = \sqrt{63}$

$\quad = \sqrt{9} \cdot \sqrt{7}$

$\quad = 3\sqrt{7}$

Section 19-5

1. D

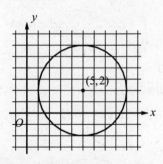

The equation of a circle with center (h,k) and
radius r is $(x-h)^2 + (y-k)^2 = r^2$.

The center of the circle shown above is $(5,2)$
and the radius is 4. Therefore, the equation of
the circle is $(x-5)^2 + (y-2)^2 = 4^2$.

2. C

Use the distance formula to find the radius.

$r = \sqrt{(x_2 - x_1)^2 + (y_2 - y_1)^2}$ $\qquad (x_1, y_1) = (-2, 0)$

$\quad = \sqrt{(0-(-2))^2 + (\dfrac{3}{2} - 0)^2}$ $\qquad (x_2, y_2) = (0, \dfrac{3}{2})$

$\quad = \sqrt{4 + \dfrac{9}{4}}$ $\qquad$ Simplify.

$\quad = \sqrt{\dfrac{16}{4} + \dfrac{9}{4}} = \sqrt{\dfrac{25}{4}}$

Therefore, the equation of the circle is

$(x-(-2))^2 + (y-0)^2 = (\sqrt{\dfrac{25}{4}})^2$.

Choice C is correct.

3. A

$x^2 + 12x + y^2 - 4y + 15 = 0$

Isolate the constant onto one side.

$x^2 + 12x + y^2 - 4y = -15$

Add $(12 \cdot \dfrac{1}{2})^2 = 36$ and $(-4 \cdot \dfrac{1}{2})^2 = 4$ to each side.

$(x^2 + 12x + 36) + (y^2 - 4y + 4) = -15 + 36 + 4$

Complete the square.

$(x+6)^2 + (y-2)^2 = 25$

The center of the circle is $(-6, 2)$ and the radius
is $\sqrt{25}$, or 5.

4. B

The center of the circle is the midpoint of the
diameter. Use the midpoint formula to find the
center of the circle.

$(h, k) = (\dfrac{x_1 + x_2}{2}, \dfrac{y_1 + y_2}{2})$

$\quad = (\dfrac{-8+2}{2}, \dfrac{4+(-6)}{2}) = (-3, -1)$

The radius is half the distance of the diameter.
Use the distance formula to find the diameter.

$d = \sqrt{(2-(-8))^2 + (-6-4)^2} = \sqrt{100+100}$

$\quad = \sqrt{200} = \sqrt{100} \cdot \sqrt{2} = 10\sqrt{2}$

$r = \dfrac{1}{2} d = \dfrac{1}{2}(10\sqrt{2}) = 5\sqrt{2}$

Therefore, the equation of the circle is

$(x-(-3))^2 + (y-(-1))^2 = (5\sqrt{2})^2$, or

$(x+3)^2 + (y+1)^2 = 50$.

5. 14

$x^2 + 2x + y^2 - 4y - 9 = 0$

Isolate the constant onto one side.

$x^2 + 2x + y^2 - 4y = 9$

Add $(2 \cdot \frac{1}{2})^2 = 1$ and $(-4 \cdot \frac{1}{2})^2 = 4$ to each side.

$(x^2 + 2x + 1) + (y^2 - 4y + 4) = 9 + 1 + 4$

Complete the square.

$(x+1)^2 + (y-2)^2 = 14$

The radius of the circle is $\sqrt{14}$.

Area of the circle is $\pi r^2 = \pi(\sqrt{14})^2 = 14\pi$.

Therefore, $k = 14$.

Chapter 19 Practice Test

1. B

An angle inscribed in a semicircle is a right angle. Therefore, $\angle ACB = 90$.

So, $\triangle ABC$ is a $30°$-$60°$-$90°$ triangle.

In a $30°$-$60°$-$90°$ triangle, the hypotenuse is twice as long as the shorter leg and the longer leg is $\sqrt{3}$ times as long as the shorter leg.

$AC = \sqrt{3}BC$

$4\sqrt{3} = \sqrt{3}BC$ $AC = 4\sqrt{3}$

$4 = BC$

$AB = 2BC = 2(4) = 8$

Therefore, the radius of circle O is 4.

Area of circle $O = \pi(4)^2 = 16\pi$

2. C

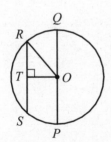

Draw $\overline{OR}$ and $\overline{OT}$ as shown above. Let the radius of the circle be r , then $OQ = OR = r$.

Since the ratio of RS to QP is 3 to 4, the ratio of RT to OQ is also 3 to 4.

Therefore, $RT = \frac{3}{4}OQ = \frac{3}{4}r$.

OT is the distance between the chord and the

diameter, which is given as $2\sqrt{7}$.

$OR^2 = RT^2 + OT^2$ Pythagorean Theorem

$r^2 = (\frac{3}{4}r)^2 + (2\sqrt{7})^2$ Substitution

$r^2 = \frac{9}{16}r^2 + 28$ Simplify.

$r^2 - \frac{9}{16}r^2 = 28$

$\frac{7}{16}r^2 = 28$

$\frac{16}{7} \cdot \frac{7}{16}r^2 = \frac{16}{7} \cdot 28$

$r^2 = 64$

$r = \sqrt{64} = 8$

3. A

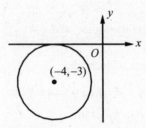

If the center of the circle is $(-4, -3)$ and the circle is tangent to the x-axis, the radius is 3.

The equation is $(x - (-4))^2 + (y - (-3))^2 = 3^2$,

or $(x+4)^2 + (y+3)^2 = 9$.

4. D

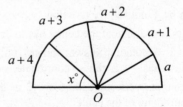

The arc length of the semicircle is

$(a+4) + (a+3) + (a+2) + (a+1) + a = 5a + 10$.

In a circle, the lengths of the arcs are proportional to the degree measures of the corresponding arcs.

Therefore, $\dfrac{\text{arc length of semicircle}}{180°} = \dfrac{a+4}{x°}$.

$\dfrac{5a+10}{180} = \dfrac{a+4}{42}$ Substitution

$42(5a+10) = 180(a+4)$ Cross Products

$210a + 420 = 180a + 720$

$30a = 300$

$a = 10$

5. B

Length of arc $AB = 2\pi r \cdot \dfrac{m\angle AOB}{360}$

$= 2\pi r \cdot \dfrac{36}{360} = \dfrac{\pi r}{5}$

Since the length of the arc is given as π,

$\dfrac{\pi r}{5} = \pi$. Solving the equation for r gives $r = 5$.

Area of sector $AOB = \pi r^2 \cdot \dfrac{m\angle AOB}{360}$

$= \pi(5)^2 \cdot \dfrac{36}{360} = \dfrac{5}{2}\pi$

6. D

$x^2 - 4x + y^2 - 6x - 17 = 0$

$x^2 - 4x + y^2 - 6x = 17$

To complete the square, add $\left(-4 \cdot \dfrac{1}{2}\right)^2 = 4$ and

$\left(-6 \cdot \dfrac{1}{2}\right)^2 = 9$ to each side.

$x^2 - 4x + 4 + y^2 - 6x + 9 = 17 + 4 + 9$

$(x-2)^2 + (y-3)^2 = 30$

The radius of the circle is $\sqrt{30}$, the area of the circle is $\pi(\sqrt{30})^2 = 30\pi$

7. A

If the diameter of the circle is 8 units, the radius of the circle is 4 units. Since the radius of the circle is 4 units, the y-coordinate of the center has to be 4 units above or below $y = 2$.

The y-coordinate of the center has to be either 6 or -2. Among the answer choices, only choice A has -2 as the y-coordinate.

No other answer choice has 6 or -2 as the y-coordinate of the center.

Choice A is correct.

8. C

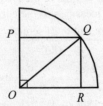

Draw $\overline{OQ}$. Since $\overline{OQ}$ is a radius, $OQ = 9$.

$OP^2 + PQ^2 = OQ^2$ Pythagorean Theorem

$OP^2 + 7^2 = 9^2$ Substitution

$OP^2 = 9^2 - 7^2 = 32$

$OP = \sqrt{32} = \sqrt{16} \cdot \sqrt{2} = 4\sqrt{2}$

Area of rectangle $OPQR = OP \times PQ$

$= 4\sqrt{2} \times 7 = 28\sqrt{2}$

9. $\dfrac{1}{3}$

Area of sector $AOB = \pi r^2 \cdot \dfrac{m\angle AOB}{360}$

The area of a sector is the fractional part of the area of a circle. The area of a sector formed by $\dfrac{2\pi}{3}$ radians of arc is $\dfrac{2\pi/3}{2\pi}$, or $\dfrac{1}{3}$, of the area of the circle.

10. 20

The distance the wheel travels in 1 minute is equal to the product of the circumference of the wheel and the number of revolutions per minute. The distance the wheel travels in 1 minute

$= 2\pi r \times$ the number of revolutions per minute

$= 2\pi(2.2 \text{ ft}) \times 400 = 1,760\pi \text{ ft}$

Total distance traveled in 1 hour

$= 1,760\pi \text{ ft} \times 60 = 105,600\pi \text{ ft}$

$= 105,600\pi \text{ ft} \times \dfrac{1 \text{ mile}}{5,280 \text{ ft}} = 20\pi \text{ miles}$

Thus, $k = 20$.

CHAPTER 20
Surface Areas and Volumes

20-1. Prisms

A **prism** is a polyhedron (a space figure whose faces are polygons) with two congruent and parallel faces. These two faces are called the **bases** of the prism. The other faces are **lateral faces**. In a prism, the lateral faces are rectangles. The **height** of a prism is a segment joining the two base planes and is perpendicular to both.

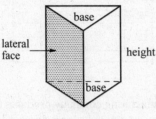

Triangular prism

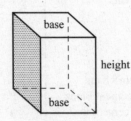

Rectangular prism

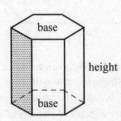

Hexagonal prism

Theorems - Prisms

The **lateral area** of a prism is the perimeter of a base times the height of the prism. $L.A. = P \cdot h$

The total **surface area** of a prism is the sum of the lateral area and the areas of the two bases. $T.A. = L.A. + 2B$

The **volume** of a prism is the area of a base times the height of the prism. $V = B \cdot h$

A **cube** is a prism in which all the faces are squares.

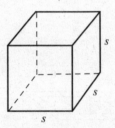

Theorems - Cubes

Volume of a cube $= s^3$

Surface area of a cube $= 6s^2$

Example 1 □ A triangular prism is shown at the right.

   a. Find the area of the base.

   b. Find the volume of the prism.

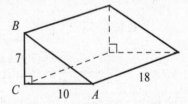

Solution □ a. $B = \dfrac{1}{2}(7)(10) = 35$ B = area of triangle ABC.

   b. $V = 35 \cdot 18 = 630$ $V = B \cdot h$

Example 2 □ A cube has a volume of 1,728 cubic inches (in^3). What is the surface area of the cube, in square inches?

Solution □ Let $s =$ the length of the cube.

   $V = s^3 = 1,728 \ in^3 \ \Rightarrow \ s = \sqrt[3]{1728 \ in^3} = (1728 \ in^3)^{\frac{1}{3}} = 12 \ in$

   Surface area of a cube $= 6s^2 = 6(12 \ in)^2 = 864 \ in^2$

Exercises – Prisms

1

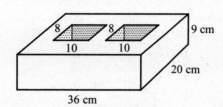

The figure above shows a cement block of
$36 \, \text{cm} \times 20 \, \text{cm} \times 9 \, \text{cm}$ with two $10 \, \text{cm} \times 8 \, \text{cm}$
openings. What is the weight of the cement block
to the nearest gram? (The density of cement is
$1.7 \, \text{gram} / \text{cm}^3$)

A) 5,040

B) 6,048

C) 7,560

D) 8,568

2

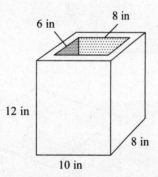

The figure above shows an aluminum block of
$10 \, \text{in} \times 8 \, \text{in} \times 12 \, \text{in}$ with an $8 \, \text{in} \times 6 \, \text{in} \times 12 \, \text{in}$
opening. What is the weight of the aluminum block
to the nearest pound? (The density of aluminum is
$0.098 \, \text{lb/in}^3$)

A) 32

B) 38

C) 42

D) 48

3

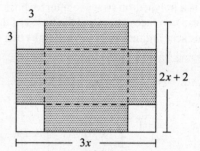

A manufacturing company produces cardboard
boxes by cutting out square corners 3 inches (in)
by 3 in. from rectangular pieces of cardboard
$3x$ in. by $2x + 2$ in. The cardboard is then folded
along the dashed lines to form a box without a top.
If the volume of the box is $162 \, \text{in}^3$, what is the
dimension of the original cardboard before cutting
out its square corners?

A) $12 \, \text{in} \times 9 \, \text{in}$

B) $14 \, \text{in} \times 10 \, \text{in}$

C) $15 \, \text{in} \times 12 \, \text{in}$

D) $16 \, \text{in} \times 14 \, \text{in}$

4

An aquarium tank in the shape of a rectangular
prism is 20 inches (in) long by 16 in wide by
12 in high. If 2,400 cubic inches of water is added
into the empty tank, how far is the surface of the
water from the top of the tank?

20-2. Cylinders and Spheres

A **cylinder** is a solid that has two congruent parallel bases that are circles. In a right cylinder, the segment joining the centers of the bases is an altitude.

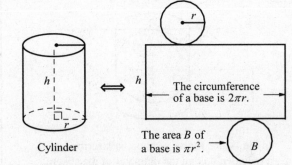

Theorems - Cylinders

The **lateral area** of a cylinder: $L.A. = 2\pi rh$

The total **surface area** of a cylinder: $T.A. = 2\pi rh + 2\pi r^2$

The **volume** of a cylinder: $V = \pi r^2 h$

Cylinder

The circumference of a base is $2\pi r$.

The area B of a base is πr^2.

A **sphere** is the set of all points in space equidistant from a given point called the center. A plane can intersect a sphere at a point or in a circle. When a plane intersects a sphere so that it contains the center of the sphere, the intersection is called a **great circle**.

Theorems - Spheres

The **surface area** of a sphere: $S.A. = 4\pi r^2$

The **volume** of a sphere: $V = \dfrac{4}{3}\pi r^3$

A plane intersects a sphere

in a circle,

in a great circle,

and

at a point.

Example 1 ☐ The volume of the cylinder shown at the right is 225π cubic inches. What is the diameter of the base of the cylinder, in inches?

9 in

Solution ☐ $V = \pi r^2 h$ Volume of a cylinder

$225\pi = \pi r^2 (9)$ Substitution

$r^2 = \dfrac{225\pi}{9\pi} = 25$ Divide both sides by 9π

$r = \sqrt{25} = 5$ Square root both sides.

diameter $= 2r = 2 \cdot 5 = 10$

Example 2 ☐ The figure at the right is a cylinder 12 feet high. It is capped by a hemisphere with a radius of 4 feet. What is the volume of the figure?

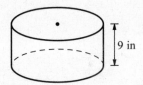

12 ft

4 ft

Solution ☐ Volume of cylinder $= \pi r^2 h = \pi(4)^2 (12) = 192\pi$

Volume of hemisphere $= \dfrac{1}{2}(\dfrac{4}{3}\pi r^3) = \dfrac{1}{2} \cdot \dfrac{4}{3}\pi(4)^3 = \dfrac{128}{3}\pi$

Volume of the figure $= 192\pi + \dfrac{128}{3}\pi = \dfrac{704}{3}\pi$

Exercises - Cylinders and Spheres

1

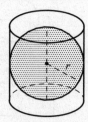

In the figure above, a sphere is inscribed in a cylinder, so that the diameter of the sphere is the same as the diameter of the cylinder and the height of the cylinder. What is the value of $\dfrac{\text{Volume of the sphere}}{\text{Volume of the cylinder}}$?

A) $\dfrac{1}{2}$

B) $\dfrac{2}{3}$

C) $\dfrac{7}{10}$

D) $\dfrac{3}{4}$

2

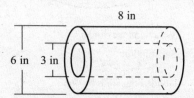

The figure above shows the mechanical part in the shape of a steel cylinder 8 inches high and 6 inches long in diameter. A hole with a diameter of 3 inches is drilled through the mechanical part. The density of steel is 490 lb/ft^3. What is the mass of the mechanical part, to the nearest pound? (1 foot = 12 inch)

A) 36

B) 42

C) 48

D) 52

3

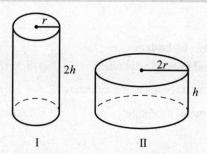

The figure above shows two cylinders. The height of cylinder I is twice the height of cylinder II and the radius of cylinder II is twice the radius of cylinder I. If the volume of cylinder I is 45π in^3, what is the volume of cylinder II in cubic inches?

A) 22.5π

B) 45π

C) 67.5π

D) 90π

4

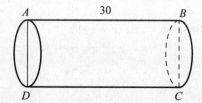

In the cylindrical tube shown above, the height of the tube is 30 and the circumference of the circular base is 32. If the tube is cut along $\overline{AB}$ and laid out flat to make a rectangle, what is the length of $\overline{AC}$ to the nearest whole number?

A) 24

B) 30

C) 34

D) 38

20-3. Pyramids and Cones

A **pyramid** is a polyhedron in which the base is a polygon and the **lateral faces** are triangles that meet at the **vertex**. The height of a lateral face is called the **slant height** of the pyramid, which is denoted by ℓ. A **regular pyramids** is a pyramid whose base is a regular polygon and whose lateral faces are congruent isosceles triangles. In SAT, you can assume that a pyramid is regular unless stated otherwise.

A **cone** is a solid that has a vertex and a circular base. The slant height ℓ is the distance from the vertex to a point on the edge of the base.

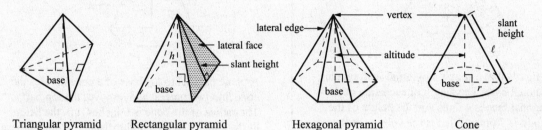

| Triangular pyramid | Rectangular pyramid | Hexagonal pyramid | Cone |

Theorems – Pyramids and Cones

The **lateral area** of a pyramid: $L.A. = \dfrac{1}{2}P\ell$

The **surface area** of a pyramid: $S.A. = L.A. + B$

The **volume** of a pyramid: $V = \dfrac{1}{3}Bh$

The **lateral area** of a cone: $L.A. = \pi r\ell$

The **surface area** of a cone: $S.A. = L.A. + B$

The **volume** of a cone: $V = \dfrac{1}{3}\pi r^2 h$

Example 1 □ A square pyramid is shown at the right.

a. Find the base area of the pyramid.

b. Find the volume of the pyramid.

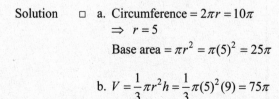

Solution □ a. Base area $= 6 \cdot 6 = 36$

b. $V = \dfrac{1}{3}Bh = \dfrac{1}{3}(36)(6) = 72$

Example 2 □ A cone with a height of 9 is shown at the right.

a. If the circumference of the base is 10π, what is the area of the base?

b. What is the volume of the cone?

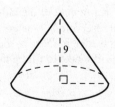

Solution □ a. Circumference $= 2\pi r = 10\pi$
  $\Rightarrow r = 5$
  Base area $= \pi r^2 = \pi(5)^2 = 25\pi$

b. $V = \dfrac{1}{3}\pi r^2 h = \dfrac{1}{3}\pi(5)^2(9) = 75\pi$

Exercises - Pyramids and Cones

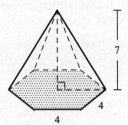

The figure above shows a pyramid with regular hexagonal base. The length of each side of the hexagonal face is 4 units and the height of the pyramid is 7 units. What is the volume of the pyramid?

A) $35\sqrt{3}$

B) $56\sqrt{3}$

C) $84\sqrt{3}$

D) $168\sqrt{3}$

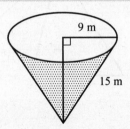

Water is pouring into a conical reservoir at the rate of 2.4 m³ per minute. If the radius of the base of the conical reservoir is 9 meters (m) and the length of the lateral edge is 15 m, to the nearest minute, how long will it take to fill up the empty reservoir?

A) 212

B) 318

C) 424

D) 530

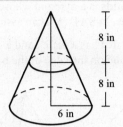

A plane parallel to the base of a cone divides the cone into two pieces, and removes the top part. The radius of the cone is 6 inches (in), the height of the cone is 16 in, and the distance from the base to the parallel plane is 8 in. What is the volume of the remaining bottom part, in cubic inches?

A) 56π

B) 84π

C) 126π

D) 168π

If the circumference of the base part of cone is 10 centimeters (cm) and the height of the cone is 8 cm, what is the volume of the cone, to the nearest cubic centimeter?

A) 18

B) 21

C) 24

D) 32

Chapter 20 Practice Test

1

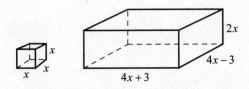

The figure above shows a cube and a rectangular prism. If the volume of the rectangular prism is 30 times the volume of the cube, what is the value of x?

A) 1.5

B) 2

C) 2.5

D) 3

2

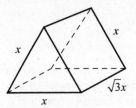

The figure above shows a triangular prism whose base is a equilateral triangle with side lengths x and height $\sqrt{3}x$. If the volume of the prism is $\dfrac{81}{4}$, what is the value of x?

A) 3

B) 4

C) 5

D) 6

3

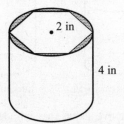

A regular hexagonal prism with edge lengths of 2 inches is created by cutting out a metal cylinder whose radius is 2 inches and height is 4 inches. What is the volume of the waste generated by creating the hexagonal prism from the cylinder, rounded to the nearest cubic inch?

A) 7

B) 9

C) 11

D) 14

4

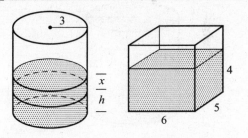

In the figure shown above, if all the water in the rectangular container is poured into the cylinder, the water level rises from h inches to $(h+x)$ inches. Which of the following is the best approximation of the value of x?

A) 3

B) 3.4

C) 3.8

D) 4.2

5

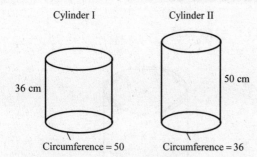

Cylinder I   Cylinder II

36 cm   50 cm

Circumference = 50   Circumference = 36

The figure above shows two cylinders that are rolled up from a poster 36 centimeter (cm) wide and 50 cm long without overlap. For cylinder I, the height is 36 cm and the circumference of the base is 50 cm. For cylinder II, the height is 50 cm and the circumference of the base is 36 cm. Which of the following is closest to the difference of volume between the two cylinders, in cubic centimeters?

A) 1,600

B) 1,800

C) 2,000

D) 2,200

6

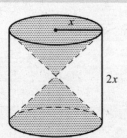

In the figure above, a double cone is inscribed in a cylinder whose radius is x and height is $2x$. What is the volume of the space inside the cylinder but outside the double cone, in terms of x?

A) $\frac{1}{2}\pi x^3$

B) $\frac{2}{3}\pi x^3$

C) $\frac{4}{3}\pi x^3$

D) $\frac{3}{2}\pi x^3$

7

The surface area of a cube is 54 square centimeters (cm^2). What is the volume of the cube in cubic centimeters?

8

A cone with a height of 10 cm and radius of 3 cm is 90 percent filled with shaved ice. What is the volume of the shaved ice, to the nearest cubic centimeter?

9

A square pyramid and a cube have equal volumes. The cube has an edge length of 4 inches and the pyramid has a base side length of 6 inches. What is the height of the pyramid in inches?

Answer Key

Section 20-1

1. D   2. B   3. C   4. 4.5

Section 20-2

1. B   2. C   3. D   4. C

Section 20-3

1. B   2. C   3. D   4. B

Chapter 20 Practice Test

1. D   2. A   3. B   4. D   5. C

6. C   7. 27   8. 85   9. $\frac{16}{3}$ or 5.33

Answers and Explanations

Section 20-1

1. **D**

   Volume of the block is $36 \times 20 \times 9 - 2(10 \times 8 \times 9)$, or $5,040$ cm^3.

   Weight of the cement block = density $\times$ volume

   $= 1.7$ gram / cm$^3 \times 5,040$ cm$^3 = 8,568$ gram.

2. **B**

   Volume of the aluminum block is
   $10 \times 8 \times 12 - 8 \times 6 \times 12$, or 384 in^3.

   Weight of the aluminum block = density $\times$ volume

   $= 0.098$ lb / in$^3 \times 384$ in$^3 = 37.632$ lb.

3. **C**

   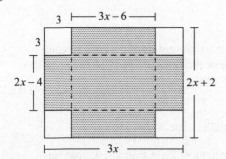

   The dimension of the box is $(3x-6) \times (2x-4) \times 3$.

   Since the volume of the box is given as 162 in^3,

   set up the following equation:

$(3x-6) \times (2x-4) \times 3 = 162$

$(3x-6) \times (2x-4) = 54$

$6x^2 - 24x + 24 = 54$

$6x^2 - 24x - 30 = 0$

$6(x^2 - 4x - 5) = 0$

$6(x-5)(x+1) = 0$

$x = 5$ or $x = -1$

The length of the side is positive, so $x = 5$.
Therefore, the dimension of the original cardboard
is (3×5) in $\times (2 \times 5 + 2)$ in, or 15 in $\times 12$ in.

4. **4.5**

   Let h be the height of water when $2,400$ cubic
   inches of water is added into the empty tank.
   Then $20 \times 16 \times h = 2,400$. Solving for h yields

   $$h = \frac{2,400}{20 \times 16} = 7.5 \text{ in}.$$

   Since the aquarium tank is 12 inches high, the
   surface of water will be $12 - 7.5$, or 4.5 inches,
   from the top of the tank.

Section 20-2

1. **B**

   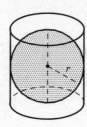

   Volume of the sphere $= \frac{4}{3}\pi r^3$

   Volume of the cylinder $= \pi r^2 \cdot$ height

   $\qquad\qquad\qquad\qquad = \pi r^2 \cdot 2r$

   $\qquad\qquad\qquad\qquad = 2\pi r^3$

   $$\frac{\text{Volume of the sphere}}{\text{Volume of the cylinder}} = \frac{\frac{4}{3}\pi r^3}{2\pi r^3} = \frac{\frac{4}{3}}{2} = \frac{2}{3}$$

2. **C**

   Volume of the mechanical part
   $= \pi(3)^2 \cdot 8 - \pi(1.5)^2 \cdot 8 = 54\pi$ in^3

   Since 1 ft $= 12$ in, 1 ft$^3 = (12$ in$)^3 = 1,728$ in^3.

   Thus 1 in$^3 = \frac{1}{1,728}$ ft^3.

Mass of the mechanical part = density × volume

$= 490 \text{ lb} / \text{ft}^3 \times 54\pi \text{ in}^3 \cdot \dfrac{1 \text{ ft}^3}{1,728 \text{ in}^3} \approx 48.1 \text{ lb}$.

3. D

Volume of cylinder I $= \pi(r)^2 \cdot 2h = 2\pi r^2 h$

Volume of cylinder II $= \pi(2r)^2 \cdot h = 4\pi r^2 h$

$\dfrac{\text{volume of cylinder I}}{\text{volume of cylinder II}} = \dfrac{2\pi r^2 h}{4\pi r^2 h} = \dfrac{1}{2}$

Thus if the volume of cylinder I is $45\pi \text{ in}^3$, the volume of cylinder II is $90\pi \text{ in}^3$.

4. C

The figure below shows the rectangle, which was laid flat from a cut along $\overline{AB}$ on the cylinder.

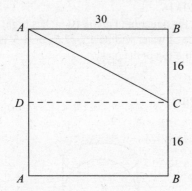

$AC^2 = AB^2 + BC^2$ Pythagorean Theorem

$AC^2 = 30^2 + 16^2$ Substitution

$\quad\; = 900 + 256$

$\quad\; = 1,156$

$AC = \sqrt{1,156} = 34$

Section 20-3

1. B

The regular hexagon consists of 6 equilateral triangles. So the area of the regular hexagon is the sum of the areas of 6 equilateral triangles. Since the area of the equilateral triangle with side

length of a is $\dfrac{\sqrt{3}}{4}a^2$, the area of the equilateral

triangle with side length of 4 is $\dfrac{\sqrt{3}}{4}(4)^2 = 4\sqrt{3}$.

The area of the hexagon is $6 \times 4\sqrt{3} = 24\sqrt{3}$.

Volume of the pyramid

$= \dfrac{1}{3}Bh = \dfrac{1}{3}(24\sqrt{3})(7) = 56\sqrt{3}$

2. C

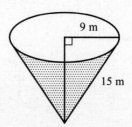

Let h = the height of the cone.

$9^2 + h^2 = 15^2$ Pythagorean Theorem

$h^2 = 15^2 - 9^2 = 144$

$h = \sqrt{144} = 12$

Volume of the cone $= \dfrac{1}{3}\pi r^2 h$

$= \dfrac{1}{3}\pi(9)^2(12) = 324\pi \text{ m}^3$

Number of minutes it takes to fill up the reservoir
= total volume ÷ rate of filling

$= 324\pi \text{ m}^3 \div 2.4 \text{ m}^3 / \text{min}$

$\approx 424.1 \text{ min}$

3. D

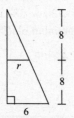

Let r = the radius of the smaller cone.
Since the bases are parallel, the proportion

$\dfrac{8}{r} = \dfrac{16}{6}$ can be used to find the radius of the

smaller cone. $\dfrac{8}{r} = \dfrac{16}{6} \implies r = 3$

Volume of the remaining bottom part
= volume of the cone − volume of the top part

$= \dfrac{1}{3}\pi(6)^2(16) - \dfrac{1}{3}\pi(3)^2(8) = 168\pi$

4. B

$$C = 2\pi r = 10 \implies r = \frac{10}{2\pi} = \frac{5}{\pi}$$

Volume of the cone

$$= \frac{1}{3}\pi r^2 h = \frac{1}{3}\pi(\frac{5}{\pi})^2(8) = \frac{200}{3\pi} \approx 21.2$$

Chapter 20 Practice Test

1. D

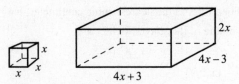

Volume of the rectangular prism

$$= (4x+3)(4x-3)(2x) = (16x^2-9)(2x)$$

Volume of the cube $= x^3$

Since the volume of the rectangular prisms is 30 times the volume of the cube, the equation $(16x^2-9)(2x) = 30x^3$ can be used to find the value of x.

$(16x^2-9)(2x)-30x^3 = 0$ Make one side 0.

$2x\left[(16x^2-9)-15x^2\right] = 0$ GCF is $2x$.

$2x(x^2-9) = 0$ Simplify.

$2x(x+3)(x-3) = 0$ Factor.

$x = 0$, $x = -3$, and $x = 3$

Since the dimension has to be positive, $x = 3$ is the correct answer.

2. A

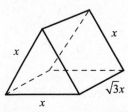

Area of the equilateral triangle with side length of x is $\frac{\sqrt{3}}{4}x^2$.

Volume of the triangular prism

$$= B \cdot h = \frac{\sqrt{3}}{4}x^2 \cdot \sqrt{3}x = \frac{3}{4}x^3$$

Since the volume of the prism is given as $\frac{81}{4}$,

the equation $\frac{3}{4}x^3 = \frac{81}{4}$ can be used to find the value of x.

$$\frac{3}{4}x^3 = \frac{81}{4} \implies 3x^3 = 81 \implies x^3 = 27$$

$$\implies x = \sqrt[3]{27} = 3$$

3. B

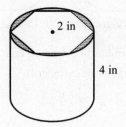

Area of the equilateral triangle with side length

of $2 = \frac{\sqrt{3}}{4}(2)^2 = \sqrt{3}$.

Area of the regular hexagon $= 6\sqrt{3}$.

Volume of the hexagonal prism $= 6\sqrt{3} \cdot 4 = 24\sqrt{3}$

Volume of the cylinder $= \pi(2)^2 \cdot 4 = 16\pi$

The volume of the waste generated by creating the hexagonal prism from the cylinder can be found by subtracting the volume of the hexagonal prism from the volume of the cylinder.

$$16\pi - 24\sqrt{3} \approx 8.69$$

The volume of the waste is about 9 cubic inches.

4. D

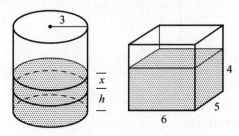

The volume of the cylinder with a radius of 3 and a height of x is $\pi(3)^2 x$, or $9\pi x$.

Volume of the water in the rectangular container is $6 \times 5 \times 4$, or 120.

To solve for x, let $9\pi x = 120$.

$$x = \frac{120}{9\pi} \approx 4.24$$

5. C

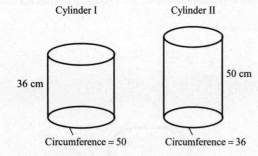

Cylinder I   Cylinder II

36 cm   50 cm

Circumference = 50   Circumference = 36

Let r_1 = the radius of cylinder I and let r_2 = the radius of cylinder II.

$$2\pi r_1 = 50 \implies r_1 = \frac{50}{2\pi} = \frac{25}{\pi}$$

$$2\pi r_2 = 36 \implies r_2 = \frac{36}{2\pi} = \frac{18}{\pi}$$

Volume of cylinder I

$$= \pi(r_1)^2 h = \pi(\frac{25}{\pi})^2(36) = \frac{22,500}{\pi}$$

Volume of cylinder II

$$= \pi(r_2)^2 h = \pi(\frac{18}{\pi})^2(50) = \frac{16,200}{\pi}$$

The difference of volume between the two cylinders is $\frac{22,500}{\pi} - \frac{16,200}{\pi} \approx 2,005.3$.

Choice C is correct.

6. C

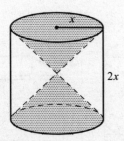

$2x$

Volume of the space inside the cylinder but outside the double cone = volume of the cylinder $-$ volume of the two cones.

$$\pi(x)^2(2x) - 2\left[\frac{1}{3}\pi(x)^2(x)\right]$$

$$= 2\pi x^3 - \frac{2}{3}\pi x^3 = \frac{4}{3}\pi x^3$$

7. 27

Surface area of the cube = $6s^2$
Since the surface area of the cube is given as 54 cm^2, $6s^2 = 54$.

$6s^2 = 54$ is simplified to $s^2 = 9$. Solving for s gives $s = 3$.
Volume of the cube = $s^3 = (3)^3 = 27$

8. 85

Volume of the cone = $\frac{1}{3}\pi(3)^2(10) = 30\pi$

Since the cone is 90 percent filled with shaved ice, the volume of the shaved ice is $30\pi \times 0.9$, or 27π cubic centimeters.

27π cm$^3 \approx 84.8$ cm^3

Therefore, to the nearest cubic centimeter, the volume of the shaved is 85 cm^3.

9. $\frac{16}{3}$ or 5.33

Let h = the height of the square pyramid.
Volume of the square pyramid

$$= \frac{1}{3}Bh = \frac{1}{3}(6)^2 h = 12h$$

Volume of the cube = $s^3 = (4)^3 = 64$

Since the square pyramid and the cube have equal volumes, $12h = 64$.

Solving for h gives $h = \frac{64}{12} = \frac{16}{3}$, or 5.33.

PSAT 10 Practice Test

Math Test – No Calculator

25 MINUTES, 17 QUESTIONS

Turn to Section 3 of your answer sheet to answer the questions in this section.

DIRECTIONS

For questions **1-13**, solve each problem, choose the best answer from the choices provided, and fill in the corresponding circle on your answer sheet. **For questions 14-17**, solve the problem and enter your answer in the grid on the answer sheet. Please refer to the directions before question 14 on how to enter your answers in the grid. You may use any available space in your test booklet for scratch work.

NOTES

1. The use of calculator **is not permitted**.

2. All variables and expressions used represent real numbers unless otherwise indicated.

3. Figures provided in this test are drawn to scale unless otherwise indicated.

4. All figures lie in a plane unless otherwise indicated.

5. Unless otherwise indicated, the domain of a given function f is the set of all real numbers x for which $f(x)$ is a real number.

REFERENCE

$A = \pi r^2$ $A = \ell w$ $A = \dfrac{1}{2}bh$ $c^2 = a^2 + b^2$ Special Right Triangles
$C = 2\pi r$

$V = \ell wh$ $V = \pi r^2 h$ $V = \dfrac{4}{3}\pi r^3$ $V = \dfrac{1}{3}\pi r^2 h$ $V = \dfrac{1}{3}\ell wh$

The number of degrees of arc in a circle is 360.
The number of radians of arc in a circle is 2π.
The sum of the measures in degrees of the angles of a triangle is 180.

CONTINUE ⟶

1

Number a is increased by the product of b and c. The result is divided by c and then decreased by b. Finally, that result is multiplied by c. Which of the following is the final result?

A) a

B) $a + bc - b$

C) $\dfrac{a}{c} + b - c$

D) $\dfrac{a}{c} + b - bc$

2

Jenny had m magazines to sell for her soccer team fundraiser. She sold j magazines on her own and her sister sold nine less than twice the amount Jenny sold. How many magazines remained unsold in terms of m and j?

A) $3j - 9 - m$

B) $3j + 9 - m$

C) $m - 3j - 9$

D) $m - 3j + 9$

3

$$\frac{y}{x} = 0.5$$
$$2(x - 3) = y$$

If (x, y) is the solution to the system of the equations above, what is the value of $x + y$?

A) 2

B) 4

C) 6

D) 8

4

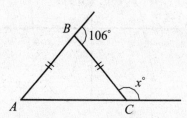

In the figure above, $AB = BC$. What is the value of x?

A) 113

B) 118

C) 123

D) 127

5

Which of the following is equivalent to
$(x^2y - 2xy^2 + 3xy) - 2(xy - xy^2 + x^2y)$?

A) $2x^2y + xy$

B) $-x^2y + xy$

C) $-x^2y + 4xy^2 + xy$

D) $2x^2y + 4xy^2 + xy$

6

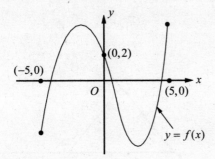

The graph of $f(x)$ is shown above for $-5 \le x \le 5$.
How many real solutions does $f(x) = 2$ have?

A) None

B) 1

C) 2

D) 3

7

$$3x^2 + 10x - 8 = 0$$

If r and s are two solutions of the equation above,
which of the following is the value of $r + s$?

A) $-\dfrac{10}{3}$

B) $-\dfrac{8}{3}$

C) $-\dfrac{5}{3}$

D) $-\dfrac{4}{3}$

8

The price of a backpack is b dollars, to which t
percent of sales tax is added at the counter. What
is the price of the backpack after tax in terms of b
and t ?

A) $b(1 + 0.01t)$ dollars

B) $b(1 + t)$ dollars

C) $(b + 0.01t)$ dollars

D) $(b + t)$ dollars

9

Perimeters and Areas of Rectangles

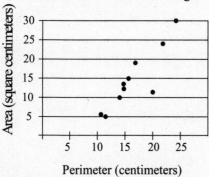

The scatter plot above shows the perimeters and areas of 10 rectangles. What is the perimeter, in centimeters, of the rectangle represented by the data point that is farthest from the line of best fit (not shown)?

A) 12

B) 17

C) 20

D) 23

10

If $(2x-3)(x-p) = 2x^2 - qx + 12$ for all values of x, what is the value of $p+q$?

A) 13

B) 15

C) 17

D) 19

Questions 11 and 12 refer to the following information.

Weekly Internet Use Time
Survey of 1,500 students

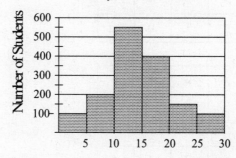

Number of Hours of Internet Use Each Week

A survey was taken to find the number of hours of internet use per week among 1,500 students.

11

Which of the following could be the median number of internet use time per week?

A) 9

B) 14

C) 16

D) 18

12

According to the histogram above, which of the following is the closest approximation of the percentage of students who use internet more than 15 hours each week?

A) 34%

B) 39%

C) 43%

D) 48%

13

Which of the following tables shows a relationship in which y is directly proportional to x?

A)

x	2	4	6
y	1	0	−1

B)

x	2	4	6
y	0	2	4

C)

x	2	4	6
y	6	9	12

D)

x	2	4	6
y	3	6	9

DIRECTIONS

For questions 14-17, solve the problem and enter your answer in the grid as described below, on the answer sheet.

1. Although not required, it is suggested that you write your answer in the boxes at the top of the columns to help you fill in the circles accurately. You will receive credit only if the circles are filled in correctly.

2. Mark no more than one circle in any column.

3. No question has a negative answer.

4. Some problems may have more than one correct answer. In such cases, grid only one answer.

5. **Mixed numbers** such as $3\frac{1}{2}$ must be gridded as 3.5 or $7/2$. (If $\boxed{3\,1\,/\,2}$ is entered into the grid, it will be interpreted as $\frac{31}{2}$ not $3\frac{1}{2}$.)

6. **Decimal answers:** If you obtain a decimal answer with more digits than the grid can accommodate, it may be either rounded or truncated, but it must fill the entire grid.

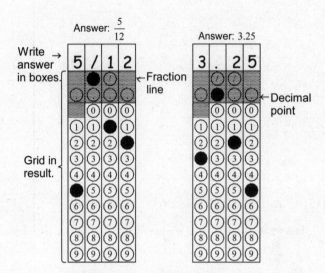

Answer: 212 - either position is correct.

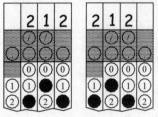

NOTE: You may start your answers in any column, space permitting. Columns you don't need to use should be left blank.

CONTINUE ➡

14

If $a = 5$ and $b = 3$, $(ac - 6) + a(b - c) =$

15

For what value of n is $n - |n - 7|$ equal to 0?

16

If x and y are positive integers, what is the value

of $\dfrac{3x^4 (2y)^2}{(2x^2 y)^2}$?

17

If $x + 3$ is a factor of $f(x) = ax^2 + bx - 15$,
in which a and b are constants, what is the
value of $3a - b$?

No Test Material On This Page

Math Test – Calculator

45 MINUTES, 31 QUESTIONS

Turn to Section 4 of your answer sheet to answer the questions in this section.

DIRECTIONS

For questions **1-27**, solve each problem, choose the best answer from the choices provided, and fill in the corresponding circle on your answer sheet. **For questions 28-31**, solve the problem and enter your answer in the grid on the answer sheet. Please refer to the directions before question 14 on how to enter your answers in the grid. You may use any available space in your test booklet for scratch work.

NOTES

1. The use of calculator **is not permitted**.

2. All variables and expressions used represent real numbers unless otherwise indicated.

3. Figures provided in this test are drawn to scale unless otherwise indicated.

4. All figures lie in a plane unless otherwise indicated.

5. Unless otherwise indicated, the domain of a given function f is the set of all real numbers x for which $f(x)$ is a real number.

REFERENCE

$A = \pi r^2$ $A = \ell w$ $A = \dfrac{1}{2}bh$ $c^2 = a^2 + b^2$ Special Right Triangles

$C = 2\pi r$

$V = \ell w h$ $V = \pi r^2 h$ $V = \dfrac{4}{3}\pi r^3$ $V = \dfrac{1}{3}\pi r^2 h$ $V = \dfrac{1}{3}\ell w h$

The number of degrees of arc in a circle is 360.
The number of radians of arc in a circle is 2π.
The sum of the measures in degrees of the angles of a triangle is 180.

CONTINUE ⟶

1

The total profit p, in dollars, from producing and selling x units of barbecue grill is given by the function $p(x) = kx - (b + 500)$, in which k and b are constants. When 120 barbecue grills were produced and sold, the total profit was $15,000 and when 200 barbecue grills were produced and sold, the total profit was $27,000. What is the value of b?

A) 1,850

B) 2,000

C) 2,250

D) 2,500

2

Arnold purchased a shirt and a pair of running shoes. The price of the shirt was s dollars and the price of the running shoes was 10 dollars less than twice the price of the shirt. He paid 8% tax for both the shoes and the shirt. If he paid 50% of the total purchase price with his debit card and paid the rest with cash, how much cash, in dollars, did he pay in terms of s?

A) $1.08s - 3.6$

B) $1.62s - 5.4$

C) $2.16s - 7.2$

D) $2.7s - 9$

3

A car traveled at an average speed of 65 miles per hour for 4 hours and consumed fuel at a rate of 32 miles per gallon. If the price of gasoline was $2.79 per gallon, what was the cost of gasoline, to the nearest cent, for the four hour trip?

A) $22.67

B) $24.74

C) $26.09

D) $27.32

4

x	-3	-1	1	3
$f(x)$	-1	0	1	2

The table above shows some values of the linear function f. Which of the following defines f?

A) $f(x) = -\dfrac{1}{2}x + \dfrac{1}{2}$

B) $f(x) = -\dfrac{1}{2}x - \dfrac{1}{2}$

C) $f(x) = \dfrac{1}{2}x + \dfrac{1}{2}$

D) $f(x) = \dfrac{1}{2}x - \dfrac{1}{2}$

Questions 5 and 6 refer to the following information.

$$A = \frac{180(n-2)}{n}$$

The formula above shows the relationship between A, the measure of each angle of a regular polygon, and n, the number of sides of a regular polygon.

5

Which of the following expresses the number of sides in terms of the measure of an angle?

A) $n = \dfrac{A - 180}{360}$

B) $n = \dfrac{A}{360} - 2$

C) $n = 180A - \dfrac{1}{2}$

D) $n = \dfrac{360}{180 - A}$

6

For which of the following number of sides will the measure of an angle be 144 degrees?

A) 6

B) 8

C) 10

D) 12

7

If $5 - n \geq 2$, what is the greatest possible value of $n + 2$?

A) 2

B) 3

C) 4

D) 5

8

$$\begin{cases} x - y < -2 \\ x + y \geq 1 \end{cases}$$

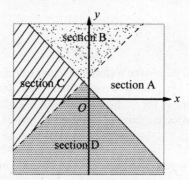

A graph and a system of inequalities are shown above. Which section of the graph could represent all of the solutions to the system?

A) Section A

B) Section B

C) Section C

D) Section D

9

A cubic meter of titanium weighs 4,540 kilograms. How much will 2,000 cubic centimeters of titanium weigh, in kilograms? (1 m = 100 cm)

A) 0.908

B) 9.08

C) 90.8

D) 908

10

When number n is divided by $\dfrac{2}{3}$, the result is the same as 6 less than $2n$. What is the value of $\dfrac{2}{3}n$?

A) 12

B) 10

C) 8

D) 6

Questions 11 and 12 refer to the following information.

Danny needs $450 to buy an iPad. He has already saved $120. He plans to earn the rest of the money by working at an office supply store. His savings can be modeled by the equation $y = 9.5x + 120$, in which x represents the number of hours he worked at the office supply store, and y represents his total savings.

11

Which of the following best describes the meaning of the number 9.5 in the equation?

A) The number of hours Danny works for the office supply store in one day.

B) The number of hours Danny works for the office supply store in one week.

C) The amount Danny get paid per day from the office supply store.

D) The amount Danny get paid per hour from the office supply store.

12

What is the minimum number of hours Danny needs to work at the office supply store to save enough money to buy an iPad?

A) 33 hours

B) 34 hours

C) 35 hours

D) 36 hours

13

If the average (arithmetic mean) of 2, a, and b is $2x$, what is the average of a and b in terms of x?

A) $2x-1$

B) $2x-2$

C) $3x-1$

D) $3x-2$

14

If a equals 120 percent of a number, then 40 percent of that number is

A) $\dfrac{1}{3}a$

B) $0.48a$

C) $3a$

D) $4.8a$

15

$$h = -4.9t^2 + 40t$$

The equation above expresses the height h, in meters, of an object t seconds after it is thrown into the air from the ground with an initial speed of 40 meters per second. After approximately how many seconds will the object reach its highest point?

A) 3

B) 4

C) 5

D) 6

16

The graph of a line on the xy- plane passes through points $(-3,1)$ and $(3,5)$. The graph of a second line contains the point $(6,0)$. If the two lines are parallel, what is the y- intercept of the second line?

A) -1

B) -2

C) -3

D) -4

17

The length and width of a large picture are respectively 18 inches and 12 inches. If each dimension is reduced by x inches to make the ratio of length to width 5 to 3, what is the value of x?

A) 6

B) 5

C) 4

D) 3

18

In a music store, 25% of the compact discs are classical. Out of these, 60% are on sale. If not more than 450 classical CDs are on sale, what could be the maximum number of CDs in the store?

A) 2,600

B) 2,800

C) 3,000

D) 3,200

19

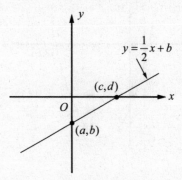

In the graph above, line $y = \dfrac{1}{2}x + b$ intersects the y-axis at point (a,b) and intersects the x-axis at point (c,d). If the value of b is equal to -3.5, what is the value of c?

A) 5.5

B) 7

C) 8.5

D) 10

20

If $y = kx^2$, in which k is a constant, and $y = -12$ when $x = -4$, what is the value of y when $x = 2$?

A) -6

B) -3

C) 3

D) 6

21

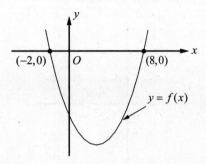

In the xy-plane above, $(-2,0)$ and $(8,0)$ are the two x-intercepts of the graph of f. If the minimum value of f is $-\dfrac{25}{2}$, which of the following is the y-intercept of the graph of f?

A) $(0,-8)$

B) $(0,-8\dfrac{1}{2})$

C) $(0,-9)$

D) $(0,-9\dfrac{1}{2})$

22

$$f(x) = -2(x^2 + 7x - 3) - a(x+2) + 1$$

In the polynomial $f(x)$ defined above, a is a constant. If $f(x)$ is divisible by x, what is the value of a?

A) $-\dfrac{5}{2}$

B) -3

C) $\dfrac{7}{2}$

D) 5

23

$$f(x) = \frac{1}{3}x - k$$

In the function above, k is a constant. If $f(-3) = k$, what is the value of $f(-\dfrac{3}{2})$?

A) -1

B) $-\dfrac{1}{2}$

C) 0

D) 1

24

The value V, in dollars, of an artist's painting t years after it was purchased is given by the function $V(t) = 5,000(4)^{\frac{t}{10}}$. What is the value, in dollars, of the painting 15 years after it was purchased?

A) $28,000$

B) $32,000$

C) $36,000$

D) $40,000$

25

A water tank in the shape of a rectangular prism has a base length of 6 meters and a base width of 4 meters. In the morning, 120 cubic meters of water from the tank was used for planting. In the afternoon, 125 percent more than the amount of water used in the morning was pumped into the tank. What is the increase in the height of the water after the water was pumped into the tank, in meters?

A) $1\frac{1}{4}$

B) $2\frac{3}{4}$

C) $4\frac{1}{2}$

D) $6\frac{1}{4}$

26

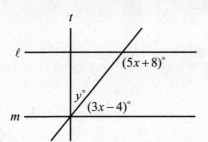

Note: Figure not drawn to scale.

In the figure above, $\ell \parallel m$ and $t \perp \ell$. What is the value of y?

A) 24

B) 28

C) 32

D) 36

27

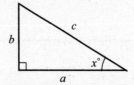

In the right triangle ABC above, which of the following must be true?

I. $\sin x° = \dfrac{b}{c}$

II. $\cos(90 - x)° = \dfrac{b}{c}$

III. $\sin(90 - x)° = \dfrac{b}{c}$

A) I only

B) II only

C) I and II only

D) I and III only

DIRECTIONS

For questions 28-31, solve the problem and enter your answer in the grid as described below, on the answer sheet.

1. Although not required, it is suggested that you write your answer in the boxes at the top of the columns to help you fill in the circles accurately. You will receive credit only if the circles are filled in correctly.

2. Mark no more than one circle in any column.

3. No question has a negative answer.

4. Some problems may have more than one correct answer. In such cases, grid only one answer.

5. **Mixed numbers** such as $3\frac{1}{2}$ must be gridded as 3.5 or $7/2$. (If $3\,1\,/\,2$ is entered into the grid, it will be interpreted as $\frac{31}{2}$ not $3\frac{1}{2}$.)

6. **Decimal answers:** If you obtain a decimal answer with more digits than the grid can accommodate, it may be either rounded or truncated, but it must fill the entire grid.

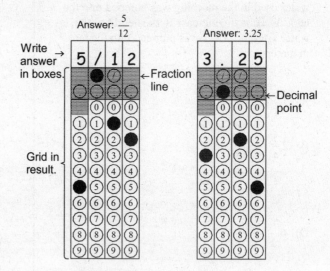

Answer: $\frac{5}{12}$

Write answer in boxes. ← Fraction line

Grid in result.

Answer: 3.25

← Decimal point

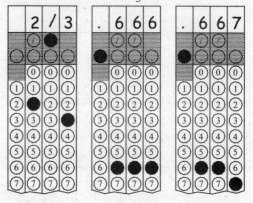

Acceptable ways to grid $\frac{2}{3}$ are:

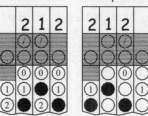

Answer: 212 - either position is correct.

NOTE: You may start your answers in any column, space permitting. Columns you don't need to use should be

CONTINUE ⟶

28

Derek paid $82 for one beanie and one mitten. If the beanie cost $8 more than the mitten, how much did Derek pay for the beanie?

29

If the slope of a line in the xy-plane that passes through the points $(\frac{1}{2}, -1)$ and $(2, b)$ is $\frac{8}{3}$, what is the value of b?

30

If x and y are positive integers, $x^2 - y^2 = \frac{8}{9}$, and $x^2 + 2xy + y^2 = \frac{16}{9}$, what is the value of $x - y$?

31

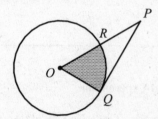

In the figure above, the radius of circle O is 3. The line segment $\overline{PQ}$ is tangent to circle O and $OR = RP$. If the area of the shaded region is $k\pi$, what is the value of k?

Answer Key

PSAT 10 Practice Test – No Calculator

1. A	2. D	3. C	4. D	5. B
6. D	7. A	8. A	9. C	10. B
11. B	12. C	13. D	14. 9	15. $\frac{7}{2}$ or 3.5
16. 3	17. 5			

PSAT 10 Practice Test – Calculator

1. D	2. B	3. A	4. C	5. D
6. C	7. D	8. B	9. B	10. A
11. D	12. C	13. C	14. A	15. B
16. D	17. D	18. C	19. B	20. B
21. A	22. C	23. C	24. D	25. D
26. B	27. C	28. 45	29. 3	30. $\frac{2}{3}$
31. $\frac{3}{2}$				

Answers and Explanations

PSAT 10 Practice Test – No Calculator

1. A

$a + b \cdot c$	Number a is increased by the product of b and c.
$\dfrac{a + b \cdot c}{c}$	The result is divided by c.
$\dfrac{a + b \cdot c}{c} - b$	Then decreased by b.
$(\dfrac{a + b \cdot c}{c} - b) \cdot c$	Finally, that result is multiplied by c.

Use distributive property to simplify the equation.

$$\frac{a + b \cdot c}{c} \cdot c - b \cdot c = a + b \cdot c - b \cdot c = a$$

The final result is a.

2. D

Jenny sold j magazines on her own and her sister sold $2j - 9$ magazines. So, they sold $j + (2j - 9)$, or $3j - 9$ magazines, together.

Therefore, there were $m - (3j - 9)$, or $m - 3j + 9$ magazines, that remained unsold.

3. C

$\dfrac{y}{x} = 0.5$	First equation
$2(x - 3) = y$	Second equation

Multiply each side of the first equation by x.

$$x(\frac{y}{x}) = (0.5)x \;\Rightarrow\; y = 0.5x$$

Substituting $0.5x$ for y in the second equation gives $2(x - 3) = 0.5x$.

$$2(x - 3) = 0.5x \;\Rightarrow\; 2x - 6 = 0.5x$$
$$\Rightarrow\; 1.5x = 6 \;\Rightarrow\; x = 4$$

Substituting 4 for x in the first equation gives $\dfrac{y}{4} = 0.5$, or $y = 2$. Therefore, the value of $x + y$ equals $4 + 2$, or 6.

4. D

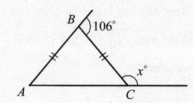

$m\angle BCA + x = 180$	Measure of straight $\angle$ equals 180.
$m\angle BCA = 180 - x$	Subtract x.
$AB = BC$	Given
$m\angle BAC = m\angle BCA$	Definition of isosceles $\triangle$.
$106 = m\angle BAC + m\angle BCA$	Exterior $\angle$ Theorem

Substituting $180 - x$ for $m\angle BCA$ and $m\angle BAC$ gives $106 = (180 - x) + (180 - x)$.

$$\Rightarrow\; 106 = 360 - 2x \;\Rightarrow\; 2x = 254 \;\Rightarrow\; x = 127$$

5. B

$$(x^2 y - 2xy^2 + 3xy) - 2(xy - xy^2 + x^2 y)$$
$$= x^2 y - 2xy^2 + 3xy - 2xy + 2xy^2 - 2x^2 y$$
$$= -x^2 y + xy$$

6. D

A real solution of a system of equations corresponds to a point of intersection of the graphs of the two equations on the xy-plane. The graph of $y = 2$ is a horizontal line that contains the point $(0, 2)$. Since the line $y = 2$ intersects $f(x)$ three times, $f(x) = 2$ has three real solutions.

7. A

If r and s are two solutions of the quadratic equation $ax^2 + bx + c = 0$, then $r + s = -\dfrac{b}{a}$.

Therefore, in the equation $3x^2 + 10x - 8 = 0$, the sum of the roots is $r + s = -\dfrac{10}{3}$.

8. A

t percent is equal to $\dfrac{1}{100}t$ or $0.01t$.

The price of a backpack is b dollars. After adding t percent tax, the price will be $b + b \cdot (0.01t) = b(1 + 0.01t)$.

9. C

In the scatter plot, the first coordinate represents the perimeter of the rectangle and the second coordinate represents the area of the rectangle. Since the data point that is farthest from the line of best fit is located at $(20, 12)$, the perimeter of the rectangle is 20.

10. B

$(2x - 3)(x - p) = 2x^2 - 2px - 3x + 3p$

$= 2x^2 - (2p + 3)x + 3p$

Thus, $2x^2 - (2p + 3)x + 3p = 2x^2 - qx + 12$.

Since the x-terms and constant terms have to be equal on both sides of the equation, $2p + 3 = q$ and $3p = 12$. Solving for p gives $p = 4$.

$q = 2p + 3 = 2(4) + 3 = 11$

Therefore, $p + q = 4 + 11 = 15$.

11. B

The median of a data set is the middle value when the data are arranged in order. Since there are 1,500 students, the middle value is the average of 750th and 751st value. There are 300 students who use internet 10 hours or less per week and there are 650 students who use internet 15 hours or more per week. So the median number should be between 10 and 15 hours per week. Therefore, of the choices given, only 14 could be the median number of internet use time in a week.

12. C

There are 650 students who use internet more than 15 hours each week. Therefore, the approximate percentage of students who use internet more than 15 hours each week is $\dfrac{650}{1500} = \dfrac{13}{30} \approx 0.43 = 43\%$.

13. D

A direct variation or a direction proportion is defined by an equation of the form $y = kx$.

Thus the graph of a direction proportion always contains the point $(0, 0)$.

Eliminate choices A and B because they do not contain the point $(0, 0)$.

Check answer choice C.

The graph contains $(2, 6)$, $(4, 9)$, and $(6, 12)$.

Substituting $x = 2$ and $y = 6$ in the equation $y = kx$ yields $6 = k(3)$ or $k = 2$. Rewrite the equation as $y = 2x$. Substitute $x = 4$ and $y = 9$ in the equation $y = 2x$. $9 = 2(4)$ is not a true equation. Therefore, choice C is not correct.

Check answer choice D.

The graph contains $(2, 3)$, $(4, 6)$, and $(6, 9)$.

Substituting $x = 2$ and $y = 3$ in the equation $y = kx$ yields $3 = k(2)$ or $k = 1.5$. Rewrite the equation as $y = 1.5x$. Substitute $x = 4$ and $y = 6$ in the equation $y = 1.5x$. $6 = 4(1.5)$ is true. Substitute $x = 6$ and $y = 9$ in the equation $y = 1.5x$. $9 = 6(1.5)$ is also true.

Choice D is correct.

14. 9

$(ac - 6) + a(b - c) = ac - 6 + ab - ac$

$= -6 + ab$

Substitute $a = 5$ and $b = 3$.

$-6 + ab = -6 + (5)(3) = -6 + 15 = 9$

15. $\dfrac{7}{2}$

$n - |n - 7| = 0$

$n = |n - 7|$

If $n = |n - 7|$, then $n = n - 7$ or $n = -(n - 7)$.

If $n = n - 7$, the equation simplifies to $0 = -7$, which does not have a solution. If $n = -(n - 7)$,

$n = -n + 7 \Rightarrow 2n = 7 \Rightarrow n = \dfrac{7}{2}$.

16. 3

$$\frac{3x^4(2y)^2}{(2x^2y)^2} = \frac{3x^4 \cdot 4y^2}{4x^4y^2} = \frac{12x^4y^2}{4x^4y^2} = 3$$

17. 5

If $x+3$ is a factor of $f(x) = ax^2 + bx - 15$, then $f(-3) = 0$.

$$f(-3) = a(-3)^2 + b(-3) - 15 = 0$$

$9a - 3b - 15 = 0$	Simplify.
$9a - 3b = 15$	Add 15 to each side.
$3(3a - b) = 15$	Factor.
$3a - b = \dfrac{15}{3} = 5$	Divide each side by 3.

PSAT 10 Practice Test – Calculator

1. D

$$p(x) = kx - (b + 500)$$
$$15,000 = k(120) - (b + 500) \quad p = 15,000,\ x = 120$$
$$27,000 = k(200) - (b + 500) \quad p = 27,000,\ x = 200$$

Subtracting the first equation from the second equation, one can get $12,000 = k(80)$, which yields $150 = k$.

Substitute 150 for k in the first equation.

$$15,000 = (150)(120) - (b + 500)$$
$$15,000 = 18,000 - (b + 500)$$
$$15,000 = 17,500 - b$$
$$b = 2,500$$

2. B

If the price of the shirt was s dollars, then the price of the running shoes was $(2s - 10)$ dollars.

$s + (2s - 10)$	Total amount before tax
$3s - 10$	Simplify.
$3s - 10 + 0.08(3s - 10)$	Total amount after 8% tax
$3s - 10 + 0.24s - 0.8$	Distributive property
$3.24s - 10.8$	Simplify.

If he paid 50% of $3.24s - 10.8$ with cash, then the amount in terms of s is $1.62s - 5.4$.

3. A

The total distance he traveled in 4 hours is 65×4, or 260 miles. The number of gasoline consumed was $260 \div 32$, or 8.125 gallons. Therefore, the cost of gasoline was $8.125 \times \$2.79$, or $\$22.67$ to the nearest cent.

4. C

Use two points, $(-1, 0)$ and $(1, 1)$ on the graph to find the slope of f.

$$\text{slope} = \frac{y_2 - y_1}{x_2 - x_1} = \frac{1 - 0}{1 - (-1)} = \frac{1}{2}$$

Eliminate choices A and B because they have incorrect slopes.
Now check the other answer choices with the points $(-1, 0)$ and $(1, 1)$ on the graph.

Check the equation $f(x) = \dfrac{1}{2}x + \dfrac{1}{2}$ in choice C.

$$0 = \frac{1}{2}(-1) + \frac{1}{2} \qquad x = -1 \text{ and } y = 0$$
$$1 = \frac{1}{2}(1) + \frac{1}{2} \qquad x = 1 \text{ and } y = 1$$

Since both equations are true, choice C is correct.

Points $(-1, 0)$ and $(1, 1)$ are not on the graph of $f(x) = \dfrac{1}{2}x - \dfrac{1}{2}$ in choice D,

5. D

$$A = \frac{180(n-2)}{n}$$

$n \cdot A = n \cdot \dfrac{180(n-2)}{n}$	Multiply each side by n.
$nA = 180(n-2)$	Simplify.
$nA = 180n - 360$	Distributive Property
$nA - 180n = -360$	Subtract $180n$.
$n(A - 180) = -360$	Factor.
$n = \dfrac{-360}{A - 180}$	Divide each side by $A - 180$.
$n = \dfrac{(-1)(-360)}{(-1)(A - 180)}$	Multiply by -1.
$n = \dfrac{360}{180 - A}$	$-(A - 180) = 180 - A$

6. C

$$n = \frac{360}{180 - A}$$
$$n = \frac{360}{180 - 144} \qquad A = 144$$
$$n = \frac{360}{36} = 10$$

7. D

$5 - n \geq 2$

$5 - n - 5 \geq 2 - 5$ Subtract 5 from each side.

$-n \geq -3$ Simplify.

$(-1)(-n) \leq (-1)(-3)$ Multiply each side by -1 and change $\geq$ to $\leq$.

$n \leq 3$

$n + 2 \leq 3 + 2$ Add 2 to each side.

$n + 2 \leq 5$

Thus, the greatest possible value of $n + 2$ is 5.

8. B

$$\begin{cases} x - y < -2 \\ x + y \geq 1 \end{cases}$$

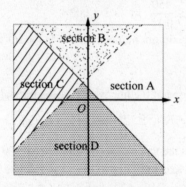

The solution set of the inequality $x - y < -2$ is the union of sections B and C of the graph. The solution set of the inequality $x + y \geq 1$ is the union of sections A and B of the graph. Therefore, section B of the graph represents all of the solutions to the system.

9. B

$1 \text{ m} = 100 \text{ cm}$

$(1 \text{ m})^3 = (100 \text{ cm})^3$ Cube each side.

$1 \text{ m}^3 = 1,000,000 \text{ cm}^3$ Simplify.

Let 2,000 cubic centimeters of titanium weigh x kilograms. Set up a proportion.

$$\frac{1 \text{ m}^3}{4540 \text{ kg}} = \frac{2000 \text{ cm}^3}{x \text{ kg}}$$

$$\frac{1,000,000 \text{ cm}^3}{4540 \text{ kg}} = \frac{2000 \text{ cm}^3}{x \text{ kg}}$$ $1 \text{ m}^3 = 1,000,000 \text{ cm}^3$

$1,000,000x = 4540 \times 2000$ Cross multiply.

$$x = \frac{4540 \times 2000}{1,000,000} = 9.08$$

2,000 cubic centimeters of titanium weigh 9.08 kilograms.

10. A

When number n is divided by $\dfrac{2}{3}$, the result is 6 less than $2n$.

The equation is $n \div \dfrac{2}{3} = 2n - 6$.

$n \times \dfrac{3}{2} = 2n - 6$ Rewrite as multiplication by the reciprocal.

$2(n \times \dfrac{3}{2}) = 2(2n - 6)$ Multiply each side by 2.

$3n = 4n - 12$ Simplify.

$-n = -12$ Subtract $4n$.

$n = 12$

11. D

In the equation $y = 9.5x + 120$, x represents the number of hours Danny worked, y represents his total savings, and 120 is the amount he already saved. Each time x increases by 1, y increases by 9.5, which is the amount Danny gets paid per hour from the office supply store.

Choice D is correct.

12. C

Danny needs $450 to buy an iPad. Therefore, the number of hours he needs to work to get enough money for one iPad can be found by solving the inequality $y = 9.5x + 120 \geq 450$.

$9.5x + 120 - 120 \geq 450 - 120$ Subtract 120.

$9.5x \geq 330$ Simplify.

$$x \geq \frac{330}{9.5} \approx 34.7$$

Therefore, the minimum number of hours he needs to work to save enough money for an iPad is 35 hours.

13. C

If the average of 2, a, and b is $2x$, the equation $2x = \dfrac{2 + a + b}{3}$ is true.

$3 \cdot 2x = 3 \cdot \dfrac{2 + a + b}{3}$ Multiply each side by 3.

$6x = 2 + a + b$ Simplify.

$6x - 2 = a + b$ Solve the equation for $a + b$.

The average of a and b is $\dfrac{a + b}{2}$. Substituting $6x - 2$ for $a + b$ yields $\dfrac{a + b}{2} = \dfrac{6x - 2}{2} = 3x - 1$.

14. A

Let the number $= n$.

$$\underset{a\ \text{equals}}{\underbrace{a\ =}}\ \underset{120\%}{\underbrace{1.2}}\ \underset{\text{of}\ n}{\underbrace{\times n}}$$

$a = 1.2n$

$\dfrac{a}{1.2} = n$ \qquad Solve for n.

40% of n is $0.4n$. Substituting $\dfrac{a}{1.2}$

for n yields $0.4n = 0.4(\dfrac{a}{1.2}) = \dfrac{1}{3}a$.

15. B

The quadratic equation $y = ax^2 + bx + c$ has its

maximum or minimum at $x = -\dfrac{b}{2a}$. Since the

leading coefficient of h is negative, h has its

maximum at $t = -\dfrac{40}{2(-4.9)} \approx 4.08$. Therefore,

the object reaches its highest point about
4 seconds after it is thrown.

16. D

The slope of the first line is $\dfrac{5-1}{3-(-3)} = \dfrac{2}{3}$.

If the two lines are parallel, their slopes are equal.

Thus, the slope of the second line is $\dfrac{2}{3}$ and it

contains $(6, 0)$.

$y = mx + b$ \qquad Slope-intercept form

$y = \dfrac{2}{3}x + b$ \qquad $m = \dfrac{2}{3}$

$0 = \dfrac{2}{3}(6) + b$ \qquad The line contains $(6, 0)$.

$0 = 4 + b$ \qquad Simplify.

$-4 = b$

Therefore the equation of the second line is

$y = \dfrac{2}{3}x - 4$ and the y-intercept is -4.

17. D

If each dimension of the large picture is reduced
by x inches, the new length will be $18 - x$ and the
new width will be $12 - x$. Since the ratio of new

length to new width is 5 to 3, $\dfrac{18-x}{12-x} = \dfrac{5}{3}$.

$3(18 - x) = 5(12 - x)$ \qquad Cross Products

$54 - 3x = 60 - 5x$ \qquad Distributive Property

$54 - 3x + 5x = 60 - 5x + 5x$ \qquad Add $5x$ to each side.

$54 + 2x = 60$ \qquad Simplify.

$2x = 6$ \qquad Subtract 54.

$x = 3$

18. C

Let $x =$ the total number of CDs in the store.
Then $0.25x =$ the number of classical CDs.
Since 60% of these classical CDs are on sale,
$0.25x \times 0.6$ are on sale. Since that number
is not more than 450, the inequality
$0.25x \times 0.6 \le 450$ must be true.

$0.25x \times 0.6 \le 450 \ \Rightarrow\ 0.15x \le 450$

$\Rightarrow\ x \le \dfrac{450}{0.15} \ \Rightarrow\ x \le 3{,}000$

The maximum number of CDs in the store is 3,000.

19. B

The slope of the line which passes through (a, b)

and (c, d) is $\dfrac{d - b}{c - a}$, which is equal to $\dfrac{1}{2}$. On the

x-axis the value of the y-coordinate is 0 and on
the y-axis the value of the x-coordinate is 0.
Therefore, $a = d = 0$. Also $b = -3.5$ is given.
Substitute these values in the slope equation.

$\dfrac{d - b}{c - a} = \dfrac{1}{2} \ \Rightarrow\ \dfrac{0 - (-3.5)}{c - 0} = \dfrac{1}{2}$

$\Rightarrow\ \dfrac{3.5}{c} = \dfrac{1}{2} \ \Rightarrow\ c = 7$

20. B

$y = kx^2$

$-12 = k(-4)^2$ \qquad $y = -12$ when $x = -4$

$-12 = 16k$

$-\dfrac{3}{4} = k$

$y = -\dfrac{3}{4}x^2$ \qquad Replace k with $-\dfrac{3}{4}$.

$y = -\dfrac{3}{4}(2)^2$ \qquad $x = 2$

$y = -3$

21. A

Since we know the two x-intercepts of the graph
of f, it is easier to start with the factored form of
a quadratic function.

The two x-intercepts are $(-2,0)$ and $(8,0)$, so the equation of f can be written as $y = a(x+2)(x-8)$, in which a is a constant. Since the x-coordinate of the vertex is the average of the two x-intercepts, $x = \dfrac{-2+8}{2} = 3$ is the x-coordinate of the vertex. The y-coordinate of the vertex is the minimum value of f, which is $-\dfrac{25}{2}$. In the equation $y = a(x+2)(x-8)$, substitute $x = 3$ and $y = -\dfrac{25}{2}$ to find the value of a.

$-\dfrac{25}{2} = a(3+2)(3-8)$ gives $a = \dfrac{1}{2}$. So the equation of f is $y = \dfrac{1}{2}(x+2)(x-8)$. To find the y-intercept of the graph of f, substitute 0 for x. $y = \dfrac{1}{2}(0+2)(0-8) = -8$.

Therefore, the y-intercept is $(0,-8)$.

22. C

If a polynomial $f(x)$ is divisible by x, then x is a factor of the polynomial. However, this is true only if the constant term of f is zero. Simplifying the equation gives

$f(x) = -2x^2 - 14x + 6 - ax - 2a + 1$
$\qquad = -2x^2 - (14+a)x + 7 - 2a$.

$7 - 2a = 0$
$-2a = -7$
$a = \dfrac{7}{2}$

23. C

$f(x) = \dfrac{1}{3}x - k$

$f(-3) = \dfrac{1}{3}(-3) - k = k$

$\Rightarrow -1 - k = k$

$\Rightarrow -\dfrac{1}{2} = k$

Therefore, $f(x) = \dfrac{1}{3}x + \dfrac{1}{2}$ and

$f(-\dfrac{3}{2}) = \dfrac{1}{3}(-\dfrac{3}{2}) + \dfrac{1}{2} = 0$

24. D

$V(t) = 5,000(4)^{\frac{t}{10}}$

$V(15) = 5,000(4)^{\frac{15}{10}} = 5,000(4)^{1.5} = 40,000$

25. D

In the morning, 120 cubic meters of water from the tank was used for planting. In the afternoon, 125 percent more than the amount of water used in the morning was pumped into the tank, which is $120 + 1.25 \times 120$, or 270 cubic meters.

Let $h =$ the increase in the height of the water, in meters, after the water was pumped into the tank.
$6 \times 4 \times h = 270 - 120$, so solving the equation for h gives $h = 6\dfrac{1}{4}$.

26. B

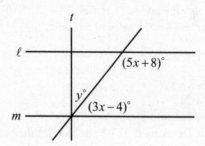

Note: Figure not drawn to scale.

If two line are parallel, consecutive interior angles are supplementary.
$(5x+8) + (3x-4) = 180$ $\qquad$ $\ell \parallel m$
$8x + 4 = 180$ $\qquad$ Simplify.
$8x = 176$
$x = 22$

In a plane, if a line is perpendicular to one of two parallel lines, it is also perpendicular to the other. Thus, $t \perp m$ and $y + (3x-4) = 90$.

$y + (3 \times 22 - 4) = 90$ $\qquad$ $x = 22$
$y + 62 = 90$ $\qquad$ Simplify.
$y = 28$

27. C

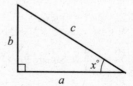

I. $\sin x° = \dfrac{\text{opposite side to angle } x}{\text{hypotenuse}} = \dfrac{b}{c}$

Roman numeral I is true.

II. $(90 - x)°$ is the angle between the sides c and b.

$\cos(90 - x)°$
$= \dfrac{\text{adjacent side to angle } (90 - x)}{\text{hypotenuse}} = \dfrac{b}{c}$

Roman numeral II is true.

III. $\sin(90 - x)°$
$= \dfrac{\text{opposite side to angle } (90 - x)}{\text{hypotenuse}} = \dfrac{a}{c}$

Roman numeral III is not true.

Choice C is correct.

28. 45

Let $m =$ the price of a mitten.
Then $m + 8 =$ the price of a beanie.

$m + (m + 8) = 82$ The cost of one beanie and one mitten is \$82.
$2m + 8 = 82$ Simplify.
$2m = 74$
$m = 37$

Thus, Derek paid $37 + 8$, or \$45, for the beanie.

29. 3

$\text{Slope} = \dfrac{y_2 - y_1}{x_2 - x_1} = \dfrac{b - (-1)}{2 - \dfrac{1}{2}} = \dfrac{b + 1}{\dfrac{3}{2}} = \dfrac{2}{3}(b + 1)$

Therefore, $\dfrac{2}{3}(b + 1) = \dfrac{8}{3}$.

$\dfrac{3}{2} \cdot \dfrac{2}{3}(b + 1) = \dfrac{3}{2} \cdot \dfrac{8}{3}$ Multiply each side by $\dfrac{3}{2}$.

$b + 1 = 4$ Simplify.
$b = 3$

30. $\dfrac{2}{3}$

$x^2 + 2xy + y^2 = \dfrac{16}{9}$

$(x + y)^2 = \dfrac{16}{9}$ Factor.

$x + y = \pm\sqrt{\dfrac{16}{9}} = \pm\dfrac{4}{3}$ Square Root Property

Since x and y are positive integers, $x + y = \dfrac{4}{3}$.

$x^2 - y^2 = \dfrac{8}{9}$

$(x + y)(x - y) = \dfrac{8}{9}$ Factor.

$\dfrac{4}{3}(x - y) = \dfrac{8}{9}$ $x + y = \dfrac{4}{3}$

$\dfrac{3}{4} \cdot \dfrac{4}{3}(x - y) = \dfrac{3}{4} \cdot \dfrac{8}{9}$ Multiply each side by $\dfrac{3}{4}$.

$x - y = \dfrac{2}{3}$

31. $\dfrac{3}{2}$

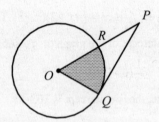

If a line is tangent to a circle, then the line is perpendicular to the radius at the point of tangency. Therefore, $\overline{PQ} \perp \overline{OQ}$ and $\triangle OPQ$ is a right triangle. If $OR = RP = 3$, then $OP = OR + RP = 3 + 3 = 6$.

If a right triangle has a hypotenuse that is twice as long as the shorter leg, then it is a $30°$-$60°$-$90°$ triangle. Thus $m\angle POQ = 60$.

Area of sector $ROQ = \pi r^2 \times \dfrac{m\angle ROQ}{360}$

$= \pi(3)^2 \times \dfrac{60}{360} = 9\pi \times \dfrac{1}{6} = \dfrac{3}{2}\pi$

If the area of the shaded region is $k\pi$, then

$k = \dfrac{3}{2}$.

SAT Practice Test 1

Math Test – No Calculator

25 MINUTES, 20 QUESTIONS

Turn to Section 3 of your answer sheet to answer the questions in this section.

DIRECTIONS

For questions **1-15**, solve each problem, choose the best answer from the choices provided, and fill in the corresponding circle on your answer sheet. **For questions 16-20**, solve the problem and enter your answer in the grid on the answer sheet. Please refer to the directions before question 16 on how to enter your answers in the grid. You may use any available space in your test booklet for scratch work.

NOTES

1. The use of calculator **is not permitted**.

2. All variables and expressions used represent real numbers unless otherwise indicated.

3. Figures provided in this test are drawn to scale unless otherwise indicated.

4. All figures lie in a plane unless otherwise indicated.

5. Unless otherwise indicated, the domain of a given function f is the set of all real numbers x for which $f(x)$ is a real number.

REFERENCE

$A = \pi r^2$ $A = \ell w$ $A = \dfrac{1}{2}bh$ $c^2 = a^2 + b^2$ Special Right Triangles
$C = 2\pi r$

$V = \ell wh$ $V = \pi r^2 h$ $V = \dfrac{4}{3}\pi r^3$ $V = \dfrac{1}{3}\pi r^2 h$ $V = \dfrac{1}{3}\ell wh$

The number of degrees of arc in a circle is 360.
The number of radians of arc in a circle is 2π.
The sum of the measures in degrees of the angles of a triangle is 180.

CONTINUE

1

If $f(x) = \dfrac{1}{2}x - 1$, what is $f(-2x+1)$ equal to?

A) $-x - \dfrac{1}{2}$

B) $-x + \dfrac{1}{2}$

C) $x - \dfrac{1}{2}$

D) $x + \dfrac{1}{2}$

2

If $x = 1 - \dfrac{a}{b}$, which of the following is

equivalent to $\dfrac{1}{x}$?

A) $\dfrac{b}{1+a}$

B) $\dfrac{b}{1-a}$

C) $\dfrac{b-1}{a}$

D) $\dfrac{b}{b-a}$

3

$$\frac{1}{2}(16 - 4x) = nx + 8 + 3x$$

If the linear equation above is an identity, what is the value of n?

A) -5

B) -3

C) -1

D) 3

4

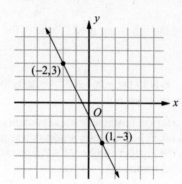

Which of the following equations represents a line that is parallel to the line shown above and contains

the point $(\dfrac{1}{2}, 3)$?

A) $y = x + \dfrac{5}{2}$

B) $y = -x + \dfrac{7}{2}$

C) $y = -2x + 4$

D) $y = -2x + 6$

Questions 5 and 6 refer to the following information.

AP Tests Taken by High School Seniors

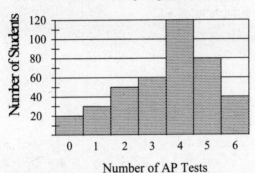

Number of AP Tests

The graph above depicts a survey of 400 senior students in a high school who took the AP tests last May. The number of AP tests taken by each student ranges from zero to six.

5

Which of the following is NOT true of the survey results?

A) The mode of the number of AP tests taken by each student was 4.

B) The average (arithmetic mean) number of AP tests taken by the senior students was greater than the median number of AP tests taken by the senior students.

C) The average (arithmetic mean) number of AP tests taken by the senior students was equal to the median number of AP tests taken by the senior students.

D) The average (arithmetic mean) number of AP tests taken by the senior students was less than the median number of AP tests taken by the senior students.

6

By what percent is the number of senior students who took 4 AP tests greater than the number of senior students who took 3 AP tests?

A) 50%

B) 75%

C) 100%

D) 200%

7

$$x + y < a$$
$$x - y > b$$

In the xy-plane, if $(0,1)$ is the solution to the system of inequalities above, which of the following relationships between a and b must be true?

A) $|a| < |b|$

B) $|a| > |b|$

C) $a - b < 2$

D) $a - b > 2$

8

Which of the following complex numbers is equivalent to $\dfrac{(1+i)^2}{1-i}$? (Note: $i = \sqrt{-1}$)

A) $-1 - i$

B) $-1 + i$

C) $1 - i$

D) $1 + i$

9

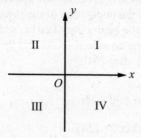

If the system of inequalities $2 - y < 2x$ and $-x \le 4 - y$ is graphed in the xy-plane above, which quadrant contains no solutions to the system?

A) Quadrant II

B) Quadrant III

C) Quadrant IV

D) There are solutions in all four quadrants.

10

A certain company produces d diskettes every m minutes. Which of the following is the number of diskettes produced in h hours, in terms of d, m, and h?

A) $\dfrac{60dh}{m}$

B) $\dfrac{60dm}{h}$

C) $\dfrac{60mh}{d}$

D) $\dfrac{dh}{60m}$

11

$$y = 2x^2 - 11x - 6$$

The equation above represents a parabola in the xy-plane. Which of the following equivalent forms of the equation displays the x-intercepts of the parabola as constants or coefficients?

A) $y = (2x - 3)(x + 2)$

B) $y = (2x + 1)(x - 6)$

C) $y = 2(x - \dfrac{11}{4})^2 - \dfrac{169}{8}$

D) $y = 2(x - \dfrac{11}{2})^2 - \dfrac{133}{4}$

12

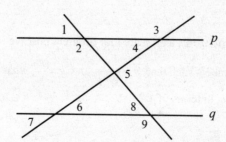

In the figure above, line p is parallel to line q. Which of the following must be true?

I. $m\angle 2 = m\angle 9$

II. $m\angle 2 + m\angle 4 = 180$

III. $m\angle 4 + m\angle 8 = m\angle 5$

A) I only

B) I and II only

C) I and III only

D) I, II, and III

13

At a coffee shop, a customer bought 10 bags of Arabian Mocha and Kona coffee. A bag of Arabian Mocha costs $18 and a bag of Kona coffee costs $28. If x is the number of bags of Arabian Mocha and the customer paid d dollars for the Arabian Mocha and Kona coffee, which of the following represents x in terms of d?

A) $x = 28 - 0.1d$

B) $x = 28 + 0.1d$

C) $x = 18 - 0.1d$

D) $x = 18 + 0.1d$

14

If p, q, r, and s are four different positive numbers such that $p = \dfrac{r}{s-r}$ and $q = \dfrac{r}{s}$, what is q in terms of s?

A) $1 + \dfrac{1}{p}$

B) $1 - \dfrac{1}{p}$

C) $\dfrac{1}{1+p}$

D) $\dfrac{p}{1+p}$

15

The population of a certain town doubles every 24 years. If the population of the town was 140,000 at the beginning of 2016, which of the following equations represents the population, P, t years after 2016?

A) $P = 140,000 + 24t$

B) $P = 140,000 + (24)^t$

C) $P = 140,000(2)^{\frac{t}{24}}$

D) $P = 140,000 \cdot \dfrac{(2)^t}{24}$

DIRECTIONS

For questions 16-20, solve the problem and enter your answer in the grid as described below, on the answer sheet.

1. Although not required, it is suggested that you write your answer in the boxes at the top of the columns to help you fill in the circles accurately. You will receive credit only if the circles are filled in correctly.

2. Mark no more than one circle in any column.

3. No question has a negative answer.

4. Some problems may have more than one correct answer. In such cases, grid only one answer.

5. **Mixed numbers** such as $3\frac{1}{2}$ must be gridded as 3.5 or $7/2$. (If ⊡ is entered into the grid, it will be interpreted as $\frac{31}{2}$ not $3\frac{1}{2}$.)

6. **Decimal answers:** If you obtain a decimal answer with more digits than the grid can accommodate, it may be either rounded or truncated, but it must fill the entire grid.

Answer: $\frac{5}{12}$

Answer: 3.25

Write answer in boxes. ←Fraction line

Grid in result.

←Decimal point

Acceptable ways to grid $\frac{2}{3}$ are:

Answer: 212 - either position is correct.

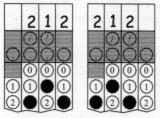

NOTE: You may start your answers in any column, space permitting. Columns you don't need to use should be left blank.

CONTINUE ⇒

16

$$-7 + a = 3$$

Given the above equation, what is the value of $10 - [(a-3)-7]$?

17

Three is subtracted from two thirds of the number k and the difference is doubled. If the result is ten more than one third of the number, what is the value of k ?

18

$$6x + ky = 3$$
$$y = 1 - 2x$$

For what value of k will the system of equations above have infinitely many solutions?

19

If $\dfrac{-2x^2 + 5x + 10}{-x + 4} = 2x + 3 - \dfrac{A}{-x + 4}$, what is the value of A ?

20

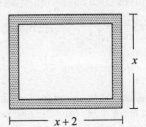

A rectangular picture, represented by the unshaded region in the figure above, is mounted in a rectangular frame, represented by the shaded region. The frame is 1 inch wide on all sides. For what value of x , in inches, is the area of the picture twice the area of the frame?

No Test Material On This Page

Math Test – Calculator

55 MINUTES, 38 QUESTIONS

Turn to Section 4 of your answer sheet to answer the questions in this section.

DIRECTIONS

For questions **1-30**, solve each problem, choose the best answer from the choices provided, and fill in the corresponding circle on your answer sheet. **For questions 31-38**, solve the problem and enter your answer in the grid on the answer sheet. Please refer to the directions before question 14 on how to enter your answers in the grid. You may use any available space in your test booklet for scratch work.

NOTES

1. The use of calculator **is not permitted**.

2. All variables and expressions used represent real numbers unless otherwise indicated.

3. Figures provided in this test are drawn to scale unless otherwise indicated.

4. All figures lie in a plane unless otherwise indicated.

5. Unless otherwise indicated, the domain of a given function f is the set of all real numbers x for which $f(x)$ is a real number.

REFERENCE

$A = \pi r^2$
$C = 2\pi r$

$A = \ell w$

$A = \dfrac{1}{2}bh$

$c^2 = a^2 + b^2$

Special Right Triangles

$V = \ell wh$

$V = \pi r^2 h$

$V = \dfrac{4}{3}\pi r^3$

$V = \dfrac{1}{3}\pi r^2 h$

$V = \dfrac{1}{3}\ell wh$

The number of degrees of arc in a circle is 360.
The number of radians of arc in a circle is 2π.
The sum of the measures in degrees of the angles of a triangle is 180.

CONTINUE ▷

1

One number is 4 times the value of another number. If their sum is -15, what is the value of the smaller of the two numbers?

A) -12

B) -9

C) -6

D) -3

2

Year	Profits
2010	108,000
2011	320,000
2012	415,000
2013	576,000
2014	842,000
2015	1,160,000

The profits of an electronic company during the six years of its operation are given in the table above. Which of the following best approximates the average rate of change of the profits from 2010 to 2015?

A) $180,000 per year

B) $210,000 per year

C) $250,000 per year

D) $280,000 per year

3

If $f(x) = \sqrt{x} + 2$ and $g(x) = (x-1)^2$, which of the following is equivalent to $g(f(a)) - 2f(a)$?

A) $\sqrt{a} + 2$

B) $\sqrt{a} - 1$

C) $a + 4$

D) $a - 3$

4

Which of the following systems of equations has no solution?

A) $\dfrac{1}{5}x + \dfrac{1}{3}y = 1$

$3x - 5y = 15$

B) $4x + 3y = 12$

$3x - 4y = 6$

C) $-3x + 2y = 7$

$\dfrac{1}{2}x - \dfrac{1}{3}y = 3$

D) $-x + 2y = 1$

$2x - 4y = -2$

5

A line in the xy- plane passes through the origin and has a slope of $-\dfrac{3}{4}$. Which of the following points does NOT lie on the line?

A) $(2, -\dfrac{3}{2})$

B) $(-4, 3)$

C) $(8, -3)$

D) $(0, 0)$

6

	Distance to Finish Line (meters)
Mike	$-12t + 1500$
Maria	$-10.5t + 1500$

Mike and Maria race on a 1500-meter course with their bikes. The expressions in the table above show the distance to the finish line t seconds after they started the race. How many meters will Maria have left to bike when Mike completes the course?

A) 165

B) 187.5

C) 210

D) 232.5

7

x	$f(x)$
−4	−10.5
−2	2.5
1	−8
2	7.5

The function f is defined by a polynomial. Some values of x and $f(x)$ are shown in the table above. What is the remainder when $f(x)$ is divided by $x + 2$?

A) −10.5

B) −8

C) 2.5

D) 7.5

8

A thermos holds 2 quarts of liquid. If $\dfrac{1}{2}$ tablespoon of ground coffee makes 4 cups of coffee, how many thermoses can be filled with the coffee made from 3 tablespoons of ground coffee?
(1 quart = 4 cups)

A) 8

B) 6

C) 4

D) 3

Questions 9 and 10 refer to the following information.

The manufacturer of a cable company sells cable for $30 per foot. The cost, C, of producing x feet of cable is $C = 12.5x + 210$. The company makes a profit when the amount of money received from selling the cable is greater than the cost of producing the cable.

9

Which of the following inequalities gives all possible values of x for which the company will make a profit?

A) $x > 12$

B) $x > 14.4$

C) $x > 16$

D) $x > 18.6$

10

What is the profit that the company could earn from the sale of 50 feet of cable?

A) $620.00

B) $635.00

C) $650.00

D) $665.00

11

Alice and Bernie both own orchards that grow only apple trees and peach trees. Alice has twice as many apple trees as Bernie has. Bernie has 1.5 times as many peach trees as Alice has. Alice's orchard has 110 more trees than Bernie's orchard. and the total number of trees in both orchards are 1,050. Let x be the number of apple trees in Bernie's orchard and y be the number of peach trees in Alice's orchard. Which of the following systems of equations can be used to find the values of the variables x and y?

A) $x + 2y = 1.5x + y + 110$
   $x + 2y + 1.5x + y = 1,050$

B) $1.5x + y = x + 2y + 110$
   $1.5x + y + x + 2y = 1,050$

C) $2x + y = x + 1.5y + 110$
   $2x + y + x + 1.5y = 1,050$

D) $2x + 1.5y = x + y + 110$
   $2x + 1.5y + x + y = 1,050$

12

The average gas mileage of Roy's car is 36 miles per gallon of gas for highway driving and 24 miles per gallon of gas for city driving. If Roy used 10 gallons of gas for driving 340 miles on both highways and cities, how many miles did he drive on highways?

A) 240

B) 260

C) 280

D) 300

13

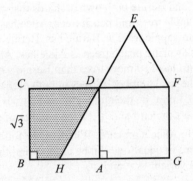

In the figure above, *ABCD* and *ADFG* are squares each with an area of 3 and *DEF* is an equilateral triangle. Line segments $\overline{AD}$, $\overline{CF}$, and $\overline{EH}$ intersect at point *D*. Which of the following represents the area of the shaded region?

A) $3 - \dfrac{\sqrt{3}}{4}$

B) $3 - \dfrac{\sqrt{3}}{2}$

C) $3 - \dfrac{3\sqrt{3}}{4}$

D) $3 - \sqrt{3}$

14

The line of a graph in the *xy*- plane contains the point $(-2, 4)$ and is parallel to a line with the equation $x + 2y = 10$. The graph of a second line passes through the points $(6, 2)$ and $(-2, -2)$. If the two lines intersect at the point (r, s), what is the value of $r + s$?

A) 5

B) 7

C) 9

D) 11

Questions 15 and 16 refer to the following information.

Revenue of the commercial banks in country X in 1995.

Banks	Percent
Bank A	40%
Bank B	29%
Bank C	15%
Bank D	8%
Other Banks	8%

$100\% = 10$ billion dollars

Revenue of the commercial banks in country X in 2005.

Banks	Percent
Bank A	36%
Bank B	21%
Bank C	18%
Bank D	10%
Other Banks	15%

$100\% = 14$ billion dollars

The tables above show the percentage of revenue of the commercial banks in country X. Total revenue of the commercial banks in 1995 was 10 billion dollars and total revenue of the commercial banks in 2005 was 14 billion dollars.

15

According to the tables above, which commercial bank had amounts of revenue that were nearly equal in 1995 and 2005?

A) Bank A

B) Bank B

C) Bank C

D) Bank D

16

According to the tables above, what is the percent increase of the revenue of Bank D from 1995 to 2005?

A) 2%

B) 20%

C) 43%

D) 75%

17

If p is 20 percent less than r, r is 20 percent less than s, and s is 20 percent less than t, which of the following is equal to p?

A) $0.4t$

B) $0.4096t$

C) $0.512t$

D) $0.64t$

18

A large container can be filled with four times as much water as a medium-sized container, or nine times as much as a small-sized container. If x small containers and x large containers are needed to fill a water tank that could be filled with 120 medium-sized containers, what is the value of x?

A) 21

B) 25

C) 27

D) 32

19

	Engineering	Humanities
Female		
Male		
Total	56	52

The incomplete table above summarizes the number of faculty members in engineering and humanities departments at a certain college. The ratio of female faculty members in engineering to male faculty members in engineering is 3 to 11, and the ratio of female faculty members in humanities to male faculty members in humanities is 9 to 4. There are a total of 56 faculty members in engineering and 52 faculty members in humanities. If one female faculty member is randomly selected, what is the probability that she will be in humanities?

A) $\dfrac{5}{8}$

B) $\dfrac{11}{16}$

C) $\dfrac{20}{27}$

D) $\dfrac{3}{4}$

20

A parabola with the equation $f(x) = a(x+1)(x-3)$ has a minimum value at $x = 1$ in the xy-plane. If $f(p) = f(-3)$, which of the following could be the value of p?

A) 4

B) 5

C) 6

D) 7

21

$$x^2 - x + y^2 + 2y - \frac{19}{4} = 0$$

The equation of a circle in the xy-plane is shown above. What is the area of the circle?

A) 6π

B) $\frac{13}{2}\pi$

C) 7π

D) $\frac{15}{2}\pi$

22

$$g(x) = -(x^2 - 6x + 5) - 4(x - c)$$

In the polynomial $g(x)$ defined above, c is a constant. If $g(x)$ is divisible by $x+1$, what is the value of c?

A) 1

B) 2

C) 3

D) 4

23

If A_0 is the initial amount deposited in a savings that earns at a fixed rate of r percent per year, and if a constant amount of c is added to the account each year, then the amount A_n of the savings, n years after the initial deposit is made, is given by the equation $A_n = (1 + \frac{r}{100}) \cdot A_{n-1} + c$.

If Alan made an initial deposit of \$10,000 that earns at a fixed rate of 4 percent per year, and he adds a constant amount of \$3,000 to his account each year, what is A_3, the amount he has in the savings three years after he made his initial deposit?

A) \$19,816.00

B) \$20,248.64

C) \$20,613.44

D) \$20,623.23

24

What are the solutions to $(x+3)(x-3) = 4x$?

A) $4 \pm \sqrt{5}$

B) $4 \pm \sqrt{13}$

C) $2 \pm \sqrt{5}$

D) $2 \pm \sqrt{13}$

25

If $x \neq \pm 1$, which of the following is equivalent to $\dfrac{\dfrac{1}{x+1}-1}{\dfrac{1}{x^2-1}+1}$?

A) $\dfrac{1+x}{x}$

B) $\dfrac{1-x}{x}$

C) $\dfrac{x}{1+x}$

D) $\dfrac{x}{1-x}$

26

The average (arithmetic mean) test score for all the students in a class is 79.6. If the average score of 16 boys in the class was 81, while that of n girls was 78, what is the value of n ?

A) 14

B) 15

C) 16

D) 17

27

The mean price of a gallon of gas in a certain state is \$2.95 with a standard deviation of 12 cents. Which of the following prices is not within 2 standard deviations of the mean price?

A) \$2.69

B) \$2.72

C) \$3.05

D) \$3.18

28

A cylindrical shape container 40 cm high inside with an internal diameter of 20 centimeters (cm) is 80 percent filled with fruit punch. If Kara pours 12 fluid ounces of fruit punch to each plastic cup, what is the largest number of plastic cups with 12 fluid ounces of fruit punch, that she can pour from the container?
(1 fluid ounce = 29.6 cubic centimeters)

A) 22

B) 25

C) 28

D) 31

29

Which of the following is NOT a factor of the polynomial $p(x) = 2x^3 - 5x^2 - 4x + 3$?

A) $2x - 1$

B) $x + 1$

C) $x - 3$

D) $x - 1$

30

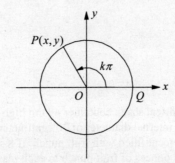

In the xy- plane above, O is the center of the unit circle, and the measure of $\angle POQ$ is $k\pi$ radians. If $\sin(k\pi) = a$, which of the following could be $\sin(k\pi + \pi)$?

A) $-\dfrac{1}{2}a$

B) $\dfrac{1}{2}a$

C) $-a$

D) a

DIRECTIONS

For questions 31-38, solve the problem and enter your answer in the grid as described below, on the answer sheet.

1. Although not required, it is suggested that you write your answer in the boxes at the top of the columns to help you fill in the circles accurately. You will receive credit only if the circles are filled in correctly.

2. Mark no more than one circle in any column.

3. No question has a negative answer.

4. Some problems may have more than one correct answer. In such cases, grid only one answer.

5. **Mixed numbers** such as $3\frac{1}{2}$ must be gridded as 3.5 or $7/2$. (If ⬚ is entered into the grid, it will be interpreted as $\frac{31}{2}$ not $3\frac{1}{2}$.)

6. **Decimal answers:** If you obtain a decimal answer with more digits than the grid can accommodate, it may be either rounded or truncated, but it must fill the entire grid.

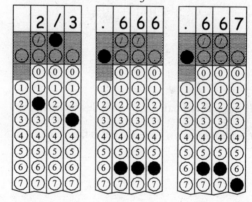

NOTE: You may start your answers in any column, space permitting. Columns you use should be left blank.

CONTINUE ▷

31

Real numbers a and b are positive, and the ratio of a to b is 2.25 times the ratio of b to a.

What is the value of $\dfrac{a}{b}$?

32

$$\frac{2}{5}x - \frac{1}{5}y = 98$$

$$\frac{2}{7}x + \frac{1}{14}y = 55$$

If the ordered pair (x, y) satisfies the system of equations shown above, what is the value of x?

33

$$p(x) = \frac{2x-1}{(x-4)^2 - 6(x-4) + 9}$$

For what value of x is the function above undefined?

34

When Jay was on vacation in China, the exchange rate for Chinese yuan to US dollars was 6.14 yuan per dollar. On her vacation in China, Jay bought two one-day Beijing tour tickets for 320 yuan each. To the nearest dollar, how many dollars did the two tickets cost?
(Disregard the $ sign when gridding your answer.)

35

If $x^4 \cdot x^9 = x^n \cdot x^n$, what is the value of n?

36

In the xy-plane, a parabola with the equation $y = -(x+3)^2 + 9$ intersects a line with the equation $y = -7$ at two points, P and Q. What is the length of $\overline{PQ}$?

37

$$y = a(x+3)(x-5)$$

In the quadratic equation above, a is a nonzero constant. The graph of the equation in the xy-plane has the vertex (h, k). If the value of k is -8, what is the value of a?

38

If $(x+2)$ is a factor of $f(x) = x^3 + x^2 + x + c$, and $(-1, p)$ lies on the graph of f, what is the value of p?

Answer Key

SAT Practice Test 1 – No Calculator

1. A	2. D	3. A	4. C	5. B
6. C	7. D	8. B	9. C	10. A
11. B	12. C	13. A	14. D	15. C
16. 10	17. 16	18. 3	19. 2	20. 10

SAT Practice Test 1 – Calculator

1. A	2. B	3. D	4. C	5. C
6. B	7. C	8. D	9. A	10. D
11. C	12. D	13. B	14. A	15. B
16. D	17. C	18. C	19. D	20. B
21. A	22. B	23. C	24. D	25. B
26. A	27. A	28. C	29. D	30. C
31. 1.5	32. 210	33. 7	34. 104	35. 6.5
36. 8	37. $\frac{1}{2}$ or 0.5	38. 5		

Answers and Explanations

SAT Practice Test 1 – No Calculator

1. A

$$f(x) = \frac{1}{2}x - 1$$

$$f(-2x+1) = \frac{1}{2}(-2x+1) - 1 \quad \text{Replace } -2x+1 \text{ for } x.$$

$$f(-2x+1) = -x + \frac{1}{2} - 1 \quad \text{Simplify.}$$

$$f(-2x+1) = -x - \frac{1}{2}$$

2. D

$$x = 1 - \frac{a}{b}$$

$$x = 1 \cdot \frac{b}{b} - \frac{a}{b} \qquad b \text{ is the LCD.}$$

$$x = \frac{b-a}{b} \qquad \text{Subtract the numerator.}$$

$$\frac{1}{x} = \frac{b}{b-a}$$

3. A

$$\frac{1}{2}(16 - 4x) = nx + 8 + 3x$$

$$8 - 2x = 8 + (n+3)x \qquad \text{Simplify.}$$

If each side of the equation is the same, the equation is an identity.
Therefore, in the simplified equation above, if $-2 = n + 3$, the equation is an identity.
Solving for n yields $n = -5$.

4. C

The slope of the line shown on the graph is $\frac{3-(-3)}{-2-1} = -2$. Therefore, the equation of the line that is parallel to the line shown on the graph, in slope-intercept form, is $y = -2x + b$.

Since the line contains $(\frac{1}{2}, 3)$, substitute $x = \frac{1}{2}$ and $y = 3$ in the equation.

$$3 = -2(\frac{1}{2}) + b \implies b = 4$$

Therefore, the equation of the line is $y = -2x + 4$.

5. B

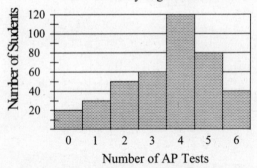

AP Tests Taken by High School Seniors

The mode of a set of data is the number that appears most frequently. Therefore, the mode of the number of AP tests taken by each student was 4.
The statement in choice A is true.

When the distribution is skewed to the left, the data set will usually have a greater median than the mean.
The statement in choice B is NOT true.
So, choice B is the correct answer.

The following shows the calculation of the mean, which you don't necessarily need to do in a real SAT test situation.

There are 160 students who took 3 or less AP tests and there are 120 students who took 5 or more AP tests. Since the median number is the average of the 200th and 201th number, the median is 4.

The mean number of AP tests taken by the senior students was

$$\frac{0\cdot 20 + 1\cdot 30 + 2\cdot 50 + 3\cdot 60 + 4\cdot 120 + 5\cdot 80 + 6\cdot 40}{400}$$

$$= 3.575$$

Therefore, the average number of AP tests taken by the senior students is less than the median number of AP tests taken by the senior students.

6. **C**

There are 120 senior students who took 4 AP tests and there are 60 students who took 3 AP tests.

The following equation represents "120 is what percent greater than 60".

$$120 = 60(1 + \underbrace{\frac{n}{100}}_{n\% \text{ more than } 60})$$

$120 = 60 + 60 \times \dfrac{n}{100}$ Distributive Property

$60 = 60 \times \dfrac{n}{100}$ Subtract 60 from each side.

$1 = \dfrac{n}{100}$ Divide each side by 60.

$n = 100$

Therefore, the number of senior students who took 4 AP tests is 100% greater than the number of senior students who took 3 AP tests.

7. **D**

$x + y < a$

$x - y > b$

Substitute $x = 0$ and $y = 1$ in the inequalities.

$0 + 1 < a$ or $1 < a$	First inequality
$0 - 1 > b$ or $-1 > b$	Second inequality
$1 < a$	
$1 < -b$	Multiply each side of second inequality by -1 and change $>$ to $<$.

$1 < a$

$+\underline{|1 < -b}$ Add the two inequalities.

$2 < a + (-b)$

Choice D is correct.

8. **B**

$$\frac{(1+i)^2}{1-i}$$

$= \dfrac{1 + 2i + i^2}{1-i}$ FOIL

$= \dfrac{1 + 2i - 1}{1-i}$ $i^2 = -1$

$= \dfrac{2i}{1-i}$ Simplify.

$= \dfrac{2i(1+i)}{(1-i)(1+i)}$ Rationalize the denominator.

$= \dfrac{2i + 2i^2}{1 - i^2}$ Distributive Property

$= \dfrac{2i - 2}{1 - (-1)}$ $i^2 = -1$

$= \dfrac{2(i-1)}{2}$ Factor.

$= i - 1$ or $-1 + i$ Simplify.

9. **C**

To determine which quadrant does not contain any solution to the system of inequalities, graph the inequalities. Graph the inequality $2 - y < 2x$ by drawing a dashed line through $(0, 2)$ and $(1, 0)$. Graph the inequality $-x \leq 4 - y$ by drawing a solid line through $(0, 4)$ and $(-4, 0)$.

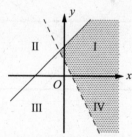

The solution to the system of inequalities is the shaded region shown above. It can be seen that the solutions only include points in quadrants I, II, and IV and do not include any points in quadrant III.

Choice C is correct.

10. **A**

Let $x =$ the number of diskettes produced in h hours.

Set up a proportion for the following:

d diskettes produced in m minutes is x diskettes produced in h hours.

$$\frac{d \text{ diskettes}}{m \text{ minutes}} = \frac{x \text{ diskettes}}{h \text{ hours}}$$

$$\frac{d \text{ diskettes}}{m \text{ minutes}} = \frac{x \text{ diskettes}}{60h \text{ minutes}} \qquad h \text{ hours} = 60h \text{ minutes}$$

$$60dh = mx \qquad \text{Cross Products}$$

$$\frac{60dh}{m} = x$$

11. B

The factored form of a quadratic function written as $y = a(x-b)(x-c)$ has x-intercepts $(b,0)$ and $(c,0)$. So, you need to factored the given equation.

$$y = 2x^2 - 11x - 6$$

Find two numbers with a sum of -11 and a product of $2 \cdot -6$ or -12. The two numbers are 1 and -12.

$$2x^2 - 11x - 6$$

$$= 2x^2 + x - 12x - 6 \qquad \text{Write } -11x \text{ as } x - 12x.$$

$$= (2x^2 + x) - (12x + 6) \qquad \text{Group terms with common factor.}$$

$$= x(2x+1) - 6(2x+1) \qquad \text{Factor each group.}$$

$$= (2x+1)(x-6) \qquad \text{Distributive Property}$$

Therefore, $y = (2x+1)(x-6)$ is the equivalent form of the equation that displays the x-intercepts of the parabola as constants or coefficients.

12. C

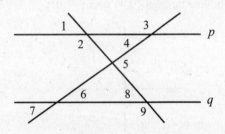

In the figure above, line p is parallel to line q.

I. If line p is parallel to line q, corresponding angles are equal in measure. Therefore, $m\angle 2 = m\angle 9$.

Statement I is true.

II. $\angle 2$ and $\angle 4$ do not have any relation. We do not know if the two angles are supplementary.

Statement II is not true.

III. $m\angle 4 = m\angle 6$ Alternate interior $\angle$s are $\cong$.

$m\angle 6 + m\angle 8 = m\angle 5$ Exterior Angle Theorem

$m\angle 4 + m\angle 8 = m\angle 5$ Substitute $m\angle 4$ for $m\angle 6$.

Statement III is true.

13. A

If x is the number of bags of Arabian Mocha, then $10 - x$ is the number of bags of Kona. The cost of Arabian Mocha is $18x$ and the cost of Kona is $28(10-x)$. The total cost is d dollars, so $18x + 28(10-x) = d$.

$$18x + 280 - 28x = d \qquad \text{Distributive Property}$$

$$-10x + 280 = d \qquad \text{Simplify.}$$

$$280 - d = 10x \qquad \text{Simplify.}$$

$$\frac{280}{10} - \frac{d}{10} = x \qquad \text{Divide each side by 10.}$$

$$28 - 0.1d = x \qquad \text{Simplify.}$$

14. D

First you need to solve the equation $p = \dfrac{r}{s-r}$ for r.

$$p(s-r) = \frac{r}{s-r}(s-r) \qquad \text{Multiply by } s-r.$$

$$ps - pr = r \qquad \text{Distributive Property}$$

$$ps = r + pr \qquad \text{Add } pr \text{ to each side.}$$

$$ps = r(1+p) \qquad \text{Factor.}$$

$$\frac{ps}{1+p} = r \qquad \text{Divide by } 1+p.$$

$$q = \frac{r}{s} = r \cdot \frac{1}{s}$$

$$q = \frac{p\!\!\!\backslash s}{1+p} \cdot \frac{1}{\backslash s} \qquad\qquad r = \frac{ps}{1+p}$$

$$q = \frac{p}{1+p} \qquad \text{Cancel out } s.$$

15. C

A population that doubles in size over equal time periods is increasing at an exponential rate. The exponential growth model can be written in the form $y = a(2)^{\frac{t}{b}}$, in which a is the population at time $t = 0$ and b is the doubling time. If the population of the town was 140,000 at the beginning of 2016 and the population doubles every 24 years, $P = 140,000(2)^{\frac{t}{24}}$ represents the population t years after 2016.

If $t = 24$, $(2)^{\frac{t}{24}} = (2)^{\frac{24}{24}} = (2)^1$.

So the population will double 24 years after 2016.

If $t = 48$, $(2)^{\frac{48}{24}} = (2)^2$. So the population will quadruple 48 years after 2016, and so on.

16. 10

$$-7 + a = 3$$
$$-7 + a + 7 = 3 + 7 \qquad \text{Add 7 to each side.}$$
$$a = 10 \qquad \text{Simplify.}$$

Hence, $10 - [(a-3) - 7] = 10 - [(10-3) - 7] = 10$.

17. 16

$\dfrac{2}{3}k - 3$	Three is subtracted from two thirds of k.
$2(\dfrac{2}{3}k - 3)$	The difference is doubled.
$2(\dfrac{2}{3}k - 3) = \dfrac{1}{3}k + 10$	The result is ten more than one third of the number.
$\dfrac{4}{3}k - 6 = \dfrac{1}{3}k + 10$	Simplify.
$3(\dfrac{4}{3}k - 6) = 3(\dfrac{1}{3}k + 10)$	Multiply each side by 3.
$4k - 18 = k + 30$	Distributive Property
$4k - 18 - k = k + 30 - k$	Subtract k from each side.
$3k - 18 = 30$	Simplify.
$3k = 48$	Add 18 to each side.
$k = 16$	Divide each side by 3.

18. 3

In order for a system of two linear equations to have infinitely many solutions, the two equations must be equivalent. The equation $6x + ky = 3$ can be rewritten as $y = \dfrac{-6}{k}x + \dfrac{3}{k}$. If the two equations are equivalent, $-\dfrac{6}{k} = -2$ and $\dfrac{3}{k} = 1$. Solving for k yields $k = 3$.

19. 2

$$\frac{-2x^2 + 5x + 10}{-x + 4} = 2x + 3 - \frac{A}{-x + 4}$$

Multiply each side of the equation by $-x + 4$.

$$(-x+4)\frac{-2x^2 + 5x + 10}{-x + 4}$$

$$= (-x+4)[2x + 3 - \frac{A}{-x+4}]$$

$$\Rightarrow \ -2x^2 + 5x + 10 = (-x+4)(2x+3) - A$$

$$\Rightarrow \ -2x^2 + 5x + 10 = -2x^2 + 5x + 12 - A$$

Since the constant terms have to be equal on both sides of the equation, $10 = 12 - A$, or $A = 2$.

20. 10

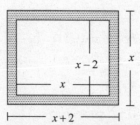

Since the width of the frame is 1 inch, it follows that the length and width of the rectangular picture, represented by the unshaded region, is x and $x - 2$ respectively. Thus the area of the rectangular picture is $x(x-2)$ square inches. The area of the outer rectangle is $x(x+2)$ square inches.

Since the area of the frame is the area of the outer rectangle minus the area of the inner rectangle, the area of the frame is $x(x+2) - x(x-2)$.

Set the expression for the area of the picture as twice the area of the frame.

$$x(x-2) = 2[x(x+2) - x(x-2)]$$
$$x^2 - 2x = 2[x^2 + 2x - x^2 + 2x]$$
$$x^2 - 2x = 8x$$
$$x^2 - 10x = 0$$
$$x(x - 10) = 0$$
$$x = 0 \text{ or } x = 10$$

Since x represents the length of the picture, discard the solution $x = 0$. Therefore, when $x = 10$, the area of the picture is twice the area of the frame.

SAT Practice Test 1 – Calculator

1. A

Let $4n$ and n be the two numbers.

$$4n + n = -15 \qquad \text{Their sum is } -15.$$
$$5n = -15 \qquad \text{Simplify.}$$
$$n = -3$$
$$4n = -12$$

Since -12 is the smaller of two numbers, choice A is correct.

2. B

Average rate of change in profit

$$= \frac{\text{change in profit}}{\text{change in years}} = \frac{1,160,000 - 108,000}{2015 - 2010}$$

$$= \frac{1,052,000}{5} = 210,400$$

3. D

If $f(x) = \sqrt{x} + 2$ and $g(x) = (x-1)^2$,

$f(a) = \sqrt{a} + 2$.

$g(f(a)) - 2f(a)$

$= g(\sqrt{a} + 2) - 2(\sqrt{a} + 2)$

$= ((\sqrt{a} + 2) - 1)^2 - 2\sqrt{a} - 4$

$= (\sqrt{a} + 1)^2 - 2\sqrt{a} - 4$

$= (\sqrt{a})^2 + 2\sqrt{a} + 1 - 2\sqrt{a} - 4$

$= a - 3$

4. C

A system of two equations has no solution if the equations have the same slope but different y-intercepts. Change each equation in each answer choice into slope-intercept form.

A) $\frac{1}{5}x + \frac{1}{3}y = 1 \Rightarrow y = -\frac{3}{5}x + 3$

$3x - 5y = 15 \Rightarrow y = \frac{3}{5}x - 3$

Their slopes are different, so they must have one solution.

B) $4x + 3y = 12 \Rightarrow y = -\frac{4}{3}x + 4$

$3x - 4y = 6 \Rightarrow y = \frac{3}{4}x - \frac{3}{2}$

Their slopes are different, so they must have one solution.

C) $-3x + 2y = 7 \Rightarrow y = \frac{3}{2}x + \frac{7}{2}$

$\frac{1}{2}x - \frac{1}{3}y = 3 \Rightarrow y = \frac{3}{2}x - 9$

The slopes are the same, but their y-intercepts are different. Therefore, the system has no solution.

5. C

If a line in the xy-plane passes through the origin and has a slope of $-\frac{3}{4}$, the equation of the line is $y = -\frac{3}{4}x$.

Check each answer choice with the equation $y = -\frac{3}{4}x$.

A) Substitute $x = 2$ and $y = -\frac{3}{2}$ in $y = -\frac{3}{4}x$.

$-\frac{3}{2} = -\frac{3}{4}(2)$ is true.

B) Substitute $x = -4$ and $y = 3$ in $y = -\frac{3}{4}x$.

$3 = -\frac{3}{4}(-4)$ is true.

C) Substitute $x = 8$ and $y = -3$ in $y = -\frac{3}{4}x$.

$-3 = -\frac{3}{4}(8)$ is not true.

Therefore, choice C is correct.

6. B

To find out the time it took for Mike to reach the finish line, solve the equation $-12t + 1,500 = 0$ for t. Solving the equation for t gives $t = 125$. Substitute 125 for t in the expression $-10.5t + 1,500$.

$-10.5(125) + 1,500 = 187.5$

Therefore, Maria has 187.5 meters to finish when Mike is on the finish line.

7. C

If the polynomial $f(x)$ is divided by $x + 2$, the remainder is $f(-2)$. Based on the table, $f(-2) = 2.5$. Therefore, when $f(x)$ is divided by $x + 2$, the remainder is 2.5.

8. D

Set up a proportion for the following.

If $\frac{1}{2}$ tablespoon of ground coffee makes 4 cups of coffee, 3 tablespoons of ground coffee makes c cups of coffee.

$$\frac{1/2 \text{ table spoon of ground coffee}}{4 \text{ cups of coffee}}$$

$$= \frac{3 \text{ table spoons of ground coffee}}{c \text{ cups of coffee}}$$

$\frac{1}{2}c = 3 \cdot 4$ Cross Product

$c = 24$ cups   Simplify.

Since a thermos holds 2 quarts of liquid, which is 8 cups, 24 cups of coffee can be filled $24 \div 8$, or 3 thermoses.

9. A

If the company sells x feet of cable, the selling price is $30x$ and the cost of producing x feet of cable is $C = 12.5x + 210$. Therefore,

profit = selling price − cost
$$= 30x - (12.5x + 210)$$
$$= 17.5x - 210$$

To make a profit, $17.5x - 210 > 0$.
Solving the inequality gives $x > 12$.

10. D

If the company sells 50 feet of cable, the profit is $17.5(50) - 210$, or 665 dollars.

11. C

If x is the number of apple trees in Bernie's orchards, $2x$ is the number of apple trees in Alice's orchards, because Alice has twice as many apple trees as Bernie has. If y is the number of peach trees in Alice's orchards, $1.5y$ is the number of peach trees in Bernie's orchards, because Bernie has 1.5 times as many peach trees as Alice. Therefore, the number of trees in Alice's orchards is $2x + y$ and the number of trees in Bernie's orchards is $x + 1.5y$. Since Alice's orchard has 110 more trees than Bernie's orchard, the expression $2x + y = x + 1.5y + 110$ is true. Since the total number of trees in both orchards is 1,050, the expression
$2x + y + x + 1.5y + 110 = 1,050$ is true.

Choice C is correct.

12. D

Let $x =$ the number of miles he drove on the highway. Let $340 - x =$ the number of miles he drove in the city. The number of gallons of gas used is the number of miles drove divided by the gas mileage. Therefore, $\dfrac{x}{36} + \dfrac{340 - x}{24} = 10$.

$72(\dfrac{x}{36} + \dfrac{340 - x}{24}) = 72(10)$ LCD is 72.
$2x + 3(340 - x) = 720$ Distributive Property
$2x + 1,020 - 3x = 720$ Distributive Property
$-x = -300$
$x = 300$

13. B

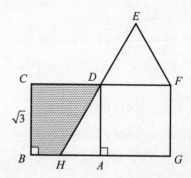

$m\angle EDF = 60$	Each $\angle$ of equilateral Δ is $60°$.
$m\angle DHA = m\angle EDF$	Corresponding angles are $\cong$.
$m\angle DHA = 60$	Substitution

Therefore, ΔDHA is a $30°$-$60°$-$90°$ triangle.

$HA \cdot \sqrt{3} = DA$	In a $30°$-$60°$-$90°$ Δ, the longer leg is $\sqrt{3}$ times the shorter leg.
$HA \cdot \sqrt{3} = \sqrt{3}$	$DA = CB = \sqrt{3}$
$HA = 1$	Divide each side by $\sqrt{3}$.

Area of $\Delta DHA = \dfrac{1}{2} HA \cdot DA = \dfrac{1}{2}(1)(\sqrt{3}) = \dfrac{\sqrt{3}}{2}$

Area of shaded region is area of square $ABCD$ minus area of triangle DHA. Therefore,

area of shaded region $= 3 - \dfrac{\sqrt{3}}{2}$.

14. A

Rewrite the equation $x + 2y = 10$ as $y = -\dfrac{1}{2}x + 5$.

The slope of the line is $-\dfrac{1}{2}$. Any line parallel to the line can be written as $y = -\dfrac{1}{2}x + b$. If the line contains the point $(-2, 4)$, substitute $x = -2$ and $y = 4$ in the equation. $4 = -\dfrac{1}{2}(-2) + b \Rightarrow b = 3$

Therefore, $y = -\dfrac{1}{2}x + 3$ is parallel to $x + 2y = 10$ and contains the point $(-2, 4)$.

The slope of the second line which passes through the points $(6, 2)$ and $(-2, -2)$ is $\dfrac{2 - (-2)}{6 - (-2)}$ or $\dfrac{1}{2}$.

The point-slope form of the second line is $y - 2 = \dfrac{1}{2}(x - 6)$, which can be rewritten as $y = \dfrac{1}{2}x - 1$. Substitute $-\dfrac{1}{2}x + 3$ for y in the equation to find the point of intersection.

$$\frac{1}{2}x - 1 = -\frac{1}{2}x + 3 \qquad \text{Substitution}$$

$$\frac{1}{2}x - 1 + \frac{1}{2}x = -\frac{1}{2}x + 3 + \frac{1}{2}x \quad \text{Add } \frac{1}{2}x.$$

$$x - 1 = 3 \qquad \text{Simplify.}$$

$$x = 4$$

$$y = \frac{1}{2}x - 1 = \frac{1}{2}(4) - 1 = 1$$

Therefore, the point of intersection $(r, s) = (4, 1)$.

$$r + s = 4 + 1 = 5$$

15. B

Actual earnings in 1995
Bank A $= 10 \times 0.4 = 4$ billion
Bank B $= 10 \times 0.29 = 2.9$ billion
Bank C $= 10 \times 0.15 = 1.5$ billion
Bank D $= 10 \times 0.08 = 0.8$ billion

Actual earnings in 2005
Bank A $= 14 \times 0.36 = 5.04$ billion
Bank B $= 14 \times 0.21 = 2.94$ billion
Bank C $= 14 \times 0.18 = 2.52$ billion
Bank D $= 14 \times 0.1 = 1.4$ billion

Bank B had actual amounts of earnings that were nearly equal in 1995 and 2005.

16. D

The actual earnings of Bank D rose from 0.8 billion in 1995 to 1.4 billion in 2005. The percent increase is

$$\frac{\text{amount of increase}}{\text{amount in 1995}} = \frac{1.4 - 0.8}{0.8} = 0.75.$$

The percent increase of the actual earnings of Bank D from 1995 to 2005 is 75 percent.

17. C

$$p = r - 0.2r \qquad p \text{ is 20\% less than } r.$$
$$p = 0.8r \qquad \text{Simplify.}$$
$$r = s - 0.2s \qquad r \text{ is 20\% less than } s.$$
$$r = 0.8s \qquad \text{Simplify.}$$
$$s = t - 0.2t \qquad s \text{ is 20\% less than } t.$$
$$s = 0.8t \qquad \text{Simplify.}$$

$$p = 0.8r = 0.8(0.8s) = 0.8(0.8(0.8t)) = 0.512t$$

18. C

Let $m =$ the capacity of the medium container, then $4m =$ the capacity of the large container,

and $\frac{4m}{9} =$ the capacity of the small container.

If x small containers and x large containers are needed to fill a water tank that could be filled with 120 medium size containers, then the equation

$$x\left(\frac{4m}{9}\right) + x(4m) = 120m \text{ can be used to solve the}$$

value of x.

$$m\left(\frac{4}{9}x + 4x\right) = 120m \qquad \text{Factor.}$$

$$\left(\frac{4}{9}x + 4x\right) = 120 \qquad \text{Divide each side by } m.$$

$$\frac{40}{9}x = 120 \qquad \text{Simplify.}$$

$$\frac{9}{40} \cdot \frac{40}{9}x = \frac{9}{40} \cdot 120 \qquad \text{Multiply each side by } \frac{9}{40}.$$

$$x = 27$$

19. D

Let the number of female faculty members in engineering be $3x$ and let the number of male faculty members in engineering be $11x$. Then $3x + 11x = 56$.

$$14x = 56 \qquad \text{Simplify.}$$
$$x = 4 \qquad \text{Divide each side by 14.}$$

So, there are 12 female and 44 male faculty members in engineering.
Let the number of female faculty members in humanities be $9y$ and let the number of male faculty members in humanities be $4y$. Then $9y + 4y = 52$.

$$13x = 52 \qquad \text{Simplify.}$$
$$y = 4 \qquad \text{Divide each side by 13.}$$

So, there are 36 female and 16 male faculty members in humanities.

Now you are able to fill in the table.

	Engineering	Humanities
Female	12	36
Male	44	16
Total	56	52

There are altogether 48 female faculty members. If one female faculty member is randomly selected, the probability that she will be in humanities is

$$\frac{36}{48} = \frac{3}{4}.$$

20. B

If the parabola has a minimum value at $x = 1$, $x = 1$ is the axis of symmetry. If $f(p) = f(-3)$, the distance from p to $x = 1$ is the same as the distance from -3 to $x = 1$. Thus, $1 - (-3) = p - 1$.

$4 = p - 1$ Simplify.

$5 = p$

21. A

$$x^2 - x + y^2 + 2y - \frac{19}{4} = 0$$

Add $\frac{19}{4}$ to each side.

$$x^2 - x + y^2 + 2y = \frac{19}{4}$$

Add $(-1 \times \frac{1}{2})^2$ and $(2 \times \frac{1}{2})^2$ to complete the square for each variable.

$$x^2 - x + \frac{1}{4} + y^2 + 2y + 1 = \frac{19}{4} + \frac{1}{4} + 1$$

$$(x - \frac{1}{2})^2 + (y + 1)^2 = 6$$

The standard equation of a circle with center (h, k) and radius r unit is $(x - h)^2 + (y - k)^2 = r^2$.

Therefore, the radius of the circle is $\sqrt{6}$ and the area of the circle is $\pi(\sqrt{6})^2 = 6\pi$.

22. B

$$g(x) = -(x^2 - 6x + 5) - 4(x - c)$$

If $g(x)$ is divisible by $x + 1$, $g(-1) = 0$.

$$g(-1) = -((-1)^2 - 6(-1) + 5) - 4(-1 - c)$$

$$= -(1 + 6 + 5) + 4 + 4c$$

$$= -12 + 4 + 4c$$

$$= -8 + 4c$$

Therefore, if $g(-1) = 0$, $-8 + 4c = 0$ or $c = 2$.

23. C

$$A_n = (1 + \frac{r}{100}) \cdot A_{n-1} + c$$

If Alan made an initial deposit of \$10,000 that earns at a fixed rate of 4 percent per year, and he adds a constant amount of \$3,000 to his account each year, then $A_0 = 10,000$, $r = 4$ and $c = 3,000$.

$$A_1 = (1 + \frac{4}{100}) \cdot 10,000 + 3,000 \qquad n = 1$$

$$= 13,400$$

$$A_2 = (1 + \frac{4}{100}) \cdot A_1 + 3,000 \qquad n = 2$$

$$= (1 + \frac{4}{100}) \cdot 13,400 + 3,000 \qquad A_1 = 13,400$$

$$= 16,936$$

$$A_3 = (1 + \frac{4}{100}) \cdot A_2 + 3,000 \qquad n = 3$$

$$= (1 + \frac{4}{100}) \cdot 16,936 + 3,000 \qquad A_2 = 16,936$$

$$= 20,613.44$$

24. D

$$(x + 3)(x - 3) = 4x$$

$$x^2 - 9 = 4x$$

$$x^2 - 4x - 9 = 0$$

Use the quadratic formula to solve the equation.

$$x = \frac{-b \pm \sqrt{b^2 - 4ac}}{2a}$$

$$= \frac{-(-4) \pm \sqrt{(-4)^2 - 4(1)(-9)}}{2(1)}$$

$$= \frac{4 \pm \sqrt{16 + 36}}{2} = \frac{4 \pm \sqrt{52}}{2}$$

$$= \frac{4 \pm \sqrt{52}}{2} = \frac{4 \pm 2\sqrt{13}}{2}$$

$$= 2 \pm \sqrt{13}$$

25. B

Since $(x^2 - 1) = (x + 1)(x - 1)$, $(x + 1)(x - 1)$ is the LCD of the numerator and the denominator.

$$\frac{\frac{1}{x+1} - 1}{\frac{1}{x^2 - 1} + 1} = \frac{(\frac{1}{x+1} - 1)(x+1)(x-1)}{(\frac{1}{x^2 - 1} + 1)(x+1)(x-1)}$$

$$= \frac{(x - 1) - (x + 1)(x - 1)}{1 + (x + 1)(x - 1)}$$

$$= \frac{x - 1 - x^2 + 1}{1 + x^2 - 1}$$

$$= \frac{x - x^2}{x^2}$$

$$= \frac{x(1 - x)}{x^2}$$

$$= \frac{1 - x}{x}$$

26. A

The weighted average of two groups is the sum of the values of group 1 plus the sum of the values of group 2 divided by the total number of the values. In this question, the weighted average of two groups is 79.6, the sum of the values of boys is 81×16, the sum of the values of girls is $78n$, and the total number of values is $16 + n$.

Use the weighted average formula.

$$79.6 = \frac{81 \times 16 + 78n}{16 + n}$$

Multiply each side of the equation by $16 + n$.

$$79.6(16 + n) = 1296 + 78n$$
$$1273.6 + 79.6n = 1296 + 78n$$
$$1.6n = 22.4$$
$$n = \frac{22.4}{1.6}$$
$$= 14$$

27. A

$2.95 + 0.12 = 3.07$	Price within one SD
$2.95 + 2 \times 0.12 = 3.19$	Price within two SD
$2.95 - 0.12 = 2.83$	Price within one SD
$2.95 - 2 \times 0.12 = 2.71$	Price within two SD

The prices between \$2.71 and \$3.19 are within two standard deviations. Thus, \$2.69 is not within two standard deviations.

28. C

Volume of the cylindrical shape container
$$= \pi r^2 h = \pi (10 \text{ cm})^2 (40 \text{ cm}) = 4,000\pi \text{ cm}^3 .$$
The container is 80 percent filled with punch, so the amount of punch in the container is
$$4,000\pi \text{ cm}^3 \times 0.8 = 3,200\pi \text{ cm}^3 .$$
Since 1 fluid ounce $= 29.6 \text{ cm}^3$, dividing the amount of cubic centimeters by 29.6 will give the number of fluid ounces.
$$(3,200\pi \text{ cm}^3) \div 29.6 \text{ cm}^3 \approx 339.63 \text{ fluid ounces}$$
To find out the number of cups, divide 339.63 by 12. $339.63 \div 12 \approx 28.3$

Therefore, the largest number of 12 ounce cups that she can pour from the container is 28.

29. D

$$p(x) = 2x^3 - 5x^2 - 4x + 3$$
Check each answer choice.

A) If $2x - 1$ is a factor of $p(x)$, $p(\frac{1}{2}) = 0$.

$$p(\frac{1}{2}) = 2(\frac{1}{2})^3 - 5(\frac{1}{2})^2 - 4(\frac{1}{2}) + 3 = 0$$
Therefore, $2x - 1$ is a factor of $p(x)$.

B) If $x + 1$ is a factor of $p(x)$, $p(-1) = 0$.
$$p(-1) = 2(-1)^3 - 5(-1)^2 - 4(-1) + 3 = 0$$
Therefore, $x + 1$ is a factor of $p(x)$.

C) If $x - 3$ is a factor of $p(x)$, $p(3) = 0$.
$$p(3) = 2(3)^3 - 5(3)^2 - 4(3) + 3 = 0$$
Therefore, $x - 3$ is a factor of $p(x)$.

D) If $x - 1$ is a factor of $p(x)$, $p(1) = 0$.
$$p(1) = 2(1)^3 - 5(1)^2 - 4(1) + 3 = -4 \neq 0$$
Therefore, $x - 1$ is NOT a factor of $p(x)$.

Choice D is correct.

30. C

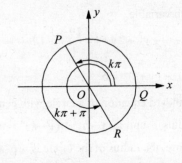

In the xy-plane above, the terminal side of $k\pi$ intersects the unit circle in quadrant II. In the unit circle, $\sin \theta = \frac{y}{1} = y$. If $\sin(k\pi) = a$, the y-coordinate of P is a, for which $a > 0$. If the terminal side of $k\pi$ is in quadrant II, the terminal side of $k\pi + \pi$ intersects the unit circle in quadrant IV. The y-coordinate in quadrant II is positive but the y-coordinate in quadrant IV is negative. Therefore,

$$\sin(k\pi + \pi) = \frac{y}{1} = y = -a.$$

31. 1.5

The ratio of a to b is 2.25 times the ratio of b to a. This can be written as $\frac{a}{b} = 2.25 \times \frac{b}{a}$.

$$\frac{a}{b} \cdot \frac{a}{b} = 2.25 \times \frac{b}{a} \cdot \frac{a}{b} \qquad \text{Multiply each side by } \frac{a}{b}.$$

$\dfrac{a^2}{b^2} = 2.25$ Simplify.

$\dfrac{a}{b} = \pm\sqrt{2.25} = \pm 1.5$ Square root each side.

Since a and b are positive, $\dfrac{a}{b} = 1.5$

32. 210

$\dfrac{2}{5}x - \dfrac{1}{5}y = 98$ First equation

$\dfrac{2}{7}x + \dfrac{1}{14}y = 55$ Second equation

$5(\dfrac{2}{5}x - \dfrac{1}{5}y) = 5(98)$ Multiply each side by 5.

$14(\dfrac{2}{7}x + \dfrac{1}{14}y) = 14(55)$ Multiply each side by 14.

$2x - y = 490$ Simplify.

$4x + y = 770$ Simplify.

Add the two equations to get $6x = 1260$.

$x = \dfrac{1260}{6} = 210$

33. 7

The expression $p(x) = \dfrac{2x-1}{(x-4)^2 - 6(x-4) + 9}$
is undefined when the denominator of $p(x)$ is
zero. Therefore, if $(x-4)^2 - 6(x-4) + 9$ is equal
to 0, $p(x)$ is undefined.

$(x-4)^2 - 6(x-4) + 9 = 0$

The expression $(x-4)^2 - 6(x-4) + 9 = 0$ is
a perfect square, which can be rewritten as
$((x-4)-3)^2 = 0$.

The expression $((x-4)-3)^2$ is equal to zero
if $(x-4)-3 = 0$. Solving for x gives $x = 7$.

34. 104

Jay bought two one-day Beijing tour tickets for
320 yuan each, so she paid 640 yuan for the
two tickets. Set up a proportion.

$\dfrac{1 \text{ dollar}}{6.14 \text{ yuans}} = \dfrac{x \text{ dollar}}{640 \text{ yuans}}$

$6.14x = 640$ Cross Products

$x = \dfrac{640}{6.14} \approx 104.234$

She paid $104 dollars for the two tickets, to the
nearest dollar.

35. 6.5

$x^4 \cdot x^9 = x^n \cdot x^n$

$x^{4+9} = x^{n+n}$ $a^m \cdot a^n = a^{m+n}$

$x^{13} = x^{2n}$ Simplify.

$13 = 2n$

$6.5 = n$

36. 8

To find the point of intersection, substitute -7
for y in the equation $y = -(x+3)^2 + 9$.

$-7 = -(x+3)^2 + 9$ Substitute -7 for y.

$-7 = -x^2 - 6x - 9 + 9$ FOIL

$-7 = -x^2 - 6x$ Simplify.

$x^2 + 6x - 7 = 0$ Make one side 0.

$(x+7)(x-1) = 0$ Factor.

$x = -7$ or $x = 1$

Since $\overline{PQ}$ is on a horizontal line, $y = -7$,

$PQ = 1 - (-7) = 8$.

37. $\dfrac{1}{2}$

The x-coordinate of the vertex of a parabola is
the average of the two x-intercepts. Therefore, if
the coordinates of the vertex of $y = a(x+3)(x-5)$
is (h, k), $h = \dfrac{-3+5}{2} = 1$. Since the value of k is
given as -8, $(h, k) = (1, -8)$. Substitute 1 for x
and -8 for y in the equation of the quadratic
function.

$-8 = a(1+3)(1-5)$

$-8 = a(-16)$

$\dfrac{1}{2} = a$

38. 5

If $(x+2)$ is a factor of $f(x) = x^3 + x^2 + x + c$,
then $f(-2) = 0$.

$f(-2) = (-2)^3 + (-2)^2 + (-2) + c = 0$

$\Rightarrow -8 + 4 - 2 + c = 0 \Rightarrow c = 6$

So, $f(x) = x^3 + x^2 + x + 6$.

Since, $(-1, p)$ lies on the graph of f, $f(-1) = p$.

$f(-1) = (-1)^3 + (-1)^2 + (-1) + 6 = p \Rightarrow p = 5$

SAT Practice Test 2

Math Test – No Calculator

25 MINUTES, 20 QUESTIONS

Turn to Section 3 of your answer sheet to answer the questions in this section.

DIRECTIONS

For questions **1-15**, solve each problem, choose the best answer from the choices provided, and fill in the corresponding circle on your answer sheet. **For questions 16-20**, solve the problem and enter your answer in the grid on the answer sheet. Please refer to the directions before question 16 on how to enter your answers in the grid. You may use any available space in your test booklet for scratch work.

NOTES

1. The use of calculator **is not permitted**.

2. All variables and expressions used represent real numbers unless otherwise indicated.

3. Figures provided in this test are drawn to scale unless otherwise indicated.

4. All figures lie in a plane unless otherwise indicated.

5. Unless otherwise indicated, the domain of a given function f is the set of all real numbers x for which $f(x)$ is a real number.

REFERENCE

$A = \pi r^2$ $A = \ell w$ $A = \dfrac{1}{2}bh$ $c^2 = a^2 + b^2$ Special Right Triangles
$C = 2\pi r$

$V = \ell wh$ $V = \pi r^2 h$ $V = \dfrac{4}{3}\pi r^3$ $V = \dfrac{1}{3}\pi r^2 h$ $V = \dfrac{1}{3}\ell wh$

The number of degrees of arc in a circle is 360.
The number of radians of arc in a circle is 2π.
The sum of the measures in degrees of the angles of a triangle is 180.

CONTINUE ⇨

1

x	-1	1	3	5
$f(x)$	9	3	-3	-9

The table above shows some values of the linear function f. Which of the following defines f?

A) $f(x) = 2x - 7$

B) $f(x) = 3x + 6$

C) $f(x) = -3x + 6$

D) $f(x) = -2x + 7$

2

For which of the following ordered pairs (x, y) is $y > x - 4$ and $x + y < 5$?

A) $(0, -5)$

B) $(0, 2)$

C) $(5, 3)$

D) $(4, -2)$

3

Which of the following equations represents a line that is parallel to the line with the equation

$$y = \frac{2}{3}x + 2 ?$$

A) $2x + 3y = 5$

B) $3x + 2y = 9$

C) $4x - 6y = 3$

D) $4x + 6y = -8$

4

If $\dfrac{3^{(a+b)^2}}{3^{(a-b)^2}} = 343$, what is the value of ab?

A) $\dfrac{5}{4}$

B) $\dfrac{3}{2}$

C) $\dfrac{7}{4}$

D) 2

5

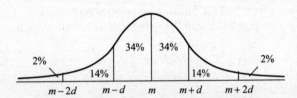

The figure above shows a normal distribution with mean m and standard deviation d, including approximate percents of the distribution corresponding to the six regions shown.

The mean value of 500 homes in a county is $225,000 and the standard deviation is $25,000.

Approximately how many of the homes in the county are between $175,000 and $225,000?

A) 310

B) 340

C) 380

D) 410

6

If a number p increased by 120 percent equals a number q decreased by 20 percent, which of the following is true?

A) $q = \dfrac{5}{2}p$

B) $q = \dfrac{11}{4}p$

C) $q = \dfrac{7}{2}p$

D) $q = \dfrac{15}{4}p$

7

Kay purchased a total of 8 bags of Colombia Coffee and Roast Espresso. Each bag of Columbia Coffee costs $25 and each bag of Roast Espresso costs $35. If Kay paid $230 for the coffee and espresso, solving which of the following systems of equations yields the number of bags of Columbia Coffee, c, and the number of bags of Roast Espresso, r?

A) $\begin{cases} c + r = 8 \\ 35c + 25r = 230 \end{cases}$

B) $\begin{cases} c = r + 8 \\ 25c + 35r = 230 \end{cases}$

C) $\begin{cases} c + r = \dfrac{230}{8} \\ 25c + 35r = 230 \end{cases}$

D) $\begin{cases} c + r = 8 \\ 25c + 35r = 230 \end{cases}$

8

$$h(x) = -px^2 + 1$$

For the function h defined above, p is a constant and $h(2) = -1$. What is the value of $h(p)$?

A) $\dfrac{7}{8}$

B) $-\dfrac{5}{4}$

C) $\dfrac{5}{4}$

D) $-\dfrac{7}{8}$

Questions 9-11 refer to the following information.

AUTOMOBILES SOLD AT MAX CAR DEALER, APRIL-AUGUST

Number of
Automobiles Sold

Month	Number
April	275
May	395
June	405
July	338
August	262

Mean Price of Automobiles Sold

Month

9

Which of the following is closest to the mean of the prices of the 670 automobiles sold in April and May?

A) $19,600

B) $19,700

C) $19,800

D) $19,900

10

What is the percent increase of the mean price of automobiles sold from May to June?

A) 7%

B) 7.5%

C) 8%

D) 8.5%

11

Max Car Dealer collected a tax equal to 8 percent of the price of each automobile sold in August. Approximately how much did Max Car Dealer collect in taxes from all automobiles sold in August?

A) $42,000

B) $44,000

C) $420,000

D) $440,000

12

$$\frac{3-i\sqrt{3}}{1-i\sqrt{3}}$$

If the expression above is rewritten in the form $a+bi$, in which a and b are real numbers, what is the value of b?

A) $-\dfrac{\sqrt{3}}{2}$

B) $\dfrac{\sqrt{3}}{2}$

C) $-\dfrac{\sqrt{3}}{4}$

D) $\dfrac{\sqrt{3}}{4}$

13

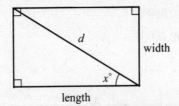

The figure above shows a rectangle with a diagonal of length d. Which of the following equations represents the area of the rectangle?

A) $d^2\cos^2 x°$

B) $d\sin^2 x°$

C) $d^2\cos x° \cdot \sin x°$

D) $d\cos x° \cdot \sin x°$

14

Which of the following is equivalent to $\dfrac{7^x \cdot x^7}{7^7 \cdot x^x}$?

A) 1

B) $(x-7)^{\frac{7}{x}}$

C) $\left(\dfrac{x}{7}\right)^{x-7}$

D) $\left(\dfrac{7}{x}\right)^{x-7}$

15

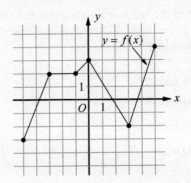

The complete graph of function f is shown in the xy-plane above, for $-5 \le x \le 5$. Which of the following are true?

I. f is strictly increasing then strictly decreasing for $-1 < x < 3$.

II. $f(-\dfrac{3}{2}) = 2$

III. f is maximum at $x = 0$.

A) I only

B) I and II only

C) II and III only

D) I, II, and III

DIRECTIONS

For questions 16-20, solve the problem and enter your answer in the grid as described below, on the answer sheet.

1. Although not required, it is suggested that you write your answer in the boxes at the top of the columns to help you fill in the circles accurately. You will receive credit only if the circles are filled in correctly.

2. Mark no more than one circle in any column.

3. No question has a negative answer.

4. Some problems may have more than one correct answer. In such cases, grid only one answer.

5. **Mixed numbers** such as $3\frac{1}{2}$ must be gridded as 3.5 or $7/2$. (If $3\,1\,/\,2$ is entered into the grid, it will be interpreted as $\frac{31}{2}$ not $3\frac{1}{2}$.)

6. **Decimal answers:** If you obtain a decimal answer with more digits than the grid can accommodate, it may be either rounded or truncated, but it must fill the entire grid.

Answer: $\frac{5}{12}$

Answer: 3.25

Acceptable ways to grid $\frac{2}{3}$ are:

Answer: 212 - either position is correct.

NOTE: You may start your answers in any column, space permitting. Columns you don't need to use should be left blank.

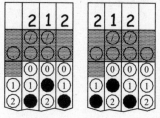

CONTINUE ⇨

16

What is the value of $9 - n$
if $n - 9 = -n + 16 - 3n$?

17

If $\dfrac{(3ab^2)(2a^2b)^3}{8a^2b^2} = 3a^m b^n$, what is the value of
$m + n$?

18

$$3x + 2y = 24$$
$$-2x + 3y = 10$$

If (x, y) is solution to the system of equations
above, what is the value of $x + y$?

19

x	$f(x)$	$g(x)$
-1	-3	-2
2	3	1
3	5	6

The table above gives values of f and g at
selected values of x. What is the value of
$g(f(2))$?

20

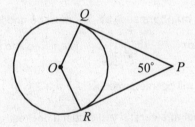

In the figure above, point O is the center of the
circle, and line segments PQ and PR are tangent
to the circle at points Q and R, respectively. If
the radius of the circle is $\dfrac{9}{\pi}$, what is the length of
the minor arc $\overarc{QR}$?

No Test Material On This Page

Math Test – Calculator

55 MINUTES, 38 QUESTIONS

Turn to Section 4 of your answer sheet to answer the questions in this section.

DIRECTIONS

For questions **1-30**, solve each problem, choose the best answer from the choices provided, and fill in the corresponding circle on your answer sheet. **For questions 31-38**, solve the problem and enter your answer in the grid on the answer sheet. Please refer to the directions before question 14 on how to enter your answers in the grid. You may use any available space in your test booklet for scratch work.

NOTES

1. The use of calculator **is not permitted**.

2. All variables and expressions used represent real numbers unless otherwise indicated.

3. Figures provided in this test are drawn to scale unless otherwise indicated.

4. All figures lie in a plane unless otherwise indicated.

5. Unless otherwise indicated, the domain of a given function f is the set of all real numbers x for which $f(x)$ is a real number.

REFERENCE

$A = \pi r^2$ $A = \ell w$ $A = \dfrac{1}{2}bh$ $c^2 = a^2 + b^2$ Special Right Triangles

$C = 2\pi r$

$V = \ell w h$ $V = \pi r^2 h$ $V = \dfrac{4}{3}\pi r^3$ $V = \dfrac{1}{3}\pi r^2 h$ $V = \dfrac{1}{3}\ell w h$

The number of degrees of arc in a circle is 360.
The number of radians of arc in a circle is 2π.
The sum of the measures in degrees of the angles of a triangle is 180.

CONTINUE

1

Half the difference of 18 and a number n is equal to the sum of n and three. What is the value of n?

A) $\dfrac{5}{2}$

B) 4

C) $\dfrac{11}{2}$

D) 6

2

If $0.14x = 2.8$, what is the value of $\dfrac{1}{x}$?

A) 0.2

B) 0.5

C) 0.02

D) 0.05

3

$$11 + 5x = kx - 3(x - 4)$$

If the linear equation above has no solution, which of the following could be the value of k?

A) -1

B) 2

C) 5

D) 8

4

If $f(2 - x) = 3x - 5$ for all values of x, what is the value of $f(-3)$?

A) -14

B) -2

C) 10

D) 14

5

The line of a graph in the xy- plane has slope $\dfrac{1}{3}$ and contains the point $(6,-1)$. The graph of a second line passes through the points $(0,1)$ and $(1,0)$. If the two lines intersect at the point (p,q), what is the value of $p \cdot q$?

A) -6

B) -3

C) 3

D) 6

6

Which of the following numbers is NOT a solution to the inequality $2-\dfrac{1}{2}x \le 2x+7$?

A) -2.5

B) -0.5

C) 0.5

D) 2.5

7

During a basketball game, the Lancers scored 15 points in the first quarter, $\dfrac{2}{7}$ of their total score in the second quarter, $\dfrac{1}{4}$ of their total score in the third quarter, and the remaining 11 points in the fourth quarter. What is the total number of points the Lancers scored in the game?

A) 48

B) 53

C) 56

D) 60

8

	Distance from Burbank (miles)
Helicopter	$-150t+260$
Plane	$-270t+440$

The expressions in the table above show the distance from Burbank to a helicopter and a plane t hours after 10:00 AM. At what time will the helicopter and the plane be equidistant from Burbank?

A) 11:00 AM

B) 11:15 AM

C) 11:30 AM

D) 11:45 AM

Questions 9 and 10 refer to the following information.

A skier starts a downhill race course that is 1,800 meters long, and the finish line is 360 meters below the start line. During the race, the skier averaged a speed of 9 meters per second.

9

Which of the following expressions gives the skier's elevation above the finish line t seconds after she started the race?

A) $360 - 0.2t$

B) $360 - 1.8t$

C) $360 - 4.5t$

D) $360 - 9t$

10

How far is the skier from the finish line one minute after she started the race?

A) 540 meters

B) 780 meters

C) 1,020 meters

D) 1,260 meters

11

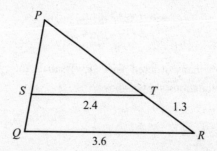

In the figure above, segments ST and QR are parallel. What is the length of $\overline{PT}$?

A) 2.6

B) 3.0

C) 3.4

D) 3.8

12

At a certain concert, all tickets are equally priced. A survey showed that decreasing the price of these tickets by 10 percent would increase the number of tickets sold by 20 percent. If each concert ticket is discounted by 10 percent, what is the percent increase in the amount of money received from the sale of tickets?

A) 8%

B) 10%

C) 12%

D) 15%

13

$$x - y = 5$$
$$y = (3x + 1)(x - 2)$$

How many ordered pairs (x, y) satisfy the system of equations shown above?

A) 0

B) 1

C) 2

D) Infinitely many

14

In the xy-plane, the graph of function f has x-intercepts at -3, 0, and 6. Which of the following could define f?

A) $f(x) = 2x^3 + 8x^2 - 24x$

B) $f(x) = 2x^3 - 8x^2 - 24x$

C) $f(x) = 2x^3 + 6x^2 - 36x$

D) $f(x) = 2x^3 - 6x^2 - 36x$

15

$$x - y = \frac{1}{2}y$$

If (x, y) is a solution to the equation above and $y \neq 0$, what is the ratio $\dfrac{x}{y}$?

A) $-\dfrac{3}{2}$

B) $-\dfrac{2}{3}$

C) $\dfrac{2}{3}$

D) $\dfrac{3}{2}$

16

Grape juice makes up 12% of brand A fruit punch and 20% of brand B fruit punch. If 10 ounces of brand A fruit punch are mixed with 15 ounces of brand B fruit punch, what percent of the mixed punch is the grape juice?

A) 14.2%

B) 15.4%

C) 16.8%

D) 20.6%

Questions 17 and 18 refer to the following information.

Metal	Density of materials ($\frac{g}{cm^3}$)
aluminum	2.7
copper	9.0
gold	19.3
iron	7.9
mercury	13.6
silver	10.5

The chart above shows approximations of the density of metals, d, in grams per cubic centimeters ($\frac{g}{cm^3}$) for six metals. The mass of an object can be found by using the formula $m = d \cdot V$, in which m is the mass of a metal measured in grams and V is the volume of a metal measured in cm^3.

17

What is the volume, in cubic centimeters, of an aluminum with a mass of 5.4 kilograms?
(1 kiligram=1,000 grams)

A) 1,450

B) 2,000

C) 14,500

D) 20,000

18

Which of the following metals with 630 grams of mass has approximately the same volume as gold with a mass of 1350 grams?

A) 630 grams of mercury

B) 630 grams of silver

C) 630 grams of copper

D) 630 grams of iron

19

A weather balloon was launched for weather forecast. At an elevation of 1,000 meters above the sea level, the outside temperature recorded $12°C$. As the balloon went up, the outside temperature decreased linearly. At an elevation of 1,500 meters above the sea level, outside temperature recorded $8.6°C$. If the temperature decreased at a constant rate as the balloon went up, which of the following models best describes temperature C at an elevation h meters above the sea level?

A) $C = -0.0136h + 25.6$

B) $C = -0.0272h + 15.2$

C) $C = -0.0068h + 18.8$

D) $C = -0.0034h + 15.4$

20

In a right triangle, one angle measures $x°$, for which $\cos x° = \frac{\sqrt{7}}{4}$. What is $\cos(90° - x°)$?

A) $\frac{\sqrt{3}}{4}$

B) $\frac{1}{2}$

C) $\frac{\sqrt{7}}{4}$

D) $\frac{3}{4}$

Questions 21 and 22 refer to the following information.

List A and List B each contains 30 numbers. Frequency distributions for each list are recorded in the histograms below.

Frequency Distribution for List A

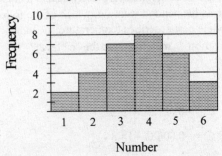

Number

Frequency Distribution for List B

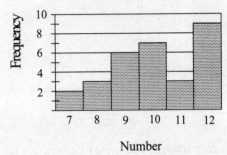

Number

The average (arithmetic mean) of the numbers in list A is 3.7, and the average of the numbers in list B is 10.1. List C contains 60 numbers: the 30 numbers of list A and the 30 numbers of list B.

21

Let M be the average and m be the median of the 60 numbers in list C. Which of the following relationships between M and m must be true?

A) $M > m$

B) $M < m$

C) $M = m$

D) The relationships between M and m cannot be determined.

22

Which of the following is true about the two lists shown for the 30 numbers?

A) The standard deviation of the numbers in list A is larger.

B) The standard deviation of the numbers in list B is larger.

C) The standard deviation of the numbers in list A is the same as that of list B.

D) The standard deviation of the numbers in the two lists cannot be determined.

23

$$y = 2(x - a)(x - b)$$

In the quadratic equation above, a and b are positive constants, with $a > b$. If the graph of the equation in the xy-plane is a parabola with vertex $(6, -18)$, what is the value of a?

A) 3

B) 6

C) 9

D) 12

24

If an event can succeed in S ways and fail in F ways, the probability of success P is given as $P = \dfrac{S}{S+F}$. Which of the following expresses S in terms of the other variables?

A) $S = \dfrac{F}{P-1}$

B) $S = \dfrac{F}{1-P}$

C) $S = \dfrac{PF}{P-1}$

D) $S = \dfrac{PF}{1-P}$

25

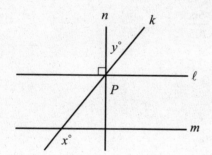

In the figure above, lines k, ℓ, and n intersect at point P. If $\ell \parallel m$ and $\ell \perp n$, which of the following is true?

A) $x = 2y$

B) $x - y = 90$

C) $x + y = 90$

D) $180 - x = y$

26

$$\begin{cases} 2x + y \ge -1 \\ 2x - 3y < 3 \end{cases}$$

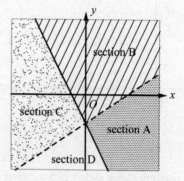

A system of inequalities and a graph are shown above. Which section or sections of the graph could represent all of the solutions to the system?

A) Section A

B) Section B

C) Section C

D) Section D

27

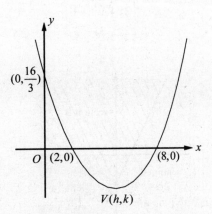

The xy- plane above shows two x- intercepts, a y- intercept, and vertex V of a parabola. Which of the following must be the coordinates of the vertex of the parabola?

A) $V(5,-3)$

B) $V(5,-\frac{10}{3})$

C) $V(5,-\frac{8}{3})$

D) $V(5,-2)$

28

	Ratings			
	1	2	3	Total
Group A	10	21	29	60
Group B	5	28	27	60
Total	15	49	56	120

The table above shows the number of people in two groups who rated a bestseller on a scale of 1 to 3.

If a person is chosen at random from those who gave a rating of at least 2, what is the probability that the person belongs to Group B ?

A) $\dfrac{49}{105}$

B) $\dfrac{50}{105}$

C) $\dfrac{55}{105}$

D) $\dfrac{56}{105}$

29

Printer A, working alone at a constant rate, prints 100 pages of documents in m minutes. Printer B, working alone at a constant rate, prints 100 pages of documents in n minutes. If printers A and B, working together at their respective constant rates, printed p pages of documents in 1 hour, which of the following equations describes p in terms of m and n?

A) $(\dfrac{m}{100}+\dfrac{n}{100})\dfrac{1}{60}=p$

B) $(100m+100n)\dfrac{1}{60}=p$

C) $(100m+100n)60=p$

D) $(\dfrac{100}{m}+\dfrac{100}{n})60=p$

30

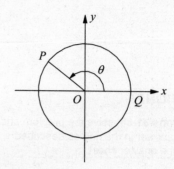

In the xy-plane above, O is the center of the circle, and the measure of $\angle POQ$ is θ. If $\sin\theta=\dfrac{a}{r}$, what is $\sin(2\pi-\theta)$?

A) $\dfrac{\sqrt{r^2-a^2}}{r}$

B) $-\dfrac{\sqrt{r^2-a^2}}{r}$

C) $-\dfrac{a}{r}$

D) $\dfrac{a}{r}$

DIRECTIONS

For questions 31-38, solve the problem and enter your answer in the grid as described below, on the answer sheet.

1. Although not required, it is suggested that you write your answer in the boxes at the top of the columns to help you fill in the circles accurately. You will receive credit only if the circles are filled in correctly.

2. Mark no more than one circle in any column.

3. No question has a negative answer.

4. Some problems may have more than one correct answer. In such cases, grid only one answer.

5. **Mixed numbers** such as $3\frac{1}{2}$ must be gridded as 3.5 or $7/2$. (If $\boxed{3\,1\,/\,2}$ is entered into the grid, it will be interpreted as $\frac{31}{2}$ not $3\frac{1}{2}$.)

6. **Decimal answers:** If you obtain a decimal answer with more digits than the grid can accommodate, it may be either rounded or truncated, but it must fill the entire grid.

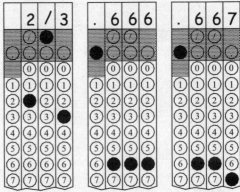

Acceptable ways to grid $\frac{2}{3}$ are:

Answer: 212 - either position is correct.

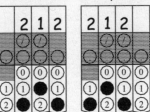

NOTE: You may start your answers in any column, space permitting. Columns you use should be left blank.

CONTINUE ⟶

31

What is the value of r if the line that passes through $(-5,4)$ and $(3,r)$ has a slope of $-\dfrac{1}{5}$?

32

At a farmers market, n pounds of avocados cost $4.50. If Gloria paid $4n$ dollars for 8 pounds of avocados, what is the value of n?

33

$$ax - 9y = 7$$
$$bx - 4y = 5$$

In the system of equations above, a and b are constants and x and y are variables. If the system of equations above has no solution, what is the value of $\dfrac{a}{b}$?

34

In a book store, hardcover copies of a certain book are priced at $24 each and paperback copies of the same book are priced at $13.50 each. Last week, the total amount collected in the sales of the hardcover and paperback copies was the same as if every book sold had cost $15.60 each. If 300 hard cover copies were sold, what was the total number of the books sold last week?

35

If $(ax-1)(bx+2) = cx^2 - x - 2$ for all values of x, and $a+b=10$, what is the value of c?

37

$$x^2(x+2) = x^2 + 8x + 12$$

If $x > 0$, what is the solution to the equation above?

36

The purchase price of a car is $24,000, and the value of the car decreases by 15 percent per year. The value V, in dollars, t years after the car is purchased is given by the function $V = 24,000(x)^t$. What is the value, in dollars, of the car 10 years after it is purchased? (Round your answer to the nearest dollar and ignore the dollar sign when gridding your answer.)

38

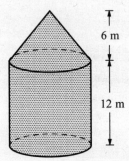

6 m

12 m

A grain silo of a barn consists of a right circular cylinder capped by a right circular cone. The heights of the cylinder and cone are represented by the figure above. If the volume of the grain silo is 224π cubic meters, what is the diameter of the silo, in meters?

Answer Key

SAT Practice Test 2 – No Calculator

1. C	2. B	3. C	4. A	5. D
6. B	7. D	8. A	9. C	10. B
11. D	12. B	13. C	14. D	15. B
16. 4	17. 8	18. 10	19. 6	20. 6.5

SAT Practice Test 2 – Calculator

1. B	2. D	3. D	4. C	5. A
6. A	7. C	8. C	9. B	10. D
11. A	12. A	13. B	14. D	15. D
16. C	17. B	18. C	19. C	20. D
21. A	22. B	23. C	24. D	25. B
26. B	27. A	28. C	29. D	30. C

31. $\frac{12}{5}$ or 2.4   32. 3   33. $\frac{9}{4}$ or 2.25   34. 1500

35. 21   36. 4725   37. 3   38. 8

Answers and Explanations

SAT Practice Test 2 – No Calculator

1. **C**

    Pick two points from the table to find the slope of f. Let's use $(-1,9)$ and $(1,3)$.

    $$\text{Slope} = \frac{3-9}{1-(-1)} = -3$$

    Only choice C has a line with slope -3.

2. **B**

    Check each answer choice to find if the ordered pairs satisfy the given inequalities, $y > x - 4$ and $x + y < 5$.

    A) $(0,-5)$ If $x = 0$ and $y = -5$,
    $-5 > 0 - 4$ is not true
    Discard choice A.

    B) $(0,2)$ If $x = 0$ and $y = 2$,
    $2 > 0 - 4$ is true
    $0 + 2 < 5$ is also true.

    Since $(0,2)$ satisfy both inequalities, choice B is correct.

3. **C**

    The slope of the line $y = \frac{2}{3}x + 2$ is $\frac{2}{3}$.

    The equation in each answer choice is written in standard form. Change the equations in each answer choice to slope-intercept form.

    A) $2x + 3y = 5 \implies y = -\frac{2}{3}x + \frac{5}{3}$

    B) $3x + 2y = 9 \implies y = -\frac{3}{2}x + \frac{9}{2}$

    C) $4x - 6y = 3 \implies y = \frac{2}{3}x - \frac{1}{2}$

    The equation in choice C has slope $\frac{2}{3}$.

4. **A**

    $$\frac{3^{(a+b)^2}}{3^{(a-b)^2}}$$

    $= 3^{(a+b)^2 - (a-b)^2}$ $\dfrac{a^m}{a^n} = a^{m-n}$

    $= 3^{(a^2+2ab+b^2)-(a^2-2ab+b^2)}$ FOIL

    $= 3^{4ab}$ Simplify.

    Therefore, $\dfrac{3^{(a+b)^2}}{3^{(a-b)^2}} = 3^{4ab} = 243$. Since $243 = 3^5$,

    we can conclude $4ab = 5$, so $ab = \dfrac{5}{4}$.

5. **D**

    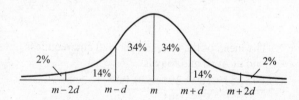

    The mean value of 500 homes in a county is $225,000 and the standard deviation is $25,000.

    Since $m = \$225,000$ and $d = 25,000$,
    $m - d = \$225,000 - \$25,000 = \$200,000$,
    $m - 2d = \$225,000 - 2 \times \$25,000 = \$175,000$,
    and $m + d = \$225,000 + \$25,000 = \$250,000$.

    Reading the graph, $14\% + 34\% + 34\%$, or 82%, of the 500 homes are priced between $175,000 ($= m - 2d$) and $225,000 ($= m + d$). Therefore, there are 0.82×500, or 410 homes.

6. B

A number p increased by 120 percent is
$p + 1.2p = 2.2p$.
A number q decreased by 20 percent is
$q - 0.2q = 0.8q$.
Therefore, $2.2p = 0.8q$. Solving the equation
for q yields, $q = \dfrac{2.2}{0.8}p = \dfrac{22}{8}p = \dfrac{11}{4}p$.

7. D

Since the total number of bags is 8, $c + r = 8$.
Each bag of Columbia Coffee costs $25. So
$25 \times c$ is the total cost for Columbia Coffee.
Each bag of Roast Espresso costs $35. So $35 \times r$
is the total cost for Roast Espresso. If Kay paid
$230 for the coffee and espresso, the equation
$25 \times c + 35 \times r = 230$ is true.

Choice D is correct.

8. A

$h(x) = -px^2 + 1$
$h(2) = -p(2)^2 + 1 = -1 \qquad h(2) = -1$
$-4p + 1 = -1 \qquad\qquad$ Simplify.

$-4p = -2 \;\Rightarrow\; p = \dfrac{1}{2}$

Therefore, $h(x) = -\dfrac{1}{2}x^2 + 1$.

Since $p = \dfrac{1}{2}$, $h(p) = h(\dfrac{1}{2}) = -\dfrac{1}{2}(\dfrac{1}{2})^2 + 1 = \dfrac{7}{8}$.

9. C

The mean of the prices of the 670 automobiles
sold in April and May is
$\dfrac{275 \times \$19,500 + 395 \times \$20,000}{275 + 395}$

$= \dfrac{\$13,262,500}{670} \approx \$19,794.78$.
The average is closest to $19,800.
Choice C is correct.

10. B

Percent increase of the mean price of automobiles
sold from May to June is
$\dfrac{\text{amount of increase}}{\text{price in May}} = \dfrac{21,500 - 20,000}{20,000}$

$= \dfrac{1500}{20,000} = 0.075 = 7.5\%$

11. D

Total amount collected from the automobile sales
in August is $262 \times \$21,000 = \$5,502,000$.

The tax is 8 percent of $5,502,000, which is
$0.08 \times \$5,502,000$, or $440,160.
Choice D is correct.

12. B

$\dfrac{3 - i\sqrt{3}}{1 - i\sqrt{3}}$

$= \dfrac{(3 - i\sqrt{3})(1 + i\sqrt{3})}{(1 - i\sqrt{3})(1 + i\sqrt{3})} \qquad$ Rationalize the denominator.

$= \dfrac{3 + 3\sqrt{3}i - \sqrt{3}i - 3i^2}{1 - 3i^2} \qquad$ FOIL

$= \dfrac{3 + 2\sqrt{3}i + 3}{1 + 3} \qquad$ Simplify. $i^2 = -1$

$= \dfrac{6 + 2\sqrt{3}i}{4} \qquad$ Simplify.

$= \dfrac{3}{2} + \dfrac{\sqrt{3}}{2}i$

Therefore, $b = \dfrac{\sqrt{3}}{2}$.

13. C

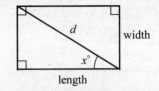

$\cos x° = \dfrac{\text{adjacent}}{\text{hypotenuse}} = \dfrac{\text{length}}{d}$

$\Rightarrow \text{length} = d \cos x°$

$\sin x° = \dfrac{\text{opposite}}{\text{hypotenuse}} = \dfrac{\text{width}}{d}$

$\Rightarrow \text{width} = d \sin x°$

Area of rectangle
$= \text{length} \times \text{width}$
$= d \cos x° \times d \sin x° = d^2 \cos x° \sin x°$

14. D

$\dfrac{7^x \cdot x^7}{7^7 \cdot x^x} = \dfrac{7^x}{7^7} \cdot \dfrac{x^7}{x^x} \qquad\qquad$ Rearrange.

$= 7^{(x-7)} \cdot x^{(7-x)}$ $\dfrac{a^m}{a^n} = a^{m-n}$

$= 7^{(x-7)} \cdot x^{-(x-7)}$ $7-x = -(x-7)$

$= 7^{(x-7)} \cdot \dfrac{1}{x^{(x-7)}}$ $a^{-m} = \dfrac{1}{a^m}$

$= \dfrac{7^{(x-7)}}{x^{(x-7)}}$ Simplify.

$= (\dfrac{7}{x})^{(x-7)}$

15. B

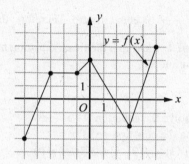

I. A function f is increasing on an interval
    if the value of f increases as x increases
    on the interval. A function f is decreasing
    on an interval if the value of f increases as
    x decreases on the interval. A function f
    is not increasing or decreasing on an interval
    if the graph of f is a horizontal line. For
    $-1 < x < 0$, f is strictly increasing and for
    $0 < x < 3$, f is strictly decreasing. Therefore,
    f is strictly increasing then strictly decreasing
    for $-1 < x < 3$.

    Statement I is true.

II. The value of f is 2 when the x-coordinate
    on the graph is $-\dfrac{3}{2}$. Therefore, $f(-\dfrac{3}{2}) = 2$.
    Statement II is true.

III. The value of f at $x = 0$ is 3.
     The value of f at $x = 5$ is 5.
     Therefore, f is maximum at $x = 5$.

     Statement III is not true.

16. 4

$n - 9 = -n + 16 - 3n$

$n - 9 = -4n + 16$ Simplify.
$5n - 9 = 16$ Add $4n$ to each side.
$5n = 25$ Add 9 to each side.
$n = 5$ Divide each side by 5.

Therefore, $9 - n = 9 - 5 = 4$.

17. 8

$\dfrac{(3ab^2)(2a^2b)^3}{8a^2b^2}$

$= \dfrac{(3ab^2)(8a^6b^3)}{8a^2b^2}$ $(a^m)^n = a^{m \cdot n}$

$= \dfrac{24a^7b^5}{8a^2b^2}$ $a^m \cdot a^n = a^{m+n}$

$= 3a^5b^3$ $\dfrac{a^m}{a^n} = a^{m-n}$

If $3a^5b^3 = 3a^m b^n$, the $m = 5$ and $n = 3$.
Therefore, $m + n = 5 + 3 = 8$.

18. 10

$3x + 2y = 24$ 1st equation
$-2x + 3y = 10$ 2nd equation
Multiply each side of the first equation by 2 and
multiply each side of the second equation by 3.
Then add the two equations.

$2(3x + 2y = 24) \Rightarrow \quad 6x + 4y = 48$
$3(-2x + 3y = 10) \Rightarrow +\underline{|-6x + 9y = 30}$
$\qquad\qquad\qquad\qquad\qquad 13y = 78$

Solving $13y = 78$ yields $y = 6$.
Substituting 6 for y in the equation
$3x + 2y = 24$ yields $3x + 2(6) = 24$.
Solving the equation for x gives $x = 4$.
So, $x + y = 4 + 6 = 10$.

19. 6

x	$f(x)$	$g(x)$
-1	-3	-2
2	3	1
3	5	6

Reading the table, when $x = 2$, $f(x) = 3$.
So, $f(2) = 3$.
$g(f(2)) = g(3)$
When $x = 3$, $g(x) = 6$
Therefore, $g(f(2)) = g(3) = 6$.

20. 6.5

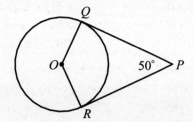

If a line is tangent to a circle, then the line is perpendicular to the radius at the point of tangency. Thus, $\overline{PQ} \perp \overline{OQ}$ and $\overline{PR} \perp \overline{OR}$, or $m\angle PQO = 90$ and $m\angle PRO = 90$.

Since the sum of the measures of the interior angles of quadrilateral is 360,

$m\angle P + m\angle PQO + m\angle QOR + m\angle PRO = 360$.

$50 + 90 + m\angle QOR + 90 = 360$ Substitution

$230 + m\angle QOR = 360$ Simplify.

$m\angle QOR = 130$

Length of the minor arc $\overset{\frown}{QR}$

$= 2\pi r \times \dfrac{m\angle QOR}{360}$

$= 2\pi(\dfrac{9}{\pi}) \times \dfrac{130}{360}$ $r = \dfrac{9}{\pi}$, $m\angle QOR = 130$

$= 6.5$

SAT Practice Test 2 – Calculator

1. **B**

$\underbrace{\dfrac{1}{2}}_{\substack{\text{half}}} \underbrace{(18 - n)}_{\substack{\text{the difference of} \\ \text{18 and a number}}} = \underbrace{n + 3}_{\substack{\text{sum of the} \\ \text{number and 3}}}$

$2 \cdot \dfrac{1}{2}(18 - n) = 2 \cdot (n + 3)$ Multiply each side by 2.

$18 - n = 2n + 6$ Distributive Property

$18 - 3n = 6$ Subtract $2n$.

$-3n = -12$ Subtract 18.

$n = 4$ Divide each side by -3.

2. **D**

$0.14x = 2.8$

$\dfrac{0.14x}{0.14} = \dfrac{2.8}{0.14}$ Divide each side by 0.14.

$x = 20$ Simplify.

$\dfrac{1}{x} = \dfrac{1}{20} = 0.05$

3. **D**

$11 + 5x = kx - 3(x - 4)$

$11 + 5x = kx - 3x + 12$

$11 + 5x - 11 = kx - 3x + 12 - 11$

$5x = kx - 3x + 1$

$5x - kx + 3x = kx - 3x + 1 - kx + 3x$

$8x - kx = 1$

$(8 - k)x = 1$

$x = \dfrac{1}{8 - k}$

The equation is undefined if the denominator of $x = \dfrac{1}{8 - k}$ is equal to zero. Therefore, the value of k for which the linear equation has no solution is 8.

4. **C**

First, solve the equation $2 - x = -3$.
Solving the equation gives $x = 5$.
So, $f(-3) = f(2 - 5) = 3(5) - 5 = 10$.

5. **A**

$y = mx + b$ Slope-Intercept Form

$y = \dfrac{1}{3}x + b$ $m = \dfrac{1}{3}$

$-1 = \dfrac{1}{3}(6) + b$ $(6, -1)$ is on the graph.

$-3 = b$

Thus equation of the line that has slope $\dfrac{1}{3}$ and contains the point $(6, -1)$ is $y = \dfrac{1}{3}x - 3$.

The slope of the second line is $\dfrac{0 - 1}{1 - 0}$, or -1.

The equation of the second line is $y - 1 = -1(x - 0)$, or $y = -x + 1$.

Substitute $-x + 1$ for y in the equation $y = \dfrac{1}{3}x - 3$.

$-x + 1 = \dfrac{1}{3}x - 3 \Rightarrow 1 = \dfrac{4}{3}x - 3 \Rightarrow 4 = \dfrac{4}{3}x$

$\Rightarrow 3 = x$

Substitute 3 for x in the equation $y = -x + 1$, to solve for y. So, $y = -(3) + 1 = -2$.

The point of intersection is $(3, -2)$.

Therefore, $p = 3$ and $q = -2$, so $p \cdot q = 3 \times -2 = -6$.

6. A

$$2 - \frac{1}{2}x \le 2x + 7$$

$2 - \frac{1}{2}x - 2x \le 2x + 7 - 2x$ Subtract $2x$.

$2 - \frac{5}{2}x \le 7$ Simplify.

$2 - \frac{5}{2}x - 2 \le 7 - 2$ Subtract 2.

$-\frac{5}{2}x \le 5$ Simplify.

$-\frac{2}{5}\left(-\frac{5}{2}x\right) \ge -\frac{2}{5}(5)$ Multiply each side by $-\frac{2}{5}$ and change $\le$ to $\ge$.

$x \ge -2$

Therefore, -2.5 is the only number in the answer choices which is not the solution to the inequality.

7. C

Let $n =$ the total number of points the Lancers scored.
Adding all the points scored in the first quarter, second quarter, third quarter, and the fourth quarter, the total score must equal n.

$n = 15 + \frac{2}{7}n + \frac{1}{4}n + 11$

$n = 26 + \frac{15}{28}n$ Simplify.

$n - \frac{15}{28}n = 26 + \frac{15}{28}n - \frac{15}{28}n$ Subtract $\frac{15}{28}n$.

$\frac{13}{28}n = 26$ Simplify.

$n = 26 \cdot \frac{28}{13}$ Multiply each side by $\frac{28}{13}$.

$n = 56$

8. C

If the helicopter and the plane is equidistant from Burbank, then $-150t + 260 = -270t + 440$.

$\Rightarrow -150t + 260 + 270t = -270t + 440 + 270t$
$\Rightarrow 120t + 260 = 440$
$\Rightarrow 120t + 260 - 260 = 440 - 260$
$\Rightarrow 120t = 180$
$\Rightarrow t = 1.5$

The helicopter and the plane will be equidistant from Burbank 1.5 hours after 10:00 AM, or at 11:30AM.

9. B

Since the skier's average speed is 9 meters per second, her distance from the start line will be $9t$ meters, t seconds after she started the race. Since the elevation drops 360 meters for 1800 meters along the slope, it follows that for $9t$ meters along the slope, the elevation drops

$9t \times \frac{360}{1800}$, or $1.8t$ meters. Therefore, the skier's

elevation above the finish line t seconds after she started the race is $360 - 1.8t$ meters.

10. D

Her speed is 9 meters per second. One minute, or 60 seconds after she started the race, her distance from the start line will be 9×60, or 540 meters. Therefore, she is $1,800 - 540$, or $1,260$ meters, from the finish line.

11. A

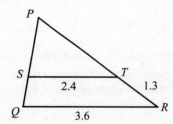

Since segments ST and QR are parallel, the following proportion is true.

$\frac{PT}{ST} = \frac{PR}{QR}$

Let $PT = x$, then $PR = PT + TR = x + 1.3$.
Substitute x for PT and $x + 1.3$ for PR, in the proportion.

$\frac{x}{2.4} = \frac{x + 1.3}{3.6}$ $ST = 2.4$ and $QR = 3.6$

$3.6x = 2.4(x + 1.3)$ Cross Products

$3.6x = 2.4x + 3.12$ Distributive Property

$1.2x = 3.12$ Subtract $2.4x$ from each side.

$x = \frac{3.12}{1.2} = 2.6$

Therefore, the length of $\overline{PT}$ is 2.6.

12. A

Let $n =$ the number of tickets sold at regular price. Let $p =$ the regular price of the tickets.
Then let $np =$ the total amount received from the sale of tickets at regular price.

If the price of tickets decreases by 10%, the new price of the tickets will be $p - 0.1p$, or $0.9p$.

If the number of tickets sold increases by 20%, the new number sold will be $n + 0.2n$, or $1.2n$. The amount of money received from the sale of tickets at the discounted price is $0.9p \times 1.2n = 1.08np$.

The total amount is increased by 8 percent.

13. B

$x - y = 5 \implies y = x - 5$

Substitute $x - 5$ for y in the equation $y = (3x+1)(x-2)$.

$x - 5 = (3x+1)(x-2)$	Substitution
$x - 5 = 3x^2 - 5x - 2$	FOIL
$3x^2 - 6x + 3 = 0$	Make one side 0.
$3(x^2 - 2x + 1) = 0$	Factor.
$3(x-1)^2 = 0$	Factor.
$x - 1 = 0$	
$x = 1$	
$y = x - 5 = 1 - 5 = -4$	Substitution

The ordered pair $(1, -4)$ satisfies the system of equations. There is only one ordered pair that satisfies the given system of equations.

14. D

If a function f has x-intercepts at -3, 0, and 6, then $(x+6)$, x, and $(x-6)$ must each be a factor of f. Therefore, $f(x)$ can be written as $f(x) = ax(x+3)(x-6)$, in which a is a constant.

$f(x) = ax(x^2 - 3x - 18)$	FOIL
$f(x) = a(x^3 - 3x^2 - 18x)$	Distributive Property

Since the leading coefficient is 2 in each answer choice, substitute 2 for a in the above polynomial equation.

$f(x) = 2(x^3 - 3x^2 - 18x)$	$a = 2$
$f(x) = 2x^3 - 6x^2 - 36x$	Distributive Property

Choice D is correct.

15. D

$$x - y = \frac{1}{2}y$$

$x - y + y = \frac{1}{2}y + y$	Add y to each side.

$x = \frac{3}{2}y$	Simplify.
$\dfrac{x}{y} = \dfrac{\frac{3}{2}y}{y}$	Divide each side by y.
$\dfrac{x}{y} = \dfrac{3}{2}$	Simplify.

16. C

Grape juice makes up 12% of brand A fruit punch and 20% of brand B fruit punch. Thus, 10 ounces of brand A fruit punch contain 0.12×10, or 1.2 ounces of grape juice, and 15 ounces of brand B fruit punch contain 0.2×15, or 3 ounces of grape juice. The percent of grape juice in the mixed punch is

$$\frac{\text{amount of grape juice}}{\text{total amount}} = \frac{1.2 + 3}{10 + 15} = 0.168.$$

There is 16.8% of grape juice in the mixed punch.

17. B

Metal	Density of materials ($\frac{g}{cm^3}$)
aluminum	2.7
copper	9.0
gold	19.3
iron	7.9
mercury	13.6
silver	10.5

The density of aluminum is 2.7 g/cm^3.

$m = d \cdot V$	
$5400 = 2.7 \times V$	$m = 5.4kg = 5400g$
$\dfrac{5400}{2.7} = V$	
$2,000 = V$	

18. C

$$m = d \cdot V \implies V = \frac{m}{d}$$

The density of gold is 19.3 g/cm^3, so the volume of gold with a mass of 1350 grams is

$$V = \frac{m}{d} = \frac{1350}{19.3} \approx 69.9 \text{ cm}^3.$$

Check each answer choice to find which metal with 630 grams of mass has approximately the same volume as gold with a mass of 1350 grams.

A) 630 grams of mercury

$$V = \frac{m}{d} = \frac{630}{13.6} \approx 46.3 \text{ cm}^3$$

B) 630 grams of silver

$$V = \frac{m}{d} = \frac{630}{10.5} \approx 60 \text{ cm}^3$$

C) 630 grams of copper

$$V = \frac{m}{d} = \frac{630}{9.0} \approx 70 \text{ cm}^3$$

So, 630 grams of copper has approximately the same volume as gold with a mass of 1350 grams.

19. C

The slope of a line is the ratio of the change in one quantity to the change in another quantity. In this question, elevation is the independent variable and the temperature is the dependent variable. Thus the rate of change in temperature

is $\dfrac{\text{change in temperature}}{\text{change in elevation}} = \dfrac{\text{change in } C}{\text{change in } h}$

$$= \frac{8.6 - 12}{1500 - 1000} = -0.0068 \text{ C/meters}.$$

The point-slope form of the equation of the line that contains $(1000, 12)$ with slope -0.0068 is

$C - 12 = -0.0068(h - 1000)$.

$C - 12 = -0.0068h + 6.8$ Distributive Property

$C = -0.0068h + 18.8$

20. D

In a right triangle, if $\cos x° = \dfrac{\sqrt{7}}{4}$, the length of the hypotenuse is 4 and the side adjacent to the angle $x°$ is $\sqrt{7}$. Sketch a right triangle with hypotenuse 4 and a side adjacent to the angle $x°$ with length $\sqrt{7}$. Let A, B, and C be the three vertex of the triangle as shown in the figure below.

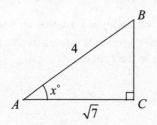

Pythagorean Theorem can be used to find the length of BC.

$BC^2 + AC^2 = AB^2$ Pythagorean Theorem

$BC^2 + (\sqrt{7})^2 = 4^2$ Substitution

$BC^2 + 7 = 16$

$BC^2 = 9$

$BC = 3$

In a right triangle, the acute angles are complementary. Therefore, $m\angle A + m\angle B = 90$.

$x + m\angle B = 90$ Substitution

$m\angle B = 90 - x$

$\cos \angle B = \cos(90 - x)° = \dfrac{BC}{AB} = \dfrac{3}{4}$

21. A

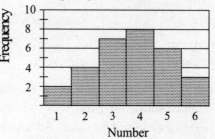

Frequency Distribution for List A

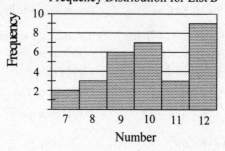

Frequency Distribution for List B

Because list A and list B each contain the same number of values, 30 numbers each, the average of the numbers in list C is the average of the individual averages of the numbers in list A and list B. Thus, the average of the numbers in list C

is $M = \dfrac{3.7 + 10.1}{2}$, or $M = 6.9$.

The median of 60 numbers in list C is the average of two middle numbers because there are even number of value in list C. The two middle numbers in list C are 6 and 7. The median is

$m = \dfrac{6 + 7}{2}$, or $m = 6.5$. Thus, the average is greater than the median of the numbers.

22. B

The standard deviation is a measure of how far the data set values are from the mean. In general, when the measures are clustered close to the mean the standard deviation is small, and when the measures are widely spread apart the standard deviation is relatively large. In list A, the data are closest to the mean. In list B, the data are more spread out, thus by observation, the standard deviation of the numbers in list B is larger.

23. C

$$y = 2(x-a)(x-b)$$

In the quadratic equation, the x-coordinate of the vertex is the average of two x-intercepts. The two x-intercepts of the given quadratic equation are a and b. Thus, $6 = \dfrac{a+b}{2}$.

$2(6) = 2\left(\dfrac{a+b}{2}\right)$	Multiply each side by 2.
$12 = a+b$	Simplify.
$12 - a = b$	Solve for b.

Since the coordinate of the vertex is $(6, -18)$, you can substitute $x = 6$ and $y = -18$ in the given equation to find the value of a and b.

$-18 = 2(6-a)(6-b)$	$x=6$ and $y=-18$
$-9 = (6-a)(6-b)$	Divide each side by 2.

Substitute $12 - a$ for b in the equation above.

$-9 = (6-a)(6-(12-a))$	Substitution
$-9 = (6-a)(-6+a)$	Simplify.
$-9 = -(6-a)(6-a)$	$-6+a = -(6-a)$
$9 = (6-a)(6-a)$	Divide each side by -1.

$9 = (6-a)^2$	
$\pm 3 = (6-a)$	Square root each side.
$3 = 6-a$ or $-3 = 6-a$	
$a = 3$ or $a = 9$	

If $a = 3$, $b = 12 - a = 12 - 3 = 9$.
If $a = 9$, $b = 12 - a = 12 - 9 = 3$.

Since $a > b$, $a = 9$ and $b = 3$.

24. D

$$P = \frac{S}{S+F}$$

Multiply each side by $S + F$.

$$(S+F)P = (S+F)\frac{S}{S+F}$$

$PS + PF = S$	Simplify.
$PS + PF - PS = S - PS$	Subtract PS.
$PF = S - PS$	Simplify.
$PF = S(1-P)$	Factor.
$\dfrac{PF}{1-P} = \dfrac{S(1-P)}{1-P}$	Divide each side by $1-P$.
$\dfrac{PF}{1-P} = S$	Simplify.

25. B

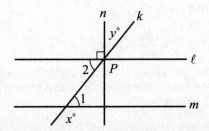

$x + m\angle 1 = 180$	Straight angle measures 180.
$m\angle 1 = 180 - x$	Subtract x from each side.
$m\angle 1 = m\angle 2$	If $\ell \parallel m$, Alternate Interior Angles are equal in measure.
$m\angle 2 = 180 - x$	Substitution: $m\angle 1 = m\angle 2$.
$m\angle 2 + 90 + y = 180$	Straight angle measures 180.
$180 - x + 90 + y = 180$	Substitution: $m\angle 2 = 180 - x$.
$270 - x + y = 180$	Simplify.
$-x + y = -90$	Subtract 270 from each side.
$(-1)(-x+y) = (-1)(-90)$	Multiply each side by -1.
$x - y = 90$	Simplify.

26. B

$$2x + y \geq -1$$
$$2x - 3y < 3$$

Select a point from each section, then test them on the inequalities. Let's use $(3,0)$, $(0,3)$, $(-3,0)$, and $(0,-3)$ from each section as test points.

$2(3) + 0 \geq -1$	$x=3$, $y=0$ is true.
$2(3) - 3(0) < 3$	$x=3$, $y=0$ is false.
$2(0) + 3 \geq -1$	$x=0$, $y=3$ is true.
$2(0) - 3(3) < 3$	$x=0$, $y=3$ is true.

Since $x = 0$ and $y = 3$ are true for both inequalities, section B represents all of the solutions to the system.

27. A

In the quadratic equation, the x-coordinate of the vertex is the average of two x-intercepts. The two x-intercepts of the given quadratic equation are 2 and 8. Thus, $h = \dfrac{2+8}{2} = 5$.

Since you know the x-coordinate of the vertex, write the equation of the parabola in vertex form, $y = a(x-h)^2 + k$.

$y = a(x-5)^2 + k$	$h = 5$
$0 = a(2-5)^2 + k$	$(2,0)$ is on the graph.
$0 = 9a + k$	Simplify.
$\dfrac{16}{3} = a(0-5)^2 + k$	$(0, \dfrac{16}{3})$ is on the graph.
$\dfrac{16}{3} = 25a + k$	Simplify.

$$\dfrac{16}{3} = 25a + k$$
$$-\;\underline{|\,0 = 9a + k\,}\qquad \text{Subtract.}$$
$$\dfrac{16}{3} = 16a$$
$$\dfrac{1}{3} = a$$

Substitute $\dfrac{1}{3} = a$ in the equation $0 = 9a + k$.

$0 = 9(\dfrac{1}{3}) + k$	$\dfrac{1}{3} = a$
$0 = 3 + k$	Simplify.
$-3 = k$	

Therefore, the coordinates of the vertex is $(5, -3)$.

28. C

There are $49 + 56$, or 105 people who gave at least 2 for the rating. Out of these $28 + 27$, or 55, people belonged to Group B.
Therefore, if a person is chosen at random from those who have given at least 2 for the rating, the probability that the person belongs to Group B is $\dfrac{55}{105}$.

29. D

If printer A, working alone at a constant rate, prints 100 pages of documents in m minutes, printer A prints $\dfrac{100}{m}$ pages in 1 minute.

If printer B, working alone at a constant rate, prints 100 pages of documents in n minutes

printer B prints $\dfrac{100}{n}$ pages in 1 minute.

In 1 hour, printers A and B working together will print $(\dfrac{100}{m} \cdot 60 + \dfrac{100}{n} \cdot 60)$ pages of document.

If printers A and B working together printed p pages of documents in 1 hour, then you can set up the equation $(\dfrac{100}{m} \cdot 60 + \dfrac{100}{n} \cdot 60) = p$

or $(\dfrac{100}{m} + \dfrac{100}{n})60 = p$.

Choice D is correct.

30. C

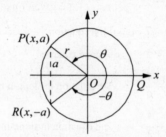

Draw $\overline{OR}$ so that $m\angle QOR = m\angle QOP = \theta$.
Since the measure of major arc QPR is $2\pi - \theta$, the measure of angle $\angle QOR$ in a circle can be expressed as $-\theta$ or $2\pi - \theta$. The sine of angle θ in a circle, by definition, is $\sin\theta = \dfrac{y}{r}$.

Therefore, if $\sin\theta = \dfrac{a}{r}$, the y-coordinate of point P must be a. If the y-coordinate of point P is a, then the y-coordinate of point R must be $-a$.

Thus, $\sin\angle QOR = \sin(2\pi - \theta) = \dfrac{-a}{r}$.

31. $\dfrac{12}{5}$ or 2.4

Use the slope formula.

$-\dfrac{1}{5} = \dfrac{r-4}{3-(-5)}$	$m = \dfrac{y_2 - y_1}{x_2 - x_1}$
$-\dfrac{1}{5} = \dfrac{r-4}{8}$	Simplify.
$5(r-4) = -8$	Cross Products
$5r - 20 = -8$	Distributive Property
$5r = 12$	Add 20 to each side.
$r = \dfrac{12}{5}$	

32. 3

If n pounds of avocados cost \$4.50 and 8 pounds of avocados cost $4n$ dollars, you can set up the following proportion.

$$\frac{n \text{ pounds}}{4.5 \text{ dollars}} = \frac{8 \text{ pounds}}{4n \text{ dollars}}$$

$n \times 4n = 4.5 \times 8$	Cross Products
$4n^2 = 36$	Simplify.
$n^2 = 9$	Divide each side by 9.
$n = \pm\sqrt{9} = \pm 3$	Square root each side.

Since the number of pounds is positive, $n = 3$.

33. $\frac{9}{4}$ or 2.25

$ax - 9y = 7$	First equation
$bx - 4y = 5$	Second equation
$y = \frac{a}{9}x - \frac{7}{9}$	1st equation in slope-intercept form
$y = \frac{b}{4}x - \frac{5}{4}$	2nd equation in slope-intercept form

If two linear equations have the same slope and have different y- intercepts, then the system of equations have no solution.

Therefore, if $\frac{a}{9} = \frac{b}{4}$, the system of equations will have no solution.

$4a = 9b$	Cross Products
$\frac{4a}{b} = \frac{9b}{b}$	Divide each side by b.
$4\frac{a}{b} = 9$	Simplify.
$\frac{1}{4} \cdot 4\frac{a}{b} = \frac{1}{4} \cdot 9$	Multiply each side by $\frac{1}{4}$.
$\frac{a}{b} = \frac{9}{4}$	Simplify.

The value of $\frac{a}{b}$ is $\frac{9}{4}$.

34. 1500

Let x = the total number of books sold, then let $x - 300$ = the number of paperback copies sold. If every book sold had cost \$15.60 each, the dollar amount collected will be $15.6x$. The amount of dollars collected from the sale of 300 hardcover copies is 300×24 and the amount of dollars collected from the sale of $x - 300$ paperback copies is $(x - 300) \times 13.5$ dollars.

If the total amount collected in the sales of the hardcover and paperback copies was the same as if every book sold had cost \$15.60 each, then you can set up the following equation.

$300 \times 24 + (x - 300) \times 13.5 = 15.6x$	
$7200 + 13.5x - 4050 = 15.6x$	Distributive Property
$3150 + 13.5x = 15.6x$	Simplify.
$3150 = 2.1x$	Subtract $13.5x$.
$\frac{3150}{2.1} = \frac{2.1x}{2.1}$	Divide by 2.1.
$1500 = x$	

The total number of the books sold last week is 1,500.

35. 21

$$(ax - 1)(bx + 2) = cx^2 - x - 2$$
$$\Rightarrow abx^2 + (2a - b)x - 2 = cx^2 - x - 2$$

The coefficient of x^2 and the coefficient of x have to be equal on both sides of the equation to make the polynomial true.

Thus, $ab = c$ and $2a - b = -1$.
Add the given equations $a + b = 10$ and $2a - b = -1$.

$$\begin{array}{r} a + b = 10 \\ + \underline{\;2a - b = -1\;} \\ 3a \quad\;\; = 9 \end{array}$$

Solving for a yields $a = 3$.
Substituting $a = 3$ in $a + b = 10$ gives $b = 7$.

Therefore, $c = ab = 3 \cdot 7 = 21$.

36. 4725

Since the value of the car decreases by 15% per year, the initial value of the car must be multiplied by a factor of $(1 - 0.15)$, or 0.85. If the value of the car is \$24,000 this year, it will be
\$24,000(0.85) one year later,
\$24,000(0.85)(0.85) two years later,
\$24,000(0.85)(0.85)(0.85) three years later,
and so on. After ten years, the value of the car will be $V = 24,000(0.85)^{10} \approx 4724.98$.

To the nearest dollar, the value of the car will be 4725 dollars.

37. 3

$$x^2(x+2) = x^2 + 8x + 12$$
$$x^2(x+2) = (x+2)(x+6) \qquad \text{Factor.}$$
$$x^2(x+2) - (x+2)(x+6) = 0 \quad \text{Make one side 0.}$$
$$(x+2)(x^2 - (x+6)) = 0 \qquad \text{Distributive Property}$$
$$(x+2)(x^2 - x - 6) = 0 \qquad \text{Simplify.}$$
$$(x+2)(x+2)(x-3) = 0 \qquad \text{Factor.}$$
$$(x+2)^2(x-3) = 0 \qquad \text{Simplify.}$$
$$x = -2 \text{ or } x = 3 \qquad \text{Zero Product Property}$$

Since $x > 0$, the solution to the equation is 3.

38. 8

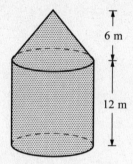

Let r be the radius of the circular cylinder and circular cone.
The volume of the grain silo is the sum of the volume of the cylinder and the volume of the cone. Since the volume of the grain silo is given as 224π cubic meters, $V = \pi r^2(12) + \frac{1}{3}\pi r^2(6) = 224\pi$.

$$\pi(12r^2 + 2r^2) = 224\pi$$
$$12r^2 + 2r^2 = 224$$
$$14r^2 = 224$$
$$r^2 = \frac{224}{14} = 16$$
$$r = \pm\sqrt{16} = \pm 4$$

The radius of the silo is 4 meters, thus the diameter of the silo is 2×4, or 8 meters.